Modern Oscilloscopes

Modern Oscilloscopes and Their Uses

BY JACOB H. RUITER, Jr.

Manager of Technical Publications, &
Advertising Manager, Instrument Division
Allen B. Du Mont Laboratories, Inc.

MURRAY HILL BOOKS, INC. • NEW YORK • TORONTO

Murray Hill Books, Inc.
is a subsidiary of
Rinehart & Company, Inc.

To my wife, Peggy, who, despite an intense aversion to any explanation even remotely technical, is entirely responsible for the completion of this book.

Preface

The author became conscious of a need for this book after receiving many inquiries as a result of his association with this field. Almost daily, at least one letter is received requesting a simple explanation of the use of the oscilloscope. Although each company furnishes an instruction book with each oscilloscope, no one company could afford to underwrite a book which would serve as general instructions to all users. The author hopes that this book will fulfill that need.

This book is written for the electronics student and for the radio technicians and repairmen who have a background in general physics. It should be helpful also to mechanical and electrical engineers who have need to use oscilloscopes in their work, but lack experience and training in the field of electronics. The explanations have been written with these types of readers in mind, and the learn-by-doing method of instruction has been employed to teach specific operations. Thus, numerous step-by-step procedures will be found throughout the book.

Inasmuch as the title of this book is "Modern Oscilloscopes and Their Uses," a brief history of oscilloscopes, the development and fundamentals of the cathode-ray tube, as well as a discussion of the circuits of the oscilloscope are included along with numerous specific examples of the applications of the oscilloscope in many fields.

The author wishes to acknowledge the cooperation of the following companies in providing data and assistance with the preparation of this volume:

Allen B. Du Mont Laboratories, Inc.
Central Scientific Company
Electro Medical Laboratories
Electronic Development Laboratories
Electro Products Laboratories
General Electric Company
General Radio Company
Hathaway Instrument Company
Hickok Electrical Instrument Company
Radio Corporation of America

Supreme Instrument Company
Sylvania Electric Products, Inc.
Waterman Products Company

Also, to a great many co-workers at the Allen B. Du Mont Laboratories, who directly and indirectly influenced this book, the author wishes to extend his thanks. Special acknowledgment is also given to Messrs. Jacobus Kuypers and John Punk, who prepared practically all of the drawings; Miss Irene Trawinski, who assisted with typing the manuscript; and Messrs. G. Robert Mezger and Walter A. Knoop, who offered many valuable suggestions during the various stages of progress.

JACOB H. RUITER, JR.

PASSAIC, NEW JERSEY,

August, 1949.

Contents

PAGE

4. FUNDAMENTAL PRINCIPLES OF CATHODE-RAY TUBE OPERATION

5. DETAILS OF THE MODERN CATHODE-RAY TUBE

6. THE GENERAL PURPOSE OSCILLOSCOPE

7. POWER-SUPPLY CIRCUITS

11. INTERPRETATION OF BASIC PATTERNS

12. AUXILIARY EQUIPMENT

13. TYPICAL APPLICATIONS IN THE ELECTRONICS INDUSTRY

14.   SERVICING A-M RADIO RECEIVERS

15.   SERVICING F-M RADIO RECEIVERS

16. SERVICING TELEVISION RECEIVERS

17.   USE AT THE RADIO TRANSMITTER

18. USING THE OSCILLOSCOPE IN TEACHING

19. ADDITIONAL INDUSTRIAL APPLICATIONS OF THE OSCILLOSCOPE

Modern Oscilloscopes

1 Introduction

What Is an Oscilloscope?   An oscilloscope is one of the most useful scientific instruments ever invented. From its meager beginnings as a laboratory device of questionable value, it has been developed into a precision instrument, contributing extensively to and largely responsible for the age of radar and television.

Although the functions of the oscilloscope are numerous and often complex, its definition is simple. An oscilloscope, as the name implies, is an instrument for viewing oscillations. This definition may seem extremely broad because there are so many different oscillations that exist in the present-day world. Then, too, since the word "vibration" is listed in the dictionary as a synonym for the word "oscillation," the implication would seem to be that the oscilloscope is an instrument for viewing any oscillation or vibration.

As broad as the original definition may seem, it is true, provided that one qualifying statement is added. The definition actually should read: "An oscilloscope is an instrument which may be used to observe and measure any vibration or oscillation that can be converted into an electrical voltage." Thus, the oscilloscope is nothing more than an a-c voltmeter that also displays the wave form of the voltage being measured.

What Are Its Applications?   The oscilloscope is most commonly used in the electronics industry, simply because it is an electronic instrument and because oscillations are so much a part of this field. Its earliest applications were purely as an indicator of electrical voltage or a magnetic field, but it has been developed into a device which actually permits the visual observation of phenomena occurring in electronic circuits. Even phenomena occurring at rates of *millions* of times per second or a phenomenon that may last for only one millionth of a second may be readily seen and carefully studied with an oscilloscope. Truly, it can be said that *an oscilloscope is to the engineer as the X-ray machine is to the physician.*

The oscilloscope is also used in many other fields of engineering. For these other applications it is necessary to convert the form of energy to be studied into electrical energy. This, however, is accomplished quite sim-

1

ply. For example, sounds of any variety, whether from a musical instrument, the human voice, machinery in motion, or the engine of an automobile, may be converted from mechanical energy into electrical energy by means of a microphone and thus viewed on an oscilloscope. The microphone, in this case, is referred to as a "transducer," since it converts one form of energy into another.

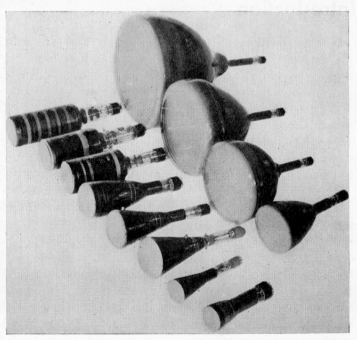

FIG. 1–1. Typical examples of modern cathode-ray tubes. (*Courtesy, Allen B. Du Mont Laboratories, Inc.*)

There are many other transducers which have been developed to convert different kinds of energy into electrical energy. The photocell transforms light into electrical energy, and the thermocouple transforms heat into electrical energy. Some of the lesser known transducers are the vibration or displacement pickup and the pressure pickup. These latter transducers are all closely related to the microphone and transform various forms of mechanical energy into electrical energy. Thus, with these means at its disposal, the oscilloscope has easily become allied with the many fields of engineering and research.

What Constitutes an Oscilloscope? An oscilloscope consists chiefly of a cathode-ray tube plus enough auxiliary electronic circuits to permit it to perform a particular function. One model is merely a cathode-ray tube and its power supply, with terminals provided for connecting an external voltage to deflect the beam of the cathode-ray tube. Another type of oscilloscope is a cathode-ray tube employing auxiliary circuits containing twenty, or even more, vacuum tubes. Both these instruments are oscilloscopes, but they are designed for entirely different purposes.

What Is a Cathode-Ray Tube? A cathode-ray tube is a vacuum tube that has been specifically designed to produce a beam of electrons and direct them toward a fluorescent screen which emits light wherever it is struck by the electron beam. Two signals are applied simultaneously to a system for deflecting the electron beam. The electron beam responds to the resultant of the instantaneous values of these two signals and thus draws a pattern on the face of the tube. A more complete discussion of the operation of the cathode-ray tube is found in Chaps. 3, 4, and 5.

Figure 1-1 illustrates some typical examples of modern cathode-ray tubes designed for various applications. Probably one of the most popular uses of this type of tube is in the field of television. In addition to their use in television and oscilloscopes, cathode-ray tubes are employed as the indicating devices in radar equipment, loran equipment, and specialized test instruments.

Function of the Oscilloscope. Generally, the function of an oscilloscope is to compare on the screen of the cathode-ray tube the variations that occur in an unknown quantity with those that occur in a known quantity. The pattern appearing on the screen from the application of these known and unknown quantities (in the form of signals or varying voltages) is a graph, since it is a plotting of the instantaneous values of one quantity with respect to another. Since this information is presented graphically on the screen of the cathode-ray tube, it lends itself to quick, easy interpretation.

Graphs have been used by practically every individual at some time or other. Probably the most common type of graph is that which uses time for one of the varying quantities. Businessmen plot sales against time and over a long period can determine business trends. Hospitals frequently keep a graphical record of a patient's temperature, pulse rate, and blood pressure over the period of the patient's confinement in order to determine the effect of their treatment.

The engineer and the technician also need graphs to gain insight into the internal operation of mechanical devices, electrical systems, and electronic circuits. Such graphs may be calculated on a theoretical basis, or they may be plotted from painstaking, point-to-point measurements which may take weeks or even months of careful investigation. With the use of the oscilloscope and of proper transducers, much time is saved, since the data may be collected and displayed instantaneously on the screen of the cathode-ray tube.

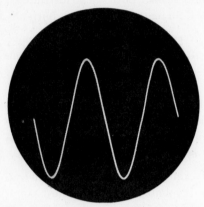

Fig. 1–2. Oscillogram showing 2 cycles of a 60-cycle a-c voltage.

Fig. 1–3. Oscillogram showing the explosion of gasoline in the cylinder of an engine.

Time is one of the most important known variables against which unknown variables are plotted, and time can be conveniently expressed in terms of electrical voltage. The following are examples of the use of an oscilloscope with unknown variables plotted against time. Figure 1-2

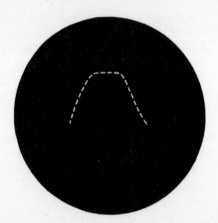

Fig. 1–4. Oscillogram showing the pattern obtained when the speed of a camera shutter is measured with an oscilloscope.

shows the alternating voltage of the normal electrical power line plotted against time. The pressure resulting from the explosion of gasoline in the cylinder of a gasoline engine can be converted into electrical voltage and plotted against time, as shown in Fig. 1-3. The action of the shutter of a camera can be displayed on the screen of an oscilloscope by converting the light that passes through the shutter into electrical energy by means of a photoelectric cell. The pattern which appears on the screen is shown in Fig. 1-4.

2 History of the Oscillograph

The Mechanical Oscillograph. The earliest instruments that were used for plotting an unknown varying quantity against a known quantity were mechanical devices. They usually contained a stylus or a pen and made permanent recordings of the variations, or oscillations, on a piece of moving paper. These devices were called "oscillographs" because they actually recorded a graph of the oscillations on paper. More sensitive oscillographs were later developed which used a beam of light to record

Fig. 2–1. The motion of a pendulum illustrates a simple oscillation.

oscillations on a strip of moving photosensitized film. This instrument also resulted in the permanent recording of these variations in the form of a graph and was likewise referred to as an "oscillograph."

Example of a Mechanical Oscillograph. One of the simplest devices for showing the principles of the operation of an oscillograph can be shown by considering the action of a pendulum. A pendulum is a weight, called a "bob," suspended at the end of a rope or wire from a fixed point. The normal rest position of this bob is directly below its point of suspension. If the bob is moved from its rest position and then released, it will swing back to its rest position and then beyond because of its inertia (see Fig. 2-1). The pendulum will continue to swing back and forth in this plane until the forces of friction (air resistance and friction between the rope and the point of suspension) gradually overcome its inertia and return it to its original rest position. This motion, the swinging back and forth of the bob through its normal rest position, is an example of an oscillation.

To record this oscillation it is merely necessary to attach a pen to the bottom of the bob and allow it to come into contact with a piece of paper. The record of this oscillation is shown as a straight line in Fig. 2-2. The straight line attained is of no particular value, since each cycle of oscillation of the bob is recorded over the previous cycle.

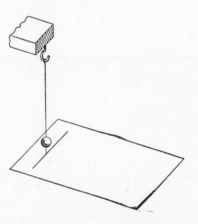

FIG. 2–2. A pen or stylus attached to the bob of the pendulum will record a straight line as the bob swings back and forth.

If, however, the paper is caused to move at a fixed rate of speed, the oscillation of the pendulum is drawn out on the paper in the form of a graph, since one varying quantity (the amplitude of the pendulum) is plotted against another varying quantity (the position of the paper) (Fig. 2-3).

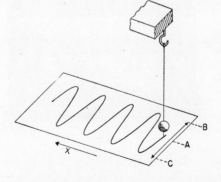

FIG. 2–3. If the paper of Fig. 2–2 is moving in the direction X, a sine wave is recorded.

Assuming the speed of the paper in the direction x to be 20 ft. per min., in 1 sec. the paper moves 4 in. Figure 2-4, then, is a graph of the amplitude of the pendulum swing against time, because time will determine the position of the paper. As a result, the amplitude of the pendulum swing may be read from the graph at any particular instant after the recording starts, or the velocity of the pendulum at any given instant may be calculated from the slope of the curve.

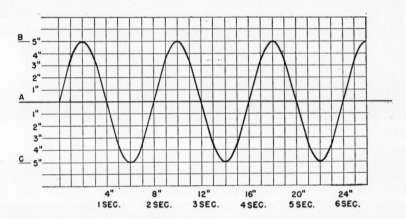

Fig. 2–4. A graph of the amplitude of the pendulum plotted against time.

The Barograph. The term "mechanical oscillograph" is a general one given to a mechanical device that is used to record one variable as a function of another. Most people, however, are acquainted with some forms of specialized mechanical oscillographs which are recognized when they are referred to by their specialized names.

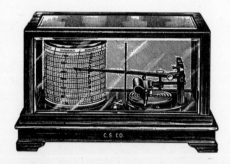

Fig. 2–5. A barograph. (*Courtesy, Central Scientific Co.*)

The barograph (Fig. 2-5) is one of the many specialized mechanical oscillographs. It is an instrument used by the weather bureau for the continuous recording of atmospheric pressure. The barograph utilizes an aneroid barometer with a pen fastened to the end of its indicating arm to record the atmospheric pressure on the proper line of graph paper. This graph paper is calibrated vertically in pressure and horizontally in hours and days, and it passes over a drum that rotates at the speed of one revolution per week. The barograph, in this way, records the atmospheric pressure throughout the day and week, showing clearly all the

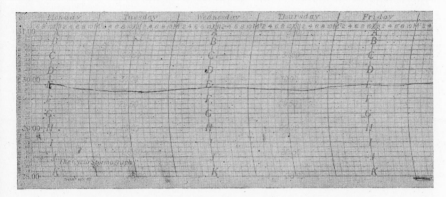

FIG. 2–6. A typical recording made from a barograph.

variations that existed and the time at which they occurred. A typical record made on a barograph is shown in Fig. 2-6.

The String Oscillograph. Another type of oscillograph, which is used for recording electrical variations, is the string oscillograph. This instrument utilizes the electromagnetic properties of a current-carrying wire or ribbon. The string, or mirror, oscillograph operates on the principle of the permanent-magnet galvanometer. It consists of a very light-

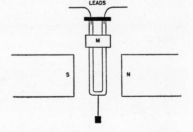

FIG. 2–7. A simplified drawing of a string oscillograph.

weight ribbon (hence, the more common reference "string") arranged as shown in Fig. 2-7. To this loop is usually fastened a mirror *M*. As the current passes through the ribbon, the magnetic field around the ribbon produces a torque that turns the coil and the ribbon about its vertical axis. The angular deflection thus produced is approximately proportional to the instantaneous current in the ribbon.

Proper operation requires a beam of light to be played on the mirror at a slight angle, usually from the bottom. The reflection from the mirror traces out the instantaneous response of the motion of the ribbon in the magnetic field when an alternating current is passed through it. The reflection may be viewed or recorded photographically by a film moving perpendicularly to the deflection of the light beam.

Fig. 2–8. A photograph of a "student's model" string oscillograph. (*Courtesy, Hathaway Instrument Co.*)

For visual observation of the oscillograph, it is necessary to present a succession of reflected light beams to the observer, in order to produce a stroboscopic effect which effectively slows up the rapid oscillations so that they may be distinguished by the human eye. This is usually accomplished with the aid of auxiliary mirrors which are synchronized to the variations being observed. An example of a string oscillograph is shown in Fig. 2-8.

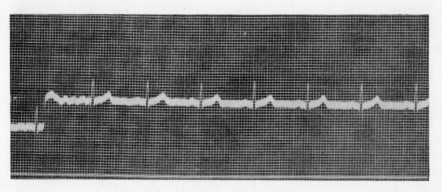

Fig. 2–9. A typical electrocardiogram.

Other Oscillographs. Many other types of oscillographs have been devised for the purpose of recording specific oscillations which occur in the various scientific fields. For example, the medical profession utilizes the *electrocardiograph*, which is also an electromagnetic device. This instrument records heart beats on a moving paper, so that they may be studied to diagnose various heart ailments. A recording from an electro-cardiograph is shown in Fig. 2-9.

The *electroencephalograph* is another oscillographic device used by the medical profession. This instrument is used to record the waves given off by the human brain. It is used in the diagnosis and study of disorders of the brain, such as epilepsy, tumors, and certain types of insanity. A photograph of a three-channel electroencephalograph is shown in Fig. 2-10. This instrument contains equipment necessary to record brain waves from three different probes simultaneously. A recording made on this device is shown in Fig. 2-11.

FIG. 2–10. A three-channel electro-encephalograph. (*Courtesy, Electro Medical Labs.*)

Advantages and Limitations of the Mechanical Oscillograph. The mechanical oscillograph has two main advantages. The first is that it can record very slow variations without limit to the slowness with which the change takes place. The other advantage is the fact that mechanical oscillographs almost invariably result in permanent recordings of the variations either on paper or on film.

The latter advantage becomes a disadvantage when high frequencies are being recorded, because it necessitates using great quantities of paper or photographic film.

Another limitation of the mechanical oscillograph is its inability to record with any degree of fidelity phenomena that occur at high fre-quencies. The upper frequency limit of the best mechanical oscillograph is hardly more than 10,000 c. The average high-frequency limit is probably 5,000 or 6,000 c.

In particular, the general-purpose string oscillograph, which is frequently used to investigate low-frequency electrical variations, draws an appreciable current from the circuit under study in order to obtain satis-

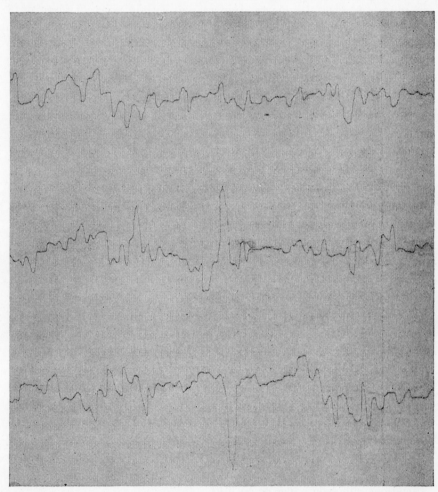

FIG. 2–11. A recording from the three-channel electroencephalograph shown in Fig. 2–10. (*Courtesy, Electro Medical Labs.*)

factory deflection. Moreover, it cannot be regarded as a very rugged instrument because of the rather fragile characteristics of the ribbon.

Need for a Better Oscillograph. With the advent of radio, which employed oscillations whose frequencies were much higher than any in the mechanical field, the mechanical oscillograph was completely inadequate. Some other means had to be found for recording or plotting these high frequencies in order to enable experimenters to progress further.

This new field required a device which would

1. Respond to frequencies as high as several million cycles per second;
2. Produce no serious loading effects upon sensitive electronic circuits;
3. Be of sufficiently rugged construction as to permit its general use as a portable instrument;
4. Have sufficient sensitivity to detect voltages as low as 1/1000 volt;
5. Display these high frequencies in the form of a graph.

The search for such an instrument led to a laboratory curiosity known as the "cathode-ray tube." Although the cathode-ray tube itself cannot fulfill all the requirements listed, it is readily adaptable to the addition of amplifiers to improve its sensitivity and to the addition of a time-base generator to enable the tube to display signals as a function of time. Thus, the complete package of a cathode-ray tube and its auxiliary circuits became known as a "cathode-ray oscillograph" and, later, as just an "oscilloscope." The inability to record very slow phenomena is one limitation of the cathode-ray tube, but the device has no other serious limitations. High-frequency phenomena can be observed on ordinary cathode-ray tubes at as high as 1,000 megacycles—and much higher on specialized high-voltage tubes. Since the deflection plates of the tube do not appreciably draw current, even the most sensitive electronic circuits can be studied without noticeable loading effect. Furthermore, the cathode-ray tube of today is of such rugged construction that an oscilloscope may be carried anywhere with normal handling and still be in good condition. As a matter of fact, there is one case on record of an oscilloscope which was used for over a year in an airplane engaged in making power dives. These dives subjected the airplane and everything in it to forces in excess of seven times the pull of gravity on the average of two or three times a week for more than a year. The oscilloscope and its cathode-ray tube survived this strain without being serviced once during that time.

Oscillograph or Oscilloscope? Considerable disagreement has arisen regarding the correct name for the instrument that is the subject of this book. Actually, it is called both "oscillo*graph*" and "oscillo*scope*," and both terms are frequently used interchangeably by many individuals.

Arguments for the term "oscillo*scope*" include the following:

1. The suffix "-scope" means "to view" or "to see," whereas the suffix "-graph" implies a device for making permanent recordings.
2. "Oscilloscope" can be abbreviated to "scope" without conflict with other existing terms.
3. Since the term "oscilloscope" has come to imply an instrument that uses a cathode-ray tube as an indicating device, the term "oscillo-

graph" is not sufficiently distinctive. The term "cathode-ray oscillograph" is necessary to describe the instrument that employs the cathode-ray tube.

Counterarguments for the term "cathode-ray oscillograph" are

1. The method of presentation of patterns on the screen of the cathode-ray tube is still in the form of a graph, whether or not the patterns are permanently recorded.

2. Permanent recordings can be made from the screen of the cathode-ray tube, if they are desired, by simple photographic methods.

Approaching the argument from the practical viewpoint, this book recognizes the fact that the terms "oscilloscope" and "cathode-ray oscillograph" do exist and may be applied interchangeaby to the same instrument. However, since the term "oscilloscope" is more convenient, and since this term has become almost universally adopted by electronic technicians who use the instrument in their daily work, the term "oscilloscope" will be used hereafter in this book.

3 Brief History of the Development of the Cathode-Ray Tube

History of the Cathode-Ray Tube. The cathode-ray tube dates back to experiments conducted by Faraday about 1865. He was experimenting with a tube similar to that shown in Fig. 3-1 to study the effects

FIG. 3–1. A drawing of a tube similar to that used by Faraday.

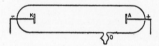

of electrical discharge in gases. The tube is cylindrical in shape and contains two platinum electrodes: a cathode K and an anode A. A small opening O in the wall of the tube permits a vacuum pump to be connected to evacuate the tube. Faraday observed that, as the pressure was reduced, less voltage was required to produce a discharge. The discharge produced in this case was due to the ionization of the gas remaining in the tubes.

Sir William Crookes and Jules Plucker working independently with similar tubes about 1880 observed that as the tube was further evacuated, less voltage was required, until a pressure of about ½ mm of mercury was reached inside the tube. As the pressure was reduced below this value, no electrical discharge occurred; instead, the sides of the tube exhibited a brilliant fluorescent glow. Plucker attributed this phenomenon to invisible rays given off by the cathode, which struck the glass with sufficient energy to cause the glass to fluoresce. Because the fluorescence was more pronounced near the cathode, Plucker called the rays "cathode rays." Although it has since been established that cathode rays do not exist in the same sense as light rays, the name still persists.

Sir William Crookes probably reached more correct conclusions in his experiments with this early cathode-ray tube than any of the other early experimenters. His name is most commonly associated with the discharge tubes used in physics laboratories in schools throughout the country. One of these tubes is shown in Fig. 3-2. It contains a cathode K and an anode A, which is cut in the form of a Maltese cross. When a high difference in potential is applied between the two electrodes, and when the Maltese cross is resting in a plane parallel to the axis of the tube, the entire end of the tube *S* fluoresces with a greenish glow. If the Maltese cross is then raised into a position perpendicular to the axis of the tube, the shadow of the cross, surrounded by the green glow, appears at the end of the tube (Fig. 3-3). Crookes concluded from this that cathode rays traveled in straight lines. From the results of later experiments, Crookes further proved, at least to his own satisfaction, that cathode rays were not truly rays, but that these phenomena were the result of moving particles.

FIG. 3–2. The present-day laboratory version of Crookes tube with the Maltese cross in a horizontal position. The entire large end of the tube emits a green glow when voltage is applied between *K* and *A*.

FIG. 3–3. Similar to Fig. 3–2 except that the Maltese cross has been raised to intercept the electrons. A shadow of the cross appears on the face of the tube.

It was not until 1895, however, that Jean Perrin definitely proved to the scientific world that cathode rays were made up of particles and that these particles carried a negative charge. Perrin's work was supplemented in 1897 by Sir J. J. Thomson, who determined both the weight and the speed of this newly found particle.

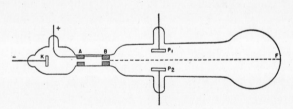

FIG. 3–4. The tube used by Thomson to determine the weight and speed of the electron.

The tube used by Thomson to make these determinations is shown in Fig. 3-4. He found it necessary to construct the anode *A-B* in the form of two thick metal discs *A* and *B*, which fill the narrow neck of the tube. The narrow neck separates the tube into two parts: one part to obtain these particles, which were later called "electrons," and the second part of the tube in which he could make his measurements.

When a difference in potential is applied between *A* and *K*, and the cathode *K* is negative, the electrons flow from *K* to *A*. Some of these electrons pass through the slit in the center of A and through the still narrower slit in the center of B and continue along the axis of the tube until they strike the face of the tube F. The slits in the anode run horizontally across the discs, so that the fluorescence on the face of the tube is in the form of a thin horizontal line of reasonably good definition.

Thomson made his measurements only on that portion of the electron beam which passed through the slit in the anode B, because that portion of the beam was completely independent of the forces between the anode and the cathode. The plates P_1 and P_2 were inserted in the wall of the deflecting chamber of the tube, so that the plane of P_1 was parallel to the plane of P_2 and the electron beam passed equidistant between them. It was then possible to measure the effect of an electrostatic field between these two plates on the electron beam. Thomson actually calculated the mass of the electron from his experiments, but it was not until Robert Millikan's work, using another method, in 1910 that the electron theory

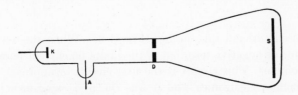

Fig. 3–5. The tube used by Karl F. Braun in his experiments.

was officially accepted. Despite the fact that Thomson worked with rather crude apparatus, it is interesting to note that his figures differed from Millikan's by only a fraction of 1 per cent.

Professor Karl F. Braun in 1898 was probably the first individual to employ the cathode-ray tube as an indicating device. He was also the first to employ an additional means of increasing the fluorescent light output. He accomplished this by coating a mica plate with a fluorescent material and using it for a screen. His tube for producing an electron beam is shown in Fig. 3-5. In this tube the anode A has been removed to the side, and a metal diaphragm D has been inserted in the neck of the tube. This diaphragm has a small hole in its center, about 2 mm in diameter, which focuses the electrons into a cylindrically shaped beam. As the beam strikes the screen S, the screen fluoresces at the point of contact. With such a positive indication given by the fluorescent spot, it was possible for Braun to use his tube to measure deflections which were produced by magnetic or electric fields.

Until the first decade of the twentieth century, all the experimenters, using cathode-ray tubes, were required to use extremely high voltages to obtain electrical discharges within the tubes. High voltages were necessary because these tubes employed cold cathodes, and large nuclear forces holding electrons to the cathode had to be overcome.

In 1883 Edison observed that when an electrode was sealed in the bulb of an incandescent lamp operated on direct current and was connected to the positive terminal of the filament through a galvanometer,

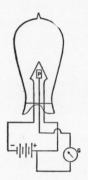

FIG. 3–6. The demonstration used by Edison from which he discovered "the Edison effect."

current passed through this circuit (Fig. 3-6). When this electrode was connected to the negative terminal of the lamp, no current passed through the galvonometer. This circuit is the first circuit to approach those used today in modern electronics, and it was the first experiment to produce evidence that heat facilitated the escape of electrons from the surface of a metal.

It was not until 1905, however, that Wehnelt incorporated the hot cathode in his version of the cathode-ray tube. Wehnelt used a hot filament in this tube as a substitute for the cathode and found that the intensity of the spot was considerably increased. Also, the hot cathode

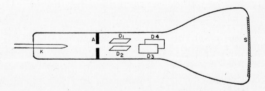

FIG. 3–7. An early version of the cathode-ray tube for quantitative measurement.

permitted the use of much lower operating voltages. Whereas the previous cold-cathode tubes required potentials of 10,000 volts and up, the hot-cathode tubes could be operated conveniently at 1,000 volts. This marked decrease in the potentials necessary for operating the tube greatly simplified the design of the power supply that furnished the operating potential.

Another improvement made by Wehnelt in the advancement of the art of making cathode-ray tubes was the inclusion of another electrode in the tube, which was known as the "grid." This, of course, was incorporated only after the development of the triode vacuum tube by Dr. Lee de Forest.

Even with these late developments, the cathode-ray tube was little more than a laboratory curiosity, chiefly because the spot obtained on the screen was too large in diameter to be useful for accurate measurements.

An early version of a cathode-ray tube using a hot cathode is shown in Fig. 3-7. The reason for the large spot in this type of tube is due to the nature of the beam itself. The beam is nothing more than a stream of electrons. Since each of these electrons is a negative charge, and since like electrical charges repel each other, the electrons along the length of the beam repel each other and diverge away from the axis of the tube in much the same manner as a stream of water diverges after leaving the nozzle of a hose. Not until John B. Johnson and van der Bijl produced the first sealed-off cathode-ray tube in 1922 was interest in this tube

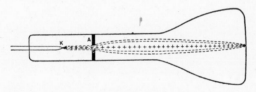

FIG. 3-8. The effect produced by inserting a small quantity of gas to focus the electron beam.

again revived. In their work they attained as nearly a perfect vacuum as possible and then inserted a small quantity of an inert gas. The presence of the inert gas improved the focusing to the point where it was possible to obtain a small spot that could be used as an accurate indicator.

Gas Focusing.   The explanation of the focusing action performed by the introduction of a small quantity of inert gas into a highly evacuated tube is quite interesting. Electrons traveling at high speed in the direction of the screen collide with some of the molecules of the inert gas. In this collision, one or more electrons are liberated from each of the gas molecules, leaving these molecules as positive ions. The positive ions thus formed are more concentrated in the geometric center of the beam as shown in Fig. 3-8. They tend to remain in the center of the beam because of their relatively large mass. Thus, the electron beam now possesses a positive core which attracts the diverging electrons causing them to converge to form a small spot on the screen. By inserting the correct amount of gas and thus obtaining the correct gas pressure within the tube, it is possible to obtain good focusing for a given size of cathode-ray tube operating under a given set of conditions.

Gas focusing has since been abandoned, however, because the presence of the gas tends to shorten the life of the tube and produce distortion in the wave forms being observed. The short tube life is due chiefly to the fact that the positive ions are attracted toward the cathode by the negative potential applied to that electrode. Although they are relatively slow-moving, their mass is great compared with that of the electron. The continual bombardment of the cathode by these heavy particles is sufficient to destroy the cathode in a relatively short time. Furthermore, the presence of these heavy positive particles in the center of the beam, which are deflected by magnetic or electrostatic fields in an opposite direction from that of the electrons (negative particles), produces distortion in any wave form being studied on the screen of the tube.

This distortion, called "origin distortion," shows itself as the beam crosses either of the two axes of the tube.

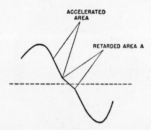

Fig. 3–9. Origin distortion affects the display of a sine wave.

In Fig. 3-7, when a positive voltage is applied to D_1, the *electrons* in the beam are attracted toward this plate, and the *positive ions* are repelled in the opposite direction toward D_2. This, again, is due to the fact that like electrical charges repel each other and unlike charges attract each other. When, on the other hand, a negative voltage is applied to D_1, the *positive ions* are attracted toward this plate, and the *electrons* are repelled toward D_2.

When an alternating voltage is applied to D_1 so that it is first charged positively and then negatively, the electrons in the beam are first attracted and then repelled while the positive ions are alternately first repelled and then attracted. Thus, as the potential on the plate D_1 changes its polarity the electrons and positive ions pass each other at the axis of the tube. Because of the force of attraction of the positive ions for the electrons, the movement of the electron beam across the axis of the tube is first accelerated, as the beam approaches the axis, and then retarded, as the beam crosses the axis. This is the cause of origin distortion. The effect of origin distortion in a sine wave displayed on a gas-focused tube is shown in Fig. 3-9.

In the cathode-ray tube of the television receiver the electron beam is swept across the screen horizontally, as well as vertically, to form a rectangle of light. If a gas-focused tube is used for this purpose, a bright cross, called a "gas cross," appears on the face of the tube as shown in Fig. 3-10. The gas cross is also due to origin distortion. Since the electron beam is retarded as it crosses both the horizontal and vertical axes of the screen, and since more light is given off by the screen when the beam is retarded, a bright line appears along the horizontal and vertical axis of the screen. Thus, gas-focused tubes were eliminated from the field of television and were found to have serious limitations in oscilloscopes.

Further Developments. Since the use of a gas-focused cathode-ray tube illustrated the value of the cathode-ray tube as an indicating device, much interest was aroused to obtain another means of focusing, which would be free of the objectionable origin distortion. Although the complete story of the development of other means of focusing is much more involved than is implied by these few lines, two methods were devised

Fig. 3–10. Origin distortion as evidenced on a television raster.

which were entirely free from origin distortion. One of these methods resulted in the addition of more electrodes and the formation of a structure known as the "electron gun." This method employed electrostatic fields to produce proper focusing of the electron beam. The other method focused the beam by means of an external magnetic field which surrounded the neck of the tube. Both of these methods proved quite successful, were developed further, and are universally used today.

Methods of deflecting the beam by electrostatic and magnetic fields were also improved. The intensity of the beam was improved by coating the cathode with electron-emitting substances and by improving the sensitivity of the screen material.

One of the leaders in the development of the cathode-ray tube in these later years is Dr. Allen B. Du Mont. In 1931 Dr. Du Mont began his research and development work on the cathode-ray tube. It was largely through his pioneering that the cathode-ray tube grew from the laboratory curiosity it was to the important position it now assumes in the field of electronics.

The High-Vacuum, Hot-Cathode, Low-Voltage Cathode-Ray Tube.
The developments outlined above required a period of many years, resulting, about 1938, in a tube which was advertised as a "high-vacuum, hot-cathode, low-voltage cathode-ray tube." High-vacuum meant, of course, that focusing was obtained without the use of gas. The hot-cathode was the means by which the tube could be operated successfully at relatively low voltages (about 1,000 volts).

The cathode-ray tube of this period and the tube of today are functionally the same, although improved manufacturing technique and further developments have resulted in better performance in the present-day types. A detailed discussion of the theory, construction, and principles of operation of the modern cathode-ray tube are given in Chaps. 4 and 5.

4 Fundamental Principles of Cathode-Ray Tube Operation

The Electron. The understanding of the operation of the cathode-ray tube demands a knowledge of the fundamentals of electrostatics. In order to establish a reference point to begin the discussion of the formation of the electron beam, the fundamental laws of electrostatics are stated and the applicable principles are reviewed in the following paragraphs.

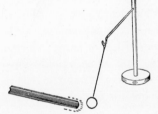

FIG. 4–1. A negatively charged rubber rod attracts a pith ball which is neutral.

The fundamental negative charge of electricity is the electron, which is a small charged particle having negligible weight or mass. The charge on each electron is negative; it is always the same; and it cannot be removed. Electrons are an integral part of all matter and may be transferred from one body or substance to another by relatively simple means. For example, combing the hair with a hard-rubber comb removes electrons from the hair. These electrons are transferred from the hair to the comb, and the comb is then said to be negatively charged while the hair is positively charged. Thus, *when a body loses electrons, it is said to be positively charged; and, conversely, when a body gains electrons, it is regarded as being negatively charged.*

Another principle of electric charges is that *like charges repel each other* and *unlike charges attract each other.* This principle is usually demonstrated in every high-school course in science by very simple experiments. A pith ball is suspended on a silk thread, as shown in Fig. 4-1. When a hard rubber rod, which is negatively charged, is brought close to the pith ball, the ball is attracted to the rod. The attraction is due to the fact that the pith ball is actually neutral with respect to ground but positive with respect to the rod, which is negative. However, once the ball

23

touches the rod, electrons are transferred from the rod to the ball and both are now negatively charged. As a result, as the rod is brought close to the pith ball for the second time (Fig. 4-2), the ball is repelled. If a positively charged glass rod is now brought close to the negatively charged pith ball, the ball is attracted toward the glass rod (Fig. 4-3).

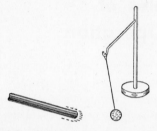

FIG. 4–2. A negatively charged rubber rod repels a pith ball which is also negatively charged.

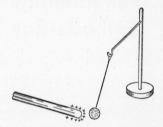

FIG. 4–3. A positively charged glass rod attracts a negatively charged pith ball.

Electrical charges, or potentials, which are applied to the various electrodes of the cathode-ray tube, are due to the fact that a given electrode has either lost or gained electrons. If the electrode is charged positively, it means that some outside force (the power supply) has caused electrons to be removed from this electrode. If an electrode is charged negatively, some outside force (the power supply again) has forced electrons into this

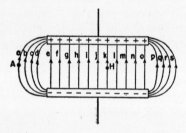

FIG. 4–4. The electrostatic field between two oppositely charged plates.

electrode, making it negative. Thus, a positively charged electrode is one that is deficient in electrons, and a negatively charged electrode is one that has an excess of electrons.

Figure 4-4 shows the resulting electrostatic field that occurs when two oppositely charged plates are brought into close proximity. The electrostatic field thus set up is made up of lines of force which show the direction in which an electron would move if it were placed in the electrostatic field. Because the electron is negatively charged, it would be attracted to the positive plate. Therefore, the direction of the electrostatic field is from the negatively charged plate toward the positively charged plate. If it were placed in the position A, it would follow the line of force indicated by a. If it were placed in position H, it would follow the line of force indicated by k.

Deflection by Means of an Electrostatic Field. If an electron or an electron stream in motion is caused to pass between the two plates that are charged oppositely, the electron beam will be attracted toward the positive plate and, if it is traveling slowly enough, will probably strike the plate. If, however, the electron stream is traveling rapidly, it will pass through the electrostatic field set up by these two plates and will merely be deflected from its straight course by the electrostatic field (Fig. 4-5). This electrostatic field exerts a force which bends the electron beam in the direction of the electrostatic field, namely, toward the positive plate.

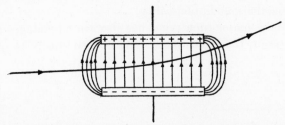

Fig. 4–5. The effect produced on an electron passing through the electrostatic field between two oppositely charged plates.

The bending of the electron stream as it passes through this electrostatic field is merely a simple problem in the resolution of forces. One force is in the initial direction of the force moving the electron beam through the electrostatic field (force Y in Fig. 4-6); the other force is the force of attraction of the electrostatic field (force X). These two forces acting in different directions cause the electron beam to assume the course of the resultant of the two forces. The resultant bending action of the electron beam is determined by the magnitudes of the two forces. In Fig.

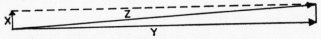

Fig. 4–6. A vector presentation showing the effect on the electron beam as it crosses each line of electrostatic force. X represents the force of the electrostatic field, Y represents the force of the electron, and Z represents the resulting path of the electron.

4-6, the vector representing the force and direction of the electron beam is much larger than that of the vector representing the force and direction of the electrostatic field.

Two Types of Cathode-Ray Tubes. There are essentially two major types of cathode-ray tubes. Classification of a tube into one of these two types is dependent upon the method employed for focusing and for deflecting the electron beam. One type employs a magnetic field to focus the beam and another magnetic field to produce deflection. The other type employs an electrostatic field to focus the beam and another electrostatic field to deflect it. Logically enough, these major types are called, respectively, "magnetic deflection and focus" and "electrostatic deflection and focus" cathode-ray tubes, or, more briefly, "magnetic type" or "electrostatic type."

It is also true that tubes have been made and used, employing electrostatic focusing and magnetic deflection, and vice versa. However, the present tendency is to use the same method to perform both functions for the sake of simplicity and practicality.

Each of these major tube types has its own advantages and limitations. As a result, the electrostatic type is used chiefly in oscilloscopes

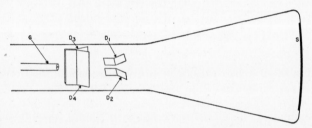

Fig. 4–7. A simplified version of an electrostatic-type tube.

and in certain radar devices, whereas the magnetic type finds its best application in the field of television and certain other types of radar equipment.

The Electrostatic-Type Cathode-Ray Tube. The electrostatic-type cathode-ray tube is a more or less pear-shaped glass tube, or bulb, containing the following major elements: an electron gun, deflection plates, and a fluorescent screen. These elements are shown in cross-sectional drawing in Fig. 4-7. The *electron gun G* serves the function of generating, focusing, and directing an electron beam at the face of the cathode-ray tube. It is so named because it figuratively "shoots" electrons at the face of the tube. A complete discussion of the structure and operation of this part of the tube is given in Chap. 5.

The *deflection plates D*1, *D*2, *D*3, and *D*4 are situated in the neck of the tube between the electron gun and the screen. They are arranged in two pairs, one pair behind the other, along the axis of the tube, so that the electron beam passes between the plates of each pair. Furthermore, the plane of one pair of deflection plates is perpendicular to the plane of the other pair.

The *screen* of the cathode-ray tube is the coating on the face of the tube that transforms the energy of the electron beam into light. This transformation of energy is accomplished by two distinctly different types of photochemical reactions. The reaction that emits light as the screen is being struck by the electron beam is called "fluorescence," and the reaction that enables the screen to continue to give off light after the electron beam has been removed from, or has passed over, a given section is called "phosphorescence." All screen materials possess both of these qualities in different degrees, the importance of which is discussed in detail in Chap. 5.

Elements of Electrostatic Deflection. Deflection of the beam of the cathode-ray tube may be accomplished by electrostatic charges applied to the deflection plates. The fact that two pairs of plates are employed at right angles to each other permits deflection of the electron beam either vertically or horizontally or along the resultant of these two forces when they are applied simultaneously. Either pair of deflection plates may be employed to produce deflection in either plane merely by turning the tube on its long axis to produce the desired result.

Since unlike charges attract each other and like charges repel each other, and since the beam of the cathode-ray tube is made up of electrons, the beam is attracted by a positively charged deflection plate and repelled by a negatively charged plate. To observe the fundamental laws governing the deflection of an electron beam, refer to Fig. 4-8a. When no voltage is applied to any of the four deflection plates ($D1$, $D2$, $D3$, and $D4$), the electron beam passes along the axis of the tube and strikes the center of the screen (Fig. 4-8a). However, if a positive charge is applied to $D1$, this plate *attracts* the beam, causing it to strike *above* the center of the screen, as illustrated in Fig. 4-8b. When the positive charge is removed from $D1$ and applied to $D2$, $D2$ *attracts* the beam, causing it to strike *below* the center of the screen (Fig. 4-8c).

Negative charges applied to the deflection plates repel the beam. For example, if a negative charge is applied only to $D2$, $D2$ will *repel* the beam, causing it to strike *above* the center of the screen. Note that this is the same result as that achieved by applying a positive charge to $D1$ and illustrated by Fig. 4-8b. Likewise, a negative charge applied to $D1$ will *repel* the beam, causing it to strike *below* the center of the screen—the same result as obtained by applying a positive charge to $D2$.

From the previous discussion, it is obvious that either a positive charge applied to $D4$ or a negative charge applied to $D3$ will deflect the beam to the left; and either a negative charge applied to $D4$ or a positive charge applied to $D3$ will deflect the beam to the right. This illustrates, qualitatively, the fundamental principles of deflection.

For a quantitative explanation of deflection, the screen of the tube should be viewed full-on. In the drawings shown in Fig. 4-9, the circle represents the screen of a 3-in.-diameter cathode-ray tube with calibra-

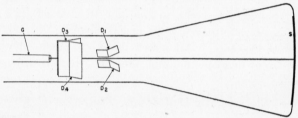

Fɪɢ. 4–8*a*. With no potential applied between $D1$ and $D2$, the electron beam strikes the center of the screen of the cathode-ray tube.

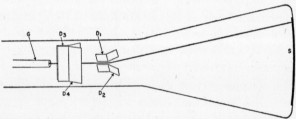

Fɪɢ. 4–8*b*. With a positive potential applied to $D1$ (or a negative potential applied to $D2$, or both) the beam is deflected upward.

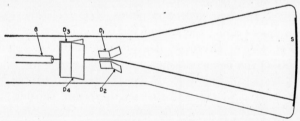

Fɪɢ. 4–8*c*. With a positive potential applied to $D2$ (or a negative potential applied to $D1$, or both) the beam is deflected downward.

Fɪɢ. 4–8. The elements of electrostatic deflection.

tion markings ½ in. apart. The deflection plates are shown outside the limits of the face of the tube to prevent confusion. The deflection plates $D3$ and $D4$ are (in these examples) the vertical deflection plates because they deflect the beam vertically. The deflection plates $D1$ and $D2$ are the horizontal deflection plates because they deflect the beam horizontally. The series of examples shown in Fig. 4-9 is made, assuming that the **de-**

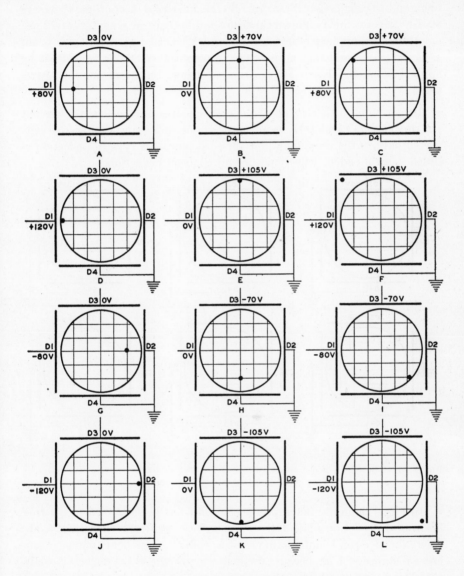

FIG. 4–9. The effect of d-c potentials applied to the deflection plates of a cathode-ray tube (single-ended deflection).

flection factor of the $D3$ and $D4$ deflection-plate pair is 70 d-c volts per inch, and the deflection factor of the $D1$ and $D2$ deflection-plate pair is 80 d-c volts per inch. This means that a difference in potential of 70 d-c volts must be applied between $D3$ and $D4$ in order to deflect the beam 1 in. vertically, and that a difference in potential of 80 d-c volts must be applied between $D1$ and $D2$ in order to deflect the beam one inch horizontally.

Because one of each pair of deflection plates is connected to ground (in this case $D2$ and $D4$), requiring that the deflecting voltages be connected only to the remaining plate of each pair, this type of deflection is called "single-ended deflection" or "unbalanced deflection."

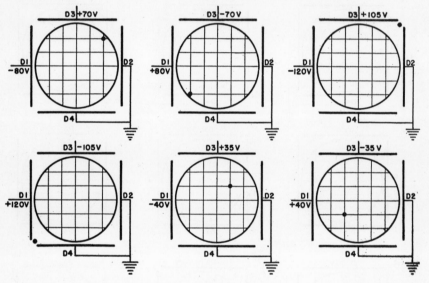

Fig. 4–10. The effect of d-c potentials applied to the deflection plates of a cathode-ray tube (single-ended deflection).

In Fig. 4-9a, a d-c potential of $+80$ volts has been applied to the free horizontal deflection plate $D1$. Because it is positively charged, $D1$ attracts the electron beam and moves it to the left. The beam moves to the left a distance of 1 in., because the deflection factor of the deflection-plate pair being used is 80 d-c volts per inch.

In Fig. 4-9b, a d-c potential of $+70$ volts has been applied to the free vertical deflection plate $D3$. Because it is positively charged, $D3$ attracts the electron beam and moves it upward. The beam moves up a distance of 1 in. because the deflection factor of the deflection-plate pair being used is 70 d-c volts per inch.

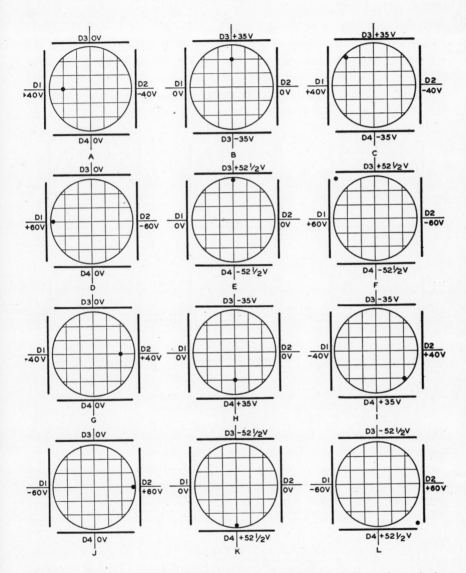

Fig. 4–11. The effect of d-c potentials applied to the deflection plates of a cathode-ray tube (double-ended deflection).

In Fig. 4-9c, a d-c potential of +70 volts has been applied to D3, and a d-c potential of +80 volts has been applied to D1. Both of these forces attract the beam simultaneously and move it along the resultant of these two forces, namely, 1 in. up and 1 in. to the left.

Deflection of the electron beam occurs in direct proportion to the voltage applied. To illustrate this, examples d, e, and f of Fig. 4-9 show the result obtained by applying 1½ times the previous voltages to the deflection plates. In example f, the electron beam is deflected along the

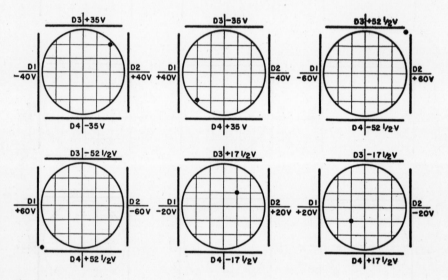

Fig. 4-12. The effect of d-c potentials applied to the deflection plates of a cathode-ray tube (double-ended deflection).

resultant of these two forces, which, because only a 3-in.-diameter tube is used, is sufficient to deflect the beam off the screen.

A negative voltage applied to the deflection plates repels the beam the same distance as an equivalent positive voltage attracts the beam. Examples g, h, and i of Fig. 4-9 illustrate this condition, and examples j, k, and l illustrate the fact that the beam is repelled in direct proportion to the negative voltage applied.

In the various examples cited in Fig. 4-9, it will be noted that the beam has only been deflected into two quadrants of the face of the tube. Suggestions of voltage combinations which will position the beam in the other two quadrants are shown in the examples of Fig. 4-10. It can readily be seen that the beam may be deflected to any position on the screen, depending upon the magnitude and the polarity of the voltage applied to the deflection plates.

Very frequently, deflection of the electron beam is accomplished by applying deflecting voltages to both plates of a pair. Deflection by this method is known by three terms: "balanced deflection," "push-pull deflection," and "double-ended deflection." Of these three terms, push-pull deflection is probably the most descriptive, since voltages of equal magnitude but opposite polarity are applied to the deflection plates. The positive voltage attracts, or "pulls," the electron beam, and the negative voltage repels, or "pushes," the beam. Figures 4-11 and 4-12 illustrate the use of

Fig. 4-13. Cross-sectional drawing of a magnetic deflection and focus cathode-ray tube with focus coil on the left and deflection yoke on the right. (*Courtesy, Allen B. Du Mont Laboratories, Inc.*)

push-pull deflection to achieve the same results as were obtained in Figs. 4-9 and 4-10, respectively. Note that the voltage applied to each deflection plate in Figs. 4-11 and 4-12 is just one-half that employed on the plates of the equivalent example in Figs. 4-9 and 4-10. However, *there is no gain in energy, since the difference in potential between the deflection plates is exactly the same in every case.*

The Magnetic-Type Cathode-Ray Tube. The magnetic-type cathode-ray tube is similar in appearance to the electrostatic-type tube, but its internal structure is quite different. This tube consists, fundamentally, of the following elements: a heater, a cathode, a control grid, a screen grid, an accelerating electrode (called the "anode"), and a screen. To perform the functions of focusing and deflection, the magnetic-type tube employs a focusing coil and a deflection yoke, separate coils which fit over the neck of the tube. Figure 4-13 shows a cross-sectional drawing of a typical magnetic tube with the focusing coil and deflection yoke in place.

The "electron gun" of the magnetic tube is the term assigned to all the electrodes of the tube. It is similar in function to that of the electrostatic-type tube, except that it does not focus the beam. The cathode and the grid cylinders are usually operated at relatively low potentials, namely, the cathode at ground potential and the grid at about −30 volts. In such a case, the screen grid is operated at a fixed potential about +250 volts more positive than the grid. This provides the initial acceleration to the electron beam and also performs a slight focusing action. In ad-

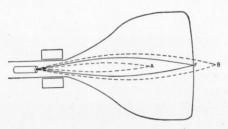

Fig. 4-14. Correct positioning of the focusing coil is indicated when all the electrons in the electron beam converge at the point F.

dition, being between the grid and the anode, it serves to prevent large changes in anode voltage from affecting the action of the grid.

The anode of the magnetic tube is the next electrode. In the modern magnetic tube it is made up of two different and distinct parts connected together electrically. One section of the anode is actually part of the gun structure, and the other section consists of a conductive coating on the inside of the glass bulb which extends nearly out to the screen of the tube. These two sections are electrically connected by friction contacts, as shown in Fig. 4-13.

The electron beam which is emitted from the electron gun is cylindrical in form. To obtain a spot of usable size on the screen, however, some means of forming this cylinder into a cone must be employed. For optimum focus it is necessary, too, that the apex of this cone be focused directly at the screen, as shown in Fig. 4-14. Improper focusing is the result if the apex of this cone is adjusted so that the electrons converge either in front of the screen, as indicated by point A, or beyond the screen as indicated by the dotted lines converging at point B.

Elements of Magnetic Focusing. The *magnetic focusing coil* is designed to produce a magnetic field which extends axially along the tube. This field is shown in the drawing in Fig. 4-15. With such a field, an electron traveling precisely along the axis of this tube is not affected by the field; however, this is a special case. Since most of the electrons do not travel along the axis of the tube, these electrons actually possess

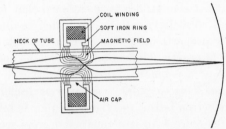

FIG. 4–15. The magnetic field produced by the focusing coil and its effect on the electron beam.

a radial component of motion, as well as an axial component. An electron penetrates the magnetic field only up to the point where the magnetic field possesses enough force to overcome the radial component and direct it back to the axis of the tube. Electrons possessing a small radial component penetrate the magnetic field only slightly; whereas electrons possessing a large radial component penetrate rather deeply. However, it

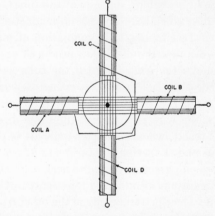

FIG. 4–16. A simplified drawing of a magnetic deflection yoke showing the magnetic fields through the neck of the cathode-ray tube.

has been proved mathematically, that, regardless of the penetration into the magnetic field, all the electrons are brought to a common focal point. It can also be shown mathematically that these electrons travel a helical path as they pass through the focusing field. This is due to the fact that they possess both a radial and an axial component.

Since the anode potential partially determines the number of electrons in the electron beam, which in turn determines the force that must be exerted by the focusing coil to produce good focus; the focusing operation must be adjustable. With magnetically focused cathode-ray tubes this adjustment is made in two steps. The physical position of the focusing coil provides a rough adjustment, while a rheostat to vary the current through the coil, thus varying the density of the magnetic field, provides a fine adjustment. It should also be mentioned that focusing coils have iron cores, but all cores have an air gap which results in the magnetic flux being directly proportional to the current through the coil.

Elements of Magnetic Deflection. Magnetic deflection is accomplished by means of a *magnetic deflection yoke,* which consists of four electromagnets operating in pairs. One pair is responsible for vertical deflection of the electron beam, and the other pair is responsible for horizontal deflection. Figure 4-16 is a functional cross-sectional drawing of the neck of a cathode-ray tube at the deflection coils with all four coils in place. Coils *A* and *B* are the pair responsible for vertical deflection, and coils *C* and *D* are the pair responsible for the horizontal deflection. It will also be noticed in this figure that the beam is passing in its normal

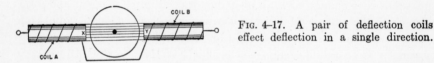

Fig. 4–17. A pair of deflection coils effect deflection in a single direction.

position (along the axis of the tube). Since no current is passing through these coils, they possess no magnetic properties.

To simplify the explanation of magnetic deflection, it is best to consider first the deflection produced only by one pair of coils. Figure 4-17 shows the same view of the tube as Figure 4-16 with only the coils in position that produce vertical deflection, that is, coils *A* and *B*. Coils *A* and *B* are wound as though they were a continuous electromagnet; that is, the wire is wound in the same direction around each of the cores. As a result, when an electric current is passed through these coils, the poles *X* and *Y* become opposite and produce a nearly linear magnetic field which passes through the neck of the cathode-ray tube. This field is practically uniform and is represented by the parallel lines of force.

The electron beam, on the other hand, possesses a magnetic field around *it,* which is similar to the field around any conductor carrying an electric current. This magnetic field is in the form of concentric lines of force, which, if the electron beam is considered to be coming out of the page toward the reader, are going around the beam in a clockwise direction (Fig. 4-18).

Since these two fields, that produced by the coils and that produced by the electron beam, cannot combine because of the difference in their pattern, the electron beam is repelled away from the center of the magnetic field produced by the deflection coils *A* and *B*. The beam will be repelled normal (perpendicular) to the direction of the field. The distance that the beam is deflected is proportional to the strength of the magnetic field, which, in turn, is proportional to the current flowing through the coils. Thus, the greater the current through the deflection coils, the greater the deflection of the electron beam.

Fig. 4–18*a*. The lines of magnetic force around an electron beam appear as concentric circles in a clockwise direction if the beam is considered coming out of the page.

Fig. 4–18*b*. The lines of magnetic force travel from the north pole to the south pole of a magnet or an electromagnet.

Fig. 4–18*c*. When the lines of force of Fig. 4-18*a* are combined with those of Fig. 4–18*b*, there is a crowding of the lines of force above the electron beam and it is repelled downward.

Fig. 4–18.   Analysis of electromagnetic deflection.

Determining the direction (in this case, either up or down) in which the electron beam will be deflected requires the use of two of the rules covered in elementary studies of electromagnetism. Figure 4-19 shows an electric current flowing in the deflection coils *A* and *B* from *T*1 to *T*2. As a result, pole *X* becomes a south magnetic pole and pole *Y* becomes a north magnetic pole. This is proved by the *right hand thumb rule* for electromagnets: *If the fingers of the right hand are wrapped around the coil in the direction of the current in the coil, the thumb will point to the north pole of the coil.* Applying this rule to coil *A*, pole *W* becomes the north pole and pole *X* becomes the south pole. Applying it to coil *B*, pole *Y* becomes the north pole and pole *Z* becomes the south pole.

It will be noted that Fig. 4-19 also indicates by an arrow that the electron beam is deflected *up* under these conditions. (As previously stated, the assumption is also made that the electron beam is flowing toward the reader.) The direction in which the electron beam is deflected can be determined by another simple rule: *Extend the thumb, index finger, and middle fingers of the right hand so that they form right angles with one another. If the hand is placed in such a position that the index finger points the direction of magnetic flux (from north to south) and the middle finger points the direction of the electron beam, the thumb will point the direction in which the beam is deflected.* Figure 4-19 also illustrates the application of this right-hand rule.

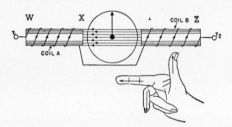

Fig. 4–19. The deflection of the electron beam is upward under the conditions in this illustration.

If, using this same set-up, the current in coils *A* and *B* is reversed, it can readily be seen by applying the right-hand thumb rules that the polarity of the electromagnets has been changed, thus changing the direction of the magnetic field. Since pole *X* has now become a north pole and pole *Y* a south pole, to apply the right hand deflection rule, the hand must be inverted showing that the beam is deflected down (Fig. 4-20). Thus, it can be seen that the direction of the deflection of the electron beam, either up or down, is dependent upon the direction of the current flowing through the deflection coils responsible for vertical deflection, commonly called the "vertical deflection coils."

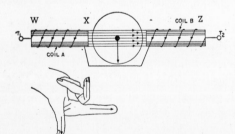

Fig. 4–20. The deflection of the electron beam is downward in the conditions of this illustration.

Horizontal deflection is produced by the two coils indicated in Fig. 4-16 as coils *C* and *D*. Figure 4-21 shows these two coils mounted in their proper position with coils *A* and *B* removed. Horizontal deflection of the electron beam is produced in the same manner as vertical deflection, except that the plane of deflection is rotated 90 deg. Figure 4-21 also illustrates the application of the right-hand deflection rule to show the direction in which the beam is deflected when current flows in the coils from $T3$ to $T4$. Figure 4-22 shows the direction in which the beam is deflected when current flows from $T4$ to $T3$.

Advantages of the Cathode-Ray Tube as an Indicator. Both types of cathode-ray tubes, the electrostatic and the magnetic, possess a distinct advantage over all other indicating devices. This advantage is the fact that the electron beam is practically free of the property of inertia. Thus, the beam of the ordinary cathode-ray tube will respond to each

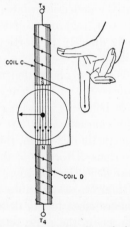

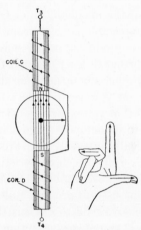

FIG. 4–21. The deflection of the electron beam is to the left under the conditions in this illustration.

FIG. 4–22. The deflection of the electron beam is to the right under the conditions in this illustration.

cycle of very-high-frequency signals and will reproduce those signals without distortion, owing entirely to the small mass of the electron. Special electrostatic-type tubes have been designed to display frequencies as high as 1,000 megacycles. When this frequency response is contrasted with the frequency response of any of the mechanical oscillographs, whose upper frequency limit is perhaps 5,000 or, at the most 10,000 c, the importance of the cathode-ray tube as an indicator is self-evident. The mechanical devices are limited by at least one moving part, which must possess some inertia and is also affected by friction. The beam of the cathode-ray tube, on the other hand, moves in a high vacuum and has no mechanically moving parts which may be hindered by friction.

The cathode-ray tube does have one disadvantage, which, quite fortunately, is easily overcome in most cases. The cathode-ray tube is quite insensitive; that is, it requires rather high voltages (for electrostatic tubes) or relatively large currents (for magnetic tubes) to deflect the beam and thus produce an indication. A voltage of 1 or 2 volts will not produce appreciable deflection on the face of the electrostatic-type tube. However, it is possible to amplify this signal and then apply it to the deflection plates. Thus, the vacuum-tube amplifier overcomes the only disadvantage of the cathode-ray tube and makes it one of the most valuable indicating devices. Also, vacuum-tube amplifiers can be used to increase the current to the deflection yoke of magnetic-type tubes so that appreciable deflection will be obtained.

The Magnetic vs the Electrostatic Cathode-Ray Tube. The electrostatic-type tube is employed in oscilloscopes practically to the exclusion of the magnetic type. One reason is that the deflection plates draw no appreciable current from the circuit under test, regardless of the deflection produced; while magnetic deflection is directly proportional to the current flowing through the deflection coils.

Another important consideration is that deflection plates depend entirely on voltage to deflect the beam, regardless of the frequency with which that voltage is applied; whereas magnetic deflecting coils inherently (due to inductance) have a frequency-response characteristic that varies practically inversely with frequency. With magnetic deflection, this frequency-response characteristic may produce serious distortion of the signal under observation. On the other hand, large deflection voltages which must be used to produce full-scale deflection in electrostatic tubes of the larger sizes tend to defocus the beam as it passes close to the deflection plate. The defocusing action is due to the charge on the plate retarding or accelerating the electron beam. This effect is objectionable in television applications because it results in a "fuzzy" outline for the images around the outer edges of the picture. The effect can be minimized by the use of push-pull deflection, since each deflection plate under this system of deflection requires but one half the voltage that is required for single-ended deflection.

Despite push-pull deflection, the defocusing effect is still present on the larger tubes. Since magnetic tubes do not produce this defocusing effect, they are more desirable for use in television. In addition, the frequency-response characteristic of their deflection coils may be compensated for, since the frequencies at which the beam is deflected are known fixed frequencies.

The use of electrostatic-type tubes in television was disputed by different manufacturers for a number of years. At present, the industry has reached certain definite conclusions:

1. Defocusing action in electrostatic-type tubes is not too objectionable in tubes whose screen diameter is 7 in. or less.

2. Television receivers employing an electrostatic-type tube are cheaper to manufacture.

3. A magnetic tube itself is cheaper to manufacture than an electrostatic tube of the same size, so that tube replacement costs are lower.

4. Magnetic-type tubes produce a higher-quality picture on screens that are larger than 7 in. in diameter.

5. Magnetic tubes are generally capable of higher beam currents that result in greater light output.

Thus, as a general rule, it will be found that electrostatic tubes are used almost exclusively for oscillographic applications and certain radar devices, and that magnetic tubes are used almost exclusively for television and as indicators in other types of radar gear.

5 Details of the Modern Cathode-Ray Tube

Introduction. Although it is not absolutely necessary for the average person who uses an oscilloscope to know the details of construction and operation of the cathode-ray tube, no book on the oscilloscope would be complete without a description of them. Furthermore, such information furnishes an appreciation of the problems involved in the development of more complicated, specialized instruments.

Classification of Cathode-Ray Tubes. Cathode-ray tubes differ in size, electrical characteristics, and the luminescent color and persistence of their screens.* These factors are always designated in the type number assigned to each different type tube. Cathode-ray tubes are assigned type numbers by the Radio Manufacturers Association just as the ordinary vacuum tubes are assigned type numbers.

One example of a cathode-ray tube type number is 5BP1. The number 5 indicates that this cathode-ray tube has a face diameter of 5 in. (± a small tolerance). The letter *B* refers to a complete electrical and mechanical specification which details the internal structure of the tube, including the connections of the various elements to the base of the tube. The letter *P* and the number 1 refer to the phosphor, the material of which the screen is made. As an illustration of this, a 5BP4 cathode-ray tube is identical with a 5BP1, except that a different screen material is used. Since, at this writing, there are fourteen different screen materials used in cathode-ray tubes, the type 5BP tube may be made with any of these screen materials, and the tube will still be electrically the same.

On the other hand, since the electrical ratings and characteristics of a tube change so drastically with different sizes of tubes, it *cannot* be concluded that a 3BP1 is exactly the same as a 5BP1 except for the size of its face. The letter following the figure that designates size is chosen in alphabetical order. For instance, the first 5-in. tube that was accepted as a standard type by the RMA was designated as a 5AP; the next, as a

---

* Since the dimensions of a cathode-ray tube are affected by the diameter of the face of the tube, and since the application of a tube determines its face diameter, the word "size" in reference to a cathode-ray tube is commonly used as a synonym for "face diameter."

42

5BP; the next, as a 5CP; and so on. Also, the first 3-in. tube that was accepted as a standard type by the RMA was designated as a 3AP; the next as a 3BP; and so forth. This is the method employed for assigning type designations to all tubes with different sizes of screen. This method of classification *does not* imply that a 5JP tube, for example, is better than a 5CP; it merely states that the 5JP type designation was granted at a later date than the 5CP. It must be remembered that different types of cathode-ray tubes are designed for different purposes, just as different

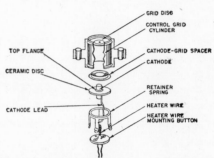

Fig. 5–1. Exploded drawing of cathode-grid assembly.

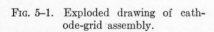

types of vacuum tubes are designed for different purposes. The more common types of cathode-ray tube are listed in Table 5-1. This table also gives the electrical characteristics of each type.

Physical Construction of the Modern Cathode-Ray Tube. The modern cathode-ray tube has a somewhat more complicated structure compared with the tube shown in Fig. 4-7. The electron gun alone contains four separate assemblies, which are mounted together on ceramic supports. These supports serve as mounting pieces as well as insulators between the electrodes. In addition, there is the deflection-plate assembly which is mounted on the electron gun. This entire assembly is inserted in the neck of the glass bulb.

Taking the electrodes in their respective order from the tube base, the first assembly is called the "control-grid assembly." This assembly consists of the first three electrodes of the cathode-ray tube, namely, the heater, the cathode, and the grid. In the modern cathode-ray tube, these three elements are carefully constructed and assembled to provide a rigid structure, thus increasing the durability of the cathode-ray tube as a scientific instrument. An exploded drawing of this assembly is shown in Fig. 5-1.

The heater is a noninductively wound coil of resistance wire, and the ends of this heater coil are welded to two rigid metal strips that are firmly held in the heater-wire mounting button. The heater wire itself is usually of tungsten and is coated with an oxide that acts as an insulator

TABLE 5-1

CHART OF ELECTROSTATIC DEFLECTION AND FOCUS CATHODE-RAY TUBES

Type No.	Nominal Diameter, In.	Over-all Length, In.	RMA Basing Designation	Heater Potential, Volts	Heater Current, Amp.	Typical Operation				Deflection Factor D-C Volts/In.	
						E_{b3}	E_{b2}	E_{b1}	E_{c1}	$D1$-$D2$	$D3$-$D4$
2AP-A	2	7-7/16	11L	6.3	0.6	....	1,000	250	-60	230	196
2BP	2	7-5/8	......	6.3	0.6	....	1,000	215	-50	114	109
3AP-A	3	11-1/2	7CE	2.5	2.1	....	15,000	450	-45	150	111
3BP-A	3	10	14G	6.3	0.6	....	1,500	430			
3GP-A	3	11-1/2	11A	6.3	0.6	....				200	148
3JP	3	10	14J	6.3	0.6	4,000	2,000	575	-60		
3KP	3	11-1/2	11M	6.3	0.6	....	2,000				
5BP-A	5	16-3/4	11N	6.3	0.6	....	2,000	450	-40	84	76
5CP-A	5	16-3/4	14J	6.3	0.6	4,000	2,000	575	-60	92	79
5UP	5	14-3/4	12E	6.3	0.6	....	2,000	490	-90	66	54
5JP-A	5	16-3/4	11E	6.3	0.6	4,000	2,000	520	-75	96	96
5LP-A	5	16-3/4	11F	6.3	0.6	4,000	2,000	500	-60	103	90
5RP-A	5	18-3/4	14F	6.3	0.6	20,000	2,000	575	-60	175	164
*5SP	5	18-3/4	14K	6.3	0.6	4,000	2,000	575	-60	92	79
7EP	7	15-1/2	11N	6.3	0.6	....	2,500	650	-60	110	95
7GP	7	14-1/2	14G	6.3	0.6	....	3,000	1,000	-60	108	89
7JP	7	14-1/2	14G	6.3	0.6	....	6,000	2,030	-120	216	177

* Dual electron gun employed in this tube. Values given are for each gun.

E_{b3} = Intensifier voltage; taken with respect to cathode.

E_{b2} = Accelerating electrode voltage (sometimes referred to as second anode voltage); taken with respect to cathode.

E_{b1} = Focusing electrode voltage (sometimes referred to as first anode voltage); taken with respect to cathode.

E_{c1} = Control grid voltage; taken with respect to cathode.

to prevent short-circuiting the respective heater coils. The heater is made small enough to pass into the hollow cylinder of the cathode.

The cathode is merely a metal cylinder closed at one end—the end farthest from the tube base. It is usually made of nickel, while most of the other electrodes of the electron gun are made of stainless steel No. 1812. The reason for using stainless steel for these electrodes is that it is nonmagnetic. The cathode cylinder is mounted in the center of a ceramic disc. This disc is held in place on the cathode by two small flanges on the outside wall of the cathode.

The control-grid electrode is a stainless steel cylinder which is closed at the end farthest from the tube base, except for a tiny aperture in the center. (The diameter of this aperture varies slightly from tube to tube, but in the tube under discussion, a type 5BP1-A, it is 0.030 in.) The control-grid cylinder is designed to contain both the heater and the cathode as well as two metal spacers, which have not yet been mentioned.

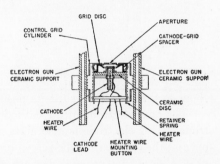

Fig. 5–2. Assembled drawing of cathode-grid assembly.

One of these spacers is the cathode-grid spacer. It is circular in shape and has the same diameter as the ceramic disc mounted on the cathode. The cathode-grid spacer fits tightly against the grid cylinder at one end and against the cathode ceramic at the other end. Thus, it is electrically in contact and is at the same potential as the grid, and it is insulated from the cathode.

The other spacer is, in reality, just a tripod retainer spring. The ceramic on which the heater is mounted snaps into grooves at the end of the legs of this retainer spring and is held rigidly in place. The flat top of this tripod supports the cathode ceramic.

The assembly of these three units—the heater, the cathode, and the grid—is quite simple. The heater ceramic, with the heater welded in place, is snapped into its grooves in the legs of the tripod retainer spring. The cathode is then slipped over the heater, and the cathode lead to the tube socket is fed through the hole in the heater ceramic provided for it. The cathode-grid spacer is inserted into the grid cylinder. Then, the assembly of the heater and the cathode is also slipped into the grid cylinder. This latter assembly is pushed in tightly until the keys on the legs of the tripod retainer spring snap into the grooves provided for them in the wall of the grid cylinder. Because this completed assembly is practically shockproof, it is known as the "locked-in cathode." A cross section of the completed assembly is shown in Fig. 5-2.

As a result of the careful engineering in this assembly, the cathode is in perfect alignment with the aperture in the end of the grid cylinder. The completed assembly is then mounted on the two ceramic mounts that sup-

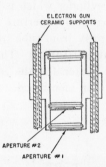

Fig. 5–3. Cross-section drawing of the preaccelerating electrode.

port all the electrodes of the electron gun and is welded tightly around them so that it cannot shift its position during normal handling.

The next electrode of the cathode-ray tube is the preaccelerating electrode. This electrode is also a stainless steel cylinder. It is completely open at the end nearest the screen of the tube, while the end nearest to the grid is closed by a metal disc which has an aperture of 0.040 in. in its

Fig. 5–4. Cross-section drawing of the focusing electrode.

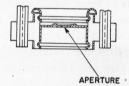

Fig. 5–5. Cross-section drawing of the accelerating electrode.

center. About one-fourth of the way up the preaccelerating electrode is another disc, which also contains a very tiny aperture. The distance between these two discs is determined by the over-all design of the particular cathode-ray tube. A drawing of the preaccelerator electrode is shown in Fig. 5-3.

The next electrode is the focusing electrode; a drawing of this is shown in Fig. 5-4. This electrode is also a stainless steel cylinder, but it is open at both ends.

The next and final electrode that makes up the electron gun is the accelerating electrode. It too is a cylinder open at both ends, but it contains another disc near the center. This disc also contains an aperture that is larger than the others used, approximately 0.080 in. (see Fig. 5-5). These dimensions are contingent upon the over-all design of the cathode-ray tube.

The previous discussion gives the details of the assembly of the electron gun. Each of these electrodes has an extension that is welded tightly around the two ceramic supports. This type of mounting ensures the correct interelectrode spacing.

These two ceramic supports also help to support the deflection plates. Fastened to the ends of the ceramic supports is a mica disc backed up by a metal ring (Fig. 5-6). This metal ring has a number of spiderlike fingers projecting from its outer edge and is, therefore, called the "spider." The mica associated with the spider is logically enough called the "spider mica." The spider mica contains a hole in its center that is cut to fit tightly around the end of the accelerating electrode. This type of construc-

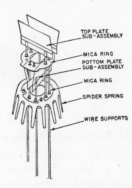

FIG. 5-6. Drawing of deflection plate assembly.

tion adds to the rigidity of the accelerating electrode, and, since the deflection plates are also mounted on the spider mica, it guarantees the alignment of the deflection plates with the electron gun.

The deflection plates are mounted in pairs—one pair at right angles to the other—on hard-drawn wires that are large enough in diameter to hold these plates firmly. Two such wires are used to mount each deflection plate. One of these wires from each plate passes through the spider mica and extends down the outside of the electron gun to make the electrical connection between the deflection plate and the socket. It should be noted that in some types of cathode-ray tubes the deflection plates are not connected electrically to the base of the tube; instead, the connections to the deflection plates may be brought out through the neck of the tube. In such cases, these connections usually terminate in caps, which are sometimes similar to the old-type grid cap, or possibly in a more modern connector sealed into the glass of the neck of the tube.

The support wires for the pair of deflection plates nearest the gun extend completely through the deflection plates and terminate in another mica ring called the "deflection-plate mica." This deflection-plate mica also has the leads to the other deflection-plate pair extending through it, these leads terminating in the deflection plates themselves. This closely knit arrangement of deflection plates and electron gun results in a structure that is sturdy and still has sufficient resilience to recover from sudden shocks without damage.

The glass bulb is also worthy of consideration. It is usually of molded glass thick enough to withstand atmospheric pressure when the tube is evacuated. The glass bulb of most small cathode-ray tubes is

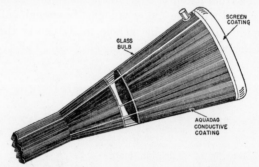

Fig. 5–7. Drawing of the glass bulb of the cathode-ray tube.

molded completely in one piece. After the molding process, it is carefully annealed to relieve any mechanical strain that may be set up in the normal cooling-off process. It is then washed very carefully to remove all particles of dust or dirt. After the bulb has been washed, the screen material is applied to the face of the tube. The screen material may be either blown on or settled on as a precipitate from a solution. If the latter is the case, the solution is then poured off very carefully. Heat must then be applied to the screen material first to make it adhere to the glass and then to activate the chemical properties of the screen. After this process, the tube is again annealed to relieve any strain. In the simpler types of tubes, an internal coating of carbon is applied on the walls with a brush as the tube is rotating. Figure 5-7 shows the completed bulb ready for the installation of the electron-gun and deflection-plate assembly.

After the conductive coating has dried, the complete electron-gun and deflection-plate assembly is inserted into the neck of the tube. The spider acts as a spring extending in all directions from the axis of the electron gun and thus centers the complete assembly in the neck of the bulb. Furthermore, the legs of the spider make contact with the internal conductive coating and maintain this coating at the same electrical potential as the accelerating electrode.

After the tube elements have been inserted, the tube is sealed and evacuated. Following the evacuation process, the base is applied, and all the leads to the tube elements are soldered into their respective base pins.

It should be noted that some tubes contain two coatings of this conductive material, separated by a space of about ½ in., applied to their walls. The conductive material nearest the screen is known as the "intensifier electrode," and connection is made through the glass bulb to this conductive coating by means of a suitable connector. Some tubes have been made with as many as six intensifier electrodes; however, these are usually specialized tubes. Figure 5-8 shows a cross-sectional drawing of a completed tube.

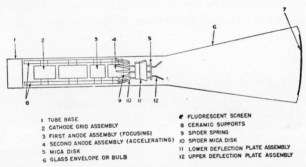

1 TUBE BASE	7 FLUORESCENT SCREEN
2 CATHODE GRID ASSEMBLY	8 CERAMIC SUPPORTS
3 FIRST ANODE ASSEMBLY (FOCUSING)	9 SPIDER SPRING
4 SECOND ANODE ASSEMBLY (ACCELERATING)	10 SPIDER MICA DISK
5 MICA DISK	11 LOWER DEFLECTION PLATE ASSEMBLY
6 GLASS ENVELOPE OR BULB	12 UPPER DEFLECTION PLATE ASSEMBLY

FIG. 5-8. Simplified cross-section drawing of a modern cathode-ray tube.

The curvature of the face of the cathode-ray tube is another factor that must receive consideration. Since the cathode-ray tube is so highly evacuated, it is necessary for the face and walls of the tube to be of very strong construction in order to withstand the force of the atmospheric air pressure. For this reason, the face of the tube is curved, since an arch construction is normally regarded as one of the strongest mechanical designs. If a large curvature is used, however, the patterns displayed on the screen, which is coated on the face of the tube, will appear very distorted because they are not on a flat surface. Thus, a compromise must be made between a flat-faced tube, which is ideal for use, and a curved-face tube, which is the ideal mechanical construction. Again, the application of the tube plays an important part. Tubes used in television must have as flat a face as possible, so that the image on the screen does not appear even slightly distorted; but tubes used in oscilloscopes can tolerate a greater face curvature, since the image being viewed is usually a single line.

As a general rule, the curvature of the face of 3- or 5-in. cathode-ray tubes, both of which are usually used in oscilloscopes, is equivalent to the curvature of the face of a sphere whose radius is 8 or, possibly, 10 in. This curvature varies with the tube type and is given in the physical specifications of each type. It is usually referred to as "radius of curvature of the face." The radius of curvature of the face of television-type tubes varies from 15 to 60 in., the average being about 25 in.

Tubes with absolutely flat faces have been made. These tubes have usually been 5-in. tubes, however. The thickness of the glass required for the face of flat-faced tubes becomes impractical as the diameter of the face is increased above 5 in.

Formation of the Electron Beam within the Cathode-Ray Tube. The function of the heater in the cathode-ray tube is merely to heat the cathode which surrounds it. Since the heater is made of high-resistance wire, current attempting to flow through this wire causes it to increase in temperature just as does the filament in an electric light bulb. The length

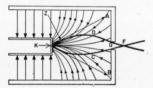

Fig. 5–9. Electrostatic field and paths of electrons within the cathode-grid assembly.

and diameter of the heater wire, which determine its resistance, are selected to cause the heater to increase in temperature to about 700° C when 6.3 volts is impressed across it. (Although some of the older type of tubes were operated at a variety of heater voltages, as low as 2.5 volts, the present tendency is to standardize on 6.3 volts as the potential to be applied to the heater of the cathode-ray tube.) The heater transmits its heat to the cathode sleeve by radiation.

When the cathode is heated to 700° C, the electron-emitting material coated on its end is capable of giving off electrons. These electrons are emitted in straight lines from the coated surface of the cathode. In normal operation of the cathode-ray tube, however, an electrostatic field exists between the grid and the cathode, the direction of which is from the grid to the cathode, as shown in Fig. 5-9. To consider the action within the grid cylinder, suppose an electron is emitted from the cathode in the direction indicated by the line KA. Each time this electron crosses a line of force of the electrostatic field, the path of this electron is bent toward the axis of the tube. This bending action is caused by the action of two opposing forces: the force with which the electron is emitted from the cathode E and the force exerted by the line of force of the electrostatic field P. The electron follows the course of the resultant of these two forces R, as shown in Fig. 5-10. If the resultant-of-force calculation is repeated for every line of force crossed by the electron, it will be found that the electron moves along the curved line KDF, as shown in Fig. 5-9. Similarly, an electron that is emitted in the direction KB is forced to follow the curved line KCF.

Regardless of the angle at which the electrons are emitted from the cathode, their path will bend so that they cross the axis of the cathode-ray tube at the point F. This condition exists because an electron which is emitted at an angle greater than KA will cross the electrostatic lines of force close to the grid cylinder. The force exerted by these lines is

FIG. 5-10. Vector drawing of the forces exerted on the electrons as they pass through the electrostatic field within the cathode-grid assembly.

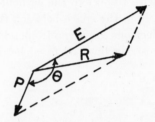

greater close to the grid cylinder. Therefore, P in Fig. 5-10 is greater, causing an increase in the angle θ, which represents a greater bending action. Conversely, electrons emitted at an angle smaller than KA will cross the electrostatic lines of force further from the grid cylinder. Thus, the force P in Fig. 5-10 is smaller, causing a decrease in the angle θ, which represents a smaller bending action.

One other factor should also be considered relative to the action between the cathode and the grid. From further study of Fig. 5-10, it should be quite evident that by increasing difference in potential between the grid and the cathode, the electrostatic field can become so strong that it overcomes the forward force of electron emission and bends the electron path so sharply that the electrons are forced back into the cathode and the beam of the tube is cut off. Even when the grid potential is such that electrons do escape from the grid cylinder to form a beam, there are still some electrons emitted from the cathode without sufficient energy to escape from the grid cylinder. These electrons are forced back into the cathode by the electrostatic field. Thus, it is evident that controlling the potential on the grid of the cathode-ray tube is an ideal method of controlling the number of electrons in the electron beam.

The point F where the electrons cross the axis of the cathode-ray tube is frequently called the "crossover point" of the electron beam. As the electrons pass this point, the normal tendency is for them to diverge again.

Accelerating and Shaping the Electron Beam. As the electrons leave the grid cylinder and pass into the space between the grid cylinder and the preaccelerating electrode, they are subjected to an exceedingly strong electrostatic field. This field is caused by the difference in potential of 1,000 to 1,500 volts between the control grid and the preaccelerating electrode.

Note: The control grid is usually maintained at a potential of from –1,000 to –1,500 volts. The preaccelerating electrode is usually at ground potential. With respect to the control grid, however, the preaccelerating electrode is 1,000 to 1,500 volts positive.

The velocity of the electrons within the grid cylinder is relatively slow, as shown by the fact that a negative potential of 50 volts on the grid with respect to the cathode is sufficient to cut off the beam.

It is in the space between the grid and the preaccelerator, then, that the electrons are given tremendous velocities. Figure 5-11 shows that the electrostatic lines of force between the grid and the preaccelerator are

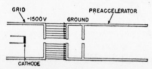

Fig. 5–11. The electrostatic field between the grid and preaccelerating electrodes.

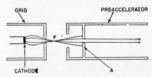

Fig. 5–12. The electron path between the grid and preaccelerating electrodes.

parallel (because the ends of the cylinders are closed) so that the electron beam remains quite concentrated as it is given its velocity.

The electron beam does diverge somewhat, however, owing to its direction as a result of the action within the grid cylinder and to the attraction of the walls of the preaccelerator before the beam acquires full velocity. This diverging action is overcome by the disc labeled *A* in Fig. 5-12. This disc contains another small aperture that eliminates from the beam the electrons that have diverged too far from the axis of the tube. These electrons are eliminated from the beam for two reasons: (1) to have a more concentrated beam resulting in better focusing and (2) to prevent the diverging electrons from striking the focusing electrode. If no electrons are permitted to strike the focusing electrode, this electrode will not draw current allowing a simpler design of the bleeder circuit of the power supply furnishing the operating potential to this electrode.

Focusing the Electron Beam. After the electron beam has been clipped by the aperture in the preaccelerating electrode, it proceeds along the axis of the tube without diverging appreciably. As it leaves the end of the preaccelerating electrode, it enters the region known as the "electron lens" of the cathode-ray tube. The electron lens in the present-day tube consists of two electrostatic fields: (1) the field between the preaccelerating and focusing electrodes and (2) the field between the focusing and accelerating electrodes. The action of these two fields is shown in Fig. 5-13.

The electrostatic field between the preaccelerating and focusing electrodes is nearly as strong as the one between the preaccelerating electrode and the grid, since the difference in potential between the preaccelerating and focusing electrodes is from 800 to 1,300 volts, depending upon the

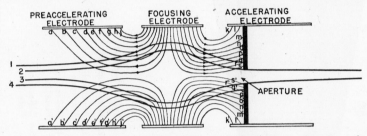

FIG. 5–13. The electron path in the electrostatic fields between the preaccelerating, focusing, and accelerating electrodes.

difference in potential used between the control grid and the preaccelerating electrode. Because the focusing electrode is negative with respect to the preaccelerating electrode, the direction of the field is from the focusing electrode to the preaccelerating electrode, as indicated in Fig. 5-13.

The path followed by a single electron, labeled 2 in the illustration, is caused to diverge away from the axis of the cathode-ray tube as it enters this electrostatic field. Since the lines of force a, b, and c are run almost opposite in direction to the path of the electron, the velocity of the electron is decreased, and the electron moves along the resultant of the two forces away from the axis of the tube. The line of force d produces much more of a divergent action than a slowing action because of the angle at which the electron crosses it. Owing to the shape of the electrostatic field, the electron must then cross each line of force again. As it crosses the line of force d for the second time, it crosses it at such an angle that this line of force bends the path of the electron back again toward the axis of the tube, as does each of the lines of force c, b, and a. The result of the action of these forces is to bend the path of the electron so that it is actually now moving parallel to the axis of the cathode-ray tube.

The electron then passes into the electrostatic field between the focusing electrode and the accelerating electrode. The direction of this field is

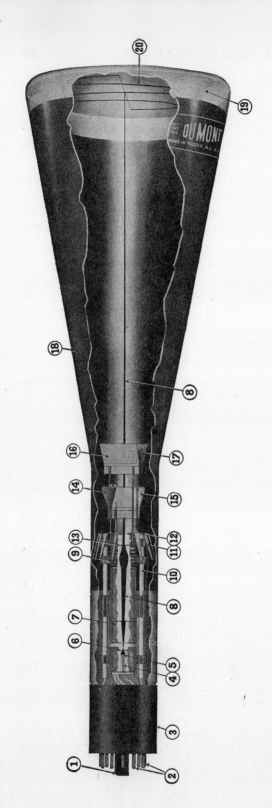

1. Key
2. Pins
3. Base
4. Heater Element
5. Cathode
6. Control Grid
7. Preaccelerating Electrode
8. Electron Beam
9. Focusing Electrode
10. Ceramic Support
11. Spider Support
12. Mica Support
13. Accelerating Electrode
14. Deflection Plate D3
15. Deflection Plate D4
16. Deflection Plate D1
17. Deflection Plate D2
18. Internal Conductive Coating
19. Fluorescent Screen Material
20. Pattern

FIG. 5-14. Cross-sectional drawing of a modern cathode-ray tube showing the shape of the electron beam within each of the electrodes. (*Courtesy, Allen B. Du Mont Laboratories, Inc.*)

from the focusing electrode to the accelerating electrode. Also, because the accelerating electrode is at the same potential as the preaccelerating electrode, this field is equal in strength to the one that was just discussed. As the electron crosses the lines of force *s, r, q,* and *p* for the first time, it crosses them at such an angle that its path is bent very sharply toward the axis of the cathode-ray tube. But as the electron crosses the line of force *p* for the second time, it crosses it at such an angle that the line of force tends again to bend the path of the electron away from the axis of the tube. This same situation is also true as the electron crosses the line of force *q*. As it reaches the lines of force *r* and *s*, however, it is traveling in almost the same direction as these two lines, so that they produce very little bending effect. Instead, they again accelerate the electron on its path toward the screen of the cathode-ray tube. The shape of the electrostatic field is such that all electrons escaping through the aperture in the accelerating electrode are accelerated along a path which is at such an angle with the axis of the tube as to result in all the electrons converging at a single point on the screen of the tube.

The path of the electron indicated as 3 in Fig. 5-13 is similar to the path labeled 2, except that this electron is on the other side of the axis of the cathode-ray tube. It can be seen in the figure that the electrons which travel along the periphery of the beam, indicated by the paths 1 and 4, are caused to follow paths similar to those of 2 and 3, but that they are mechanically clipped from the beam by the disc in the preaccelerating electrode. These electrons are too far from the axis of the tube to permit them to be focused on the screen of the cathode-ray tube and are, therefore, eliminated from the beam. They are absorbed by the accelerating electrode, which is at ground potential. A complete picture of the action of each of the electrodes on the beam of electrons is shown in Fig. 5-14.

Deflecting the Electron Beam. The mechanics of deflecting the electron beam were discussed carefully in the preceding chapter. The explanation of how this beam is deflected has already been given, but a few more points should be stressed.

Earlier, it was explained that deflection of the beam is dependent upon the velocity of the electrons and the intensity of the electrostatic field between the deflection plates. A third factor entering into the discussion of deflection is the length of the electrostatic field.

For example, if a pair of deflection plates has a difference in potential of 100 volts applied to them, they are separated a distance of ½ in.; they are ¾ in. long; and they will not deflect an electron beam passing between them to as great an angle as another pair of deflection plates subjected to the same conditions whose length is 1 in. The explanation is that by elongating the deflection plates the electrostatic field is elongated, and the electron beam is subjected to the force of the field for a greater length of time. Actually, this results in the same effect, as far as deflection is concerned, as though the beam moved more slowly through the field.

In the development of the cathode-ray tube, the deflection plates were continually made longer to obtain better deflection sensitivity up to the point where the electron beam actually hit the deflection plate when a relatively low potential was applied. It was then discovered that the deflection plate could be bent and thus maintain a long plate and obtain high deflection sensitivity without the size of the plate having any limiting effect.

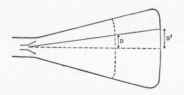

Fig. 5–15. Drawing to show the effect of length of tube on deflection sensitivity.

Another factor affecting deflection sensitivity is the distance from the deflection plate to the screen of the cathode-ray tube, illustrated plainly in Fig. 5-15. The farther the screen is from the deflection plate, the greater the deflection sensitivity of the cathode-ray tube; that is, the greater the deflection produced on the screen for a given difference in potential applied to the deflection plates. For the same reason, the deflection-plate pair that is nearer the gun of the cathode-ray tube is more sensitive than the deflection-plate pair that is nearer the screen.

The Intensifier Electrode. The addition of one more electrode, called the "intensifier electrode," to the cathode-ray tube is an improvement in increasing the light output of the screen material without an appreciable loss in deflection sensitivity. The intensifier electrode consists of another conductive coating on the inside of the glass envelope. This intensifier coating is separated by approximately ½ in. from the coating that is connected to the accelerating electrode. Connection is made to the coating from a connector which resembles a grid cap through the wall of the bulb. A high positive voltage is applied to the intensifier. This positive voltage is usually equal to the difference in potential between the grid and the accelerating electrode. The reason that this intensifier electrode does not appreciably decrease the deflection sensitivity is that the intensifier electrode accelerates the electrons in the beam after deflection has taken place. The accelerating action of the electron beam is due to the electrostatic field between the graphite coating to which the accelerating electrode is connected (maintained at ground potential) and the intensifier coating maintained at a high positive potential. The lines of electrostatic force run from the first graphite coating to the graphite coating of the intensifier, as shown in Fig. 5-16. Thus, the electron beam traveling through this field is traveling in the same direction as the lines of force and these lines tend to accelerate the electron beam as it travels along them. Since the beam has already been deflected, the deflection sensitivity is not appreciably affected.

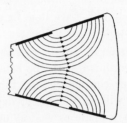

FIG. 5–16. Electrostatic field between the accelerating electrode and the intensifier band.

Accelerating Potential. The term "accelerating potential" refers to the difference in potential between the cathode and the final accelerating electrode. In tubes that have no intensifier, the accelerating electrode of the electron gun is the final accelerating electrode; but in tubes that employ an intensifier, the accelerating potential is the difference in potential between the cathode and the intensifier. This is usually referred to as "over-all accelerating potential" applied to the tube. As an example, a normal tube may be operated with the cathode at –1,500 volts, the accelerating electrode at ground, and the intensifier at +1,500 volts. In this case, the accelerating potential applied to the electron gun is 1,500 volts, the difference between the cathode and the accelerating electrode. The over-all accelerating potential applied to the tube, however, is 3,000 volts, the difference in potential between the cathode and the intensifier.

The term "accelerating potential" is used chiefly in the consideration of over-all tube performance. The accelerating potential applied to the electron gun determines the velocity of the electrons as they pass between the deflection plates. Thus, all other factors being equal, the accelerating potential applied to the electron gun determines the deflection sensitivity of the tube, i.e., the greater the accelerating potential, the lower the deflection sensitivity.

On the other hand, the over-all accelerating potential determines for the most part the brightness of the pattern on the screen. The greater the velocity of the electrons, the more energy they impart to the screen material, and, therefore, the greater the light output of the screen. The advantage, then, of tubes that employ intensifiers is that since they accelerate the electron beam after it has been deflected, they obtain a greater light output without appreciably decreasing the deflection sensitivity.

Screen Materials. Only a few materials have the ability to emit light when they are struck by an electron beam. As mentioned in Chap. 4, this property is known as "fluorescence." Since all these materials possess some degree of persistence after they have been excited, they also possess the quality known as "phosphorescence." The light emitted by these materials through either of these two processes is commonly called "cold light," since it is light that is generated without the generation of large quantities of heat.

Screen materials, referred to technically as "phosphors," are classified in accordance with the color of light that they emit and with their persistence characteristics. Since both the color and persistence characteristics will vary widely, depending upon the materials from which the screen is made as well as upon the treatment to which the screen is subjected during the manufacture of the tube, the RMA has standardized certain types of screens.

At this writing there are 14 different screens which have been designated as standard. These range in number from P1 consecutively to P14. Of these 14 different screens, only about 6 are really very popular, viz., the P1, P2, P4, P5, P7, and P11 screens. The 14 standard RMA phosphors are listed in Table 5-2, along with their characteristic colors and chief uses.

Factors Affecting the Light Output of Screens. The light emitted from a fluorescent screen depends upon (1) the over-all accelerating potential applied to the tube; (2) the material from which the screen is made; (3) the thickness of the screen material; and (4) the speed at which the electron beam passes over a given area of screen (writing speed).

Cascade Screens. Cascade screens, as the name implies, are two screens coated one on top of the other. The screen material near the outside of the tube is usually a material with long persistence characteristic; whereas the inner coating is usually of a material with short persistence but a very high efficiency. The screen coating near the outside, i.e., the long-persistence coating, is activated by both the electron beam and the light from the inner coating and thus receives more energy than it would from the electron beam alone. As a result, the persistence obtained from a cascade screen is usually longer than that obtained from a single screen. The P7 and the P14 screen types are two examples of cascade screens.

TABLE 5-2

RMA STANDARD PHOSPHORS—THEIR CHARACTERISTICS AND CHIEF USES

Screen	Persistence	Composition	Fluorescence	Phosphorescence	Applications
P1	Medium	Zinc orthosilicate	Green	Green	Most common screen used for visual observation in oscilloscopes; its efficiency is rather high, resulting in bright traces with relatively low accelerating potential
P2	Long	Zinc sulphide	Blue-green	Yellow-green	The general-purpose screen for use in oscilloscopes employing accelerating potentials of 3,000 volts or more; its long persistence makes it useful for the visual observation of transients
P3	Medium	Zinc beryllium silicate	Yellow	Yellow	Chiefly used in oscilloscopes, but not so efficient as P1; its persistence has an exponential decay characteristic that is chiefly of interest in television
P4	Medium	Zinc sulphide and zinc beryllium silicate	White	White	Chiefly used in television-type cathode-ray tubes
P5	Short	Calcium wilomite	Blue	Blue	Chiefly used for photography on continuous-motion film for frequencies above 200 kc
P6	Medium	Zinc sulphide and a complex compound of zinc and calcium sulphide	White	White	Developed chiefly for use in color television
P7	Long	Zinc sulphide cascaded on zinc and calcium sulphide	Blue-white	Orange	Originally developed for radar; similar in characteristics to P2 screen but having longer persistence
P8	Same as P7	(Reserved by the British as being confidential during World War II)			
P9	Long	Calcium phosphate	White	White	In addition to the long persistence, this screen gives very high definition; developed for radar applications
P10	Very long	Potassium chloride	Magenta on white	Magenta on white	Also developed for radar; its chief advantage is its efficiency even under high ambient-light conditions
P11	Short	Zinc sulphide	Blue	Blue	Used chiefly in oscilloscopes for photography; it has a higher visual and photographic efficiency than the P5, but it cannot be used for recordings on continuous-motion film at frequencies above 200 kc per second, because its persistence is slightly longer than the P5
P12	Long	Zinc magnesium fluoride	Orange	Orange	Used for fire-control radar for scanning rates between 4 and 16 scans per second
P13	Discontinued		Red	Red	Also developed for fire-control radar
P14	Long	Zinc sulphide cascaded on zinc and calcium sulphide	White	Orange	Developed for radar operating at a scanning rate of about 1 scan per second

Long-persistence screens are used in oscilloscopes for observing low-frequency signals, signals that occur at low repetition rates, or transient signals. A transient signal is one that occurs only once for any given set of conditions. In addition to the factors affecting the light output of any screen material, the persistence of any screen is also affected by the ambient light conditions. Any external light that strikes the face of the tube is referred to as "ambient light."

6 The General-Purpose Oscilloscope

Introduction. In order to use an oscilloscope intelligently, it is necessary to know first, the uses to which an oscilloscope may be put; second, how the various circuits of the oscilloscope will display the signal; and third, the effect of each control on the circuit to which it is connected.

Chapter 1 states that any oscillation or vibration that can be converted into electrical energy may be studied by means of the oscilloscope. Thus, an oscilloscope is an instrument for measuring a varying voltage, which, to eliminate confusion, is usually called a "signal voltage," or, for brevity, a "signal." Also, it is pointed out in Chap. 1 that the signal under test or examination with an oscilloscope may be from any number of sources, as long as it has been converted into a voltage before it enters the oscilloscope.

Since it is desirable, in most cases, to study the variations in the signal voltage as a function of time, an electronic circuit has been devised to produce a voltage that varies in direct proportion to time. This is called the "sweep frequency" and the circuit in which it is developed is called a "time-base generator" and is incorporated as an integral part of oscilloscopes that are produced to display the variations in signal voltage with respect to time. Such an oscilloscope is so comprehensive in its application that it is referred to as a "general-purpose oscilloscope."

General Description of the Oscilloscope. A typical general-purpose oscilloscope may be broken down into its major parts, usually referred to as "blocks," as in Fig. 6-1. Here, it can be seen that such an instrument contains the following units: a cathode-ray tube, a time-base generator, a horizontal amplifier, a vertical amplifier, a power supply that furnishes a positive low voltage, a power supply that furnishes a negative high voltage, and, in some cases, a third power supply that furnishes a positive high voltage. In addition, a number of switches are shown which add to the versatility and operating convenience of the instrument.

The cathode-ray tube serves, of course, as the indicating device for the instrument. With the exception of the power supplies, the remaining blocks transmit the two signals, one to each of the two sets of deflection plates. Generally, the vertical amplifier, which may consist of a number of amplifying stages, plus any switching and related circuits, is referred to as the "vertical channel." The vertical channel carries the signal that is impressed on the pair of plates in the cathode-ray tube which produce vertical deflection of the beam.

It was also stated previously that the oscilloscope presents the unknown signal as a function of the known signal in the form of a graph on the face of the cathode-ray tube. Since the conventional method for

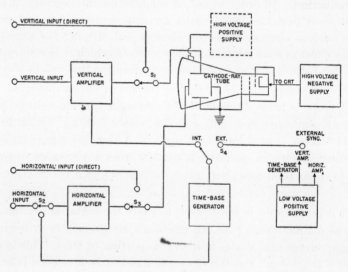

Fig. 6–1. Block diagram of a general-purpose oscilloscope.

plotting graphs is to use the horizontal axis of the graph to measure or record the independent quantity and the vertical axis to measure the dependent quantity, the oscilloscope manufacturers have conformed to this convention. The unknown signal is applied to the vertical channel of the oscilloscope, and the known signal is applied to the horizontal channel. Typical examples of signals plotted against time have already been shown in Chap. 1 in Figs. 1-2, 1-3, and 1-4.

It is also worth noting that some manufacturers have gone a step further in carrying over the mathematical graph by calling the vertical channel the "Y axis" and the horizontal channel the "X axis." This method is often convenient to the operator who is familiar with mathematics, but to prevent confusion, this book will continue to use the terms "vertical" and "horizontal."

Summarizing the block diagram in Fig. 6-1, we find that the signal to be studied is connected to the vertical amplifier, amplified, and im-

pressed on the vertical deflection plates of the cathode-ray tube to produce vertical deflection of the beam. The time-base generator furnishes
a signal, whose voltage varies as a linear function of time, to the horizontal amplifier, which amplifies this signal and applies it to the horizontal plates of the cathode-ray tube. The cathode-ray tube beam
responds to the resultant of these two signals applied simultaneously and
traces a pattern on the screen. The interpretation of these patterns will
be discussed in a later chapter. The function of the various power supplies is to furnish the proper operating voltages to the horizontal and
vertical amplifiers, and to the various electrodes of the cathode-ray tube.

The Cathode-Ray Tube.   It is convenient to have some control over
the action of the cathode-ray tube as it is employed in the general-purpose oscilloscope. As a result, controls labeled INTENSITY, FOCUS, VERTICAL

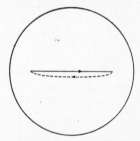

FIG. 6–2. Drawing showing the deflection produced by a linear time-base
generator. The return trace has been
displaced so that it can be seen.

POSITIONING, and HORIZONTAL POSITIONING are usually found on the front
panel. As previously implied, the latter two controls are sometimes called
Y POSITION and X POSITION, respectively. The INTENSITY control decreases
or increases the bias on the grid of the cathode-ray tube so that, respectively, more or fewer electrons are allowed to pass through the control
grid and strike the screen. The FOCUS control changes the voltage on the
focusing electrode of the cathode-ray tube and thus exerts a more or
less constricting force on the electron beam, depending upon the number
of electrons in that beam.

The function of the VERTICAL POSITIONING control is to move the beam,
or trace, to any desired position in a vertical plane. The function of the
HORIZONTAL POSITIONING control is similar, except that it moves the beam
in a horizontal plane.

The Time-Base Generator.   The time-base generator furnishes a
voltage that varies linearly with respect to time. When this voltage is
applied to the horizontal deflection plates, the spot formed by the beam
of the cathode-ray tube is deflected to the left side of the screen and then
moved to the right at a definite rate of speed. When the spot reaches the
right side of the screen, the time-base generator causes it to move rapidly

back to the left side of the screen and begin its trace again. This movement is illustrated in the drawing in Fig. 6-2. In the figure the return trace has been moved down so that it can be seen. Standard practice calls for the spot to move from left to right, since this is the conventional direction used in plotting graphs. Consequently, most commercial oscilloscopes are constructed to meet this convention. However, if right-to-left movement of the spot is desired, it is necessary only to reverse the connections to the horizontal-deflection plates.

To produce a sweep in a tube equipped for single-ended deflection, it is necessary that a varying voltage (see Fig. 6-4) be applied to the horizontal deflection plate. The voltage must vary from positive to negative, so that the beam is first attracted by the left horizontal plate (as the

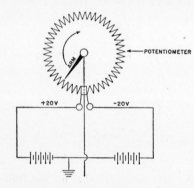

Fig. 6-3. A mechanical means for generating a saw-toothed wave.

operator views the tube) and is gradually attracted less until the beam reaches the center of the tube, at which time the potential on this plate reaches zero. As the plate then becomes more and more negative, the beam is repelled beyond the center of the tube to the right side.

Although it is not common practice but serves the purpose of an excellent analogy, such a varying voltage can be generated mechanically by the potentiometer shown in Fig. 6-3. It has a rotating arm which is capable of complete rotation. By rotating the arm, the voltage on it will vary from +20 to −20 volts for about 355 deg of rotation. As the arm is rotated further, the voltage varies from −20 to +20 volts for the remaining 5 deg., and the cycle repeats as the rotation continues. A graph of this waveform is shown in Fig. 6-4. From this graph it is easy to see how the waveform obtained its name as a "saw-toothed wave." If this wave were placed on the left horizontal deflection plate, the time required for the voltage to change from A to B represents the time of the sweep, i.e., the time required for the beam to move from the left side of the screen to the right side. The time from B to C is the time of the return trace, i.e., the time required by the beam to return to the left side of the screen.

The frequency with which the beam is swept across the screen must be variable for the instrument to be versatile. To change the frequency of the saw-toothed wave generated by the mechanical apparatus shown in Fig. 6-3, it is necessary to rotate the arm either more or less rapidly. A more rapid rotation of the arm causes the beam to complete more sweeps across the screen in a given length of time (a higher frequency sweep, Fig. 6-5), and a less rapid rotation results in fewer sweeps in the same period of time (a lower frequency sweep, Fig. 6-6).

Another consideration is that of the linearity of the sweep. If the sweep voltage does not change in direct proportion to time, the line *AB* of Fig. 6-4 will not be straight. If the potentiometer arm is not rotating

FIG. 6-4. A graphical representation of a saw-toothed wave whose frequency is *x* cps.

FIG. 6-5. A graphical representation of a saw-toothed wave whose frequency is 2*x* cps.

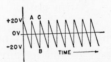

FIG. 6-6. A graphical representation of a saw-toothed wave whose frequency is ½*x* cps.

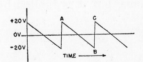

with uniform motion, or if the resistance of the potentiometer is not uniform, the voltage may vary from *A* to *B*, as shown in Fig. 6-7*a*, with the result that a sine wave impressed simultaneously on the vertical deflection plate will look like that in Fig. 6-7*b*. Contrast this with the proper appearance of a sine wave on a linear sweep shown in Fig. 1-2. If the voltage varies according to the curve shown in Fig. 6-8*a*, the sine wave will look like that in Fig. 6-8*b*. A lack of linearity of the sweep may very easily mislead the operator, particularly if he doesn't realize that the sweep is not linear.

If the cathode-ray tube employed is for balanced deflection, it is necessary to generate two waveforms simultaneously, which are actually mirror images (i.e., 180 deg. out of phase) of each other, and apply one to each deflection plate. These waveforms, for analogy again, can be generated by the apparatus shown in Fig. 6-9. Two potentiometers, similar to the one previously used, may be used with their arms coupled together in the same angular position on a single, insulated shaft. It will be noticed that the voltage of each waveform is only one half the voltage of the waveform generated for single-ended deflection. However, the difference in potential between the two waves at any instant is identical with the

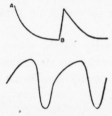

FIG. 6–7. The upper nonlinear saw-toothed wave, applied to the horizontal deflection plates will produce a distorted sine wave similar to that shown below it when a sine wave is simultaneously applied to the vertical deflection plates.

FIG. 6–8. The upper nonlinear saw-toothed wave, above, applied to the horizontal deflection plates will produce a distorted sine wave similar to that shown below it when a sine wave is simultaneously applied to the vertical deflection plates.

difference in potential measured between the single-ended saw-toothed wave and ground for any given position of the beam.

This method of obtaining saw-toothed waveforms is not only cumbersome, but it is limited by mechanical considerations to use at low fre-

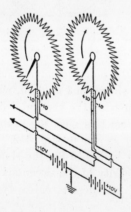

FIG. 6–9. A mechanical means for generating two saw-toothed waves 180 deg out of phase with each other for balanced deflection.

quencies only. It is *not* the method employed in present-day general-purpose oscilloscopes. The method was presented, however, because it is often quite helpful to understand mechanical analogies of some of the more basic electronic principles. The time-base generator in the general-purpose oscilloscope develops the same waveforms as shown here, but it develops them with vacuum-tube circuits. These circuits are discussed in Chap. 9.

The frequency of the time-base sweep is usually varied by two different controls: a COARSE FREQUENCY control and a FINE FREQUENCY control. A COARSE FREQUENCY control is usually a rotary switch, which adjusts the circuit to a desired range of frequencies, and the FINE FREQUENCY control can be used to adjust to a specific frequency within this selected range. Other positions of the COARSE FREQUENCY switch will give other ranges over which the FINE FREQUENCY control will operate.

Synchronization.   In order to view a pattern intelligently on the screen of the cathode-ray tube, it is necessary to have that pattern fixed on the screen so that it does not move. This can almost be accomplished by setting the FINE FREQUENCY control carefully. Regardless of the setting, however, the time-base generator is not capable of holding a definite frequency without drifting somewhat from it. This drift causes the entire pattern to drift slowly across the screen of the cathode-ray tube. To compensate for this frequency drift, a portion of the signal under observation is fed into the sweep generator to synchronize the sweep frequency with the frequency of the wave under observation. An amplitude control enables the operator to apply just enough synchronizing voltage to maintain synchronization, i.e., to keep the pattern in a fixed position on the screen. To obtain the most satisfactory pattern on the screen, the FINE FREQUENCY control should be set as close to the correct frequency as possible before any synchronizing voltage is applied. Provision is frequently made, as shown in Fig. 6-1, for selecting this synchronizing voltage from either the vertical amplifier or an external source. The switch S4 in Fig. 6-1 is the SYNCHRONIZING SELECTOR switch.

Horizontal Amplifier.   Amplifiers are provided in both the horizontal and vertical channels of the oscilloscope to amplify low-level signals so that they will produce sufficient deflection on the cathode-ray tube to be studied conveniently.

The amplifier provided in the horizontal channel may be used to amplify either the sweep output of the time-base generator or an external signal that is applied to the HORIZONTAL INPUT terminal. The switch S2 selects the input to this amplifier as determined by the operator. A gain control for this amplifier gives the operator control of the signal voltage applied to the horizontal deflection plates.

The amplifier may have any number of stages, depending on the gain and frequency response desired of the amplifier. Care should be taken by the operator to stay within the frequency limitations of the amplifier, otherwise he may obtain patterns that will be as misleading as those in

Figs. 6-7 and 6-8. Frequency limitations of amplifiers are explained in greater detail in Chap. 8.

Vertical Amplifier. Many oscilloscope manufacturers build general-purpose oscilloscopes with identical amplifiers in the vertical and horizontal channels. However, it is also true that many oscilloscopes are built containing vertical amplifiers that have a better frequency response and more gain than the horizontal amplifiers. Again, the operator should be careful not to exceed the frequency limits of the vertical amplifier. As in the horizontal amplifier, a gain control is also available in the vertical amplifier to give the operator control over the input voltage and thus over the amount of vertical deflection.

Deflection-Plate Connections. Occasionally, it is desirable to connect a signal to the deflection plates without passing it through the amplifiers; e.g., if the frequency of the signal being observed is beyond the frequency limits of the amplifier. This condition may be true of either one or both of the horizontal and vertical channels. For this reason, some commercial oscilloscopes provide facilities for shunting or by-passing the amplifiers. This is usually accomplished merely by placing a switch in each channel, as shown in Fig. 6-1.

Power Supply. As previously stated, various voltages are required to operate the cathode-ray tube. Also, the other circuits of the oscilloscope require certain voltages for their operation. The average general-purpose oscilloscope really contains two distinctly separate power supplies: a negative high-voltage supply and a positive low-voltage supply. The negative high-voltage supply furnishes approximately from −1,000 to −1,500 volts to operate the cathode-ray tube. This voltage is rectified and filtered and connected through a high-resistance bleeder to ground. The different voltages to the various electrodes of the cathode-ray tube are obtained from this bleeder. The current through the bleeder may vary from 3 to 5 ma, depending upon design features. The positive low-voltage supply furnishes between +300 and +400 volts to operate all the other tubes and the positioning circuits of the cathode-ray tube. The current drain on this supply varies appreciably with the number of tubes in the instrument.

Occasionally, some manufacturers use the positive low-voltage supply also to furnish a positive voltage to the intensifier electrode of intensifier-type cathode-ray tubes and thus add 300 or 400 volts to the over-all accelerating potential of the tube. It is customary, however, to add another power supply if an intensifier-type cathode-ray tube is used. This supply is a positive high-voltage supply and may furnish up to approximately +1,500 volts to operate the intensifier electrode. The current drain on this supply, like that of the negative high-voltage supply, is approximately 3 to 5 ma.

Warning

From the preceding description of the power supplies, it can readily be seen that such voltages are dangerous. Personal contact with these voltages will produce severe burns and may even cause death. For this reason, never operate an oscilloscope with its case removed. Even when the power is turned off, certain conditions may exist that leave dangerous potentials on capacitors and will cause severe shock and burns if contacted. *Always* remove the power cord from the socket and *always* discharge the capacitors before attempting any repair work on an oscilloscope.

Other Operating Switches. The various switches shown in Fig. 6-1 are for the convenience of the operator. All these switches may not be found in every commercial oscilloscope, but at least two or three will be present in each general-purpose model.

As previously mentioned, the switch $S1$ permits signals to be applied directly to the vertical-deflection plates of the cathode-ray tube. A modification of this circuit may be incorporated, using a double-pole double-throw switch in this position. The lead from the vertical input terminal is connected to one of the other poles, as shown in Fig. 6-10, to permit the use of only one VERTICAL INPUT terminal.

FIG. 6-10. The circuit showing the use of a double-pole double-throw switch for shunting the vertical amplifier.

The switch $S3$ serves the same function in the horizontal channel as does $S1$ in the vertical channel. Figure 6-11 shows how the circuit may be connected to utilize a single HORIZONTAL INPUT terminal.

The switches $S2$ and $S4$ have been discussed previously in this chapter, so there is no necessity for reviewing their functions.

Occasionally, it is convenient to have a fifth switch, which is not shown in Fig. 6-1. This switch is frequently called the "beam switch," and is connected in the high-voltage power supply to switch off the beam of the cathode-ray tube. It enables the operator to leave his oscilloscope in readiness without the danger of burning the screen of the cathode-ray tube. When it becomes necessary to use the oscilloscope, the beam switch

FIG. 6–11. The circuit showing the use of a double-pole double-throw switch for shunting the horizontal amplifier.

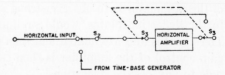

is thrown on, and the instrument is ready for use without waiting for the usual "warm-up" period.

Other Types of Oscilloscopes. The general-purpose oscilloscope, as just described, is probably the most popular type in use today. However, there are many others whose circuits are designed for specific purposes. Some oscilloscopes are much simpler than the general-purpose oscilloscope, e.g., the National type CRV. This instrument contains merely a cathode-ray tube, a power supply, and terminals to permit external signals to be connected to the deflection plates of the cathode-ray tube. It is designed primarily as a modulation monitor for use with radio transmitters.

At the other extreme, there are those oscilloscopes which are much more complex than the general-purpose model, e.g., the RCA type 715-B and the DuMont type 248-A. They contain 33 and 35 tubes, respectively, and are designed primarily for the precise measurement of high-frequency electrical signals.

Within this wide range of oscilloscopes, from the simple to the complex, there are many more features incorporated in the more complex instruments than have been enumerated in the preceding discussion. Some of these features are merely utility devices, whereas others are necessary for certain applications of the oscilloscope in the various industrial fields.

Stepped Attenuators. Stepped attenuators are resistance-capacitance circuits connected to various contacts of a switch, which are often incorporated in the vertical and horizontal channels, to reduce the voltage of the input signal. They usually reduce the signal in steps by a ratio of 10:1 or 100:1, or sometimes both, and are compensated so that the waveform of the signal is not distorted. Since the normal gain control is, in reality, a continuous attenuator, and since the stepped attenuator provides additional attenuation, an oscilloscope employing the stepped attenuator in addition to its gain control can display signals having a wide range of voltages. As an example, it may be desirable to examine the waveform at the input and the output of an amplifier. If the input signal is examined first, the output signal may be large enough to produce more than full-scale deflection. Use of the attenuator would reduce the signal by a definite ratio so that it could be observed. Another use of the attenuator is to observe strong signals which, if connected directly to the deflection plates, would produce more than full-scale deflection. The signal is first attenuated and then passed through the amplifier. The gain control of the amplifier is then capable of controlling signal amplitude to any desired deflection.

Beam Modulation. Occasionally, it is desirable to know the exact time interval between two given points on the signal being observed. Such a measurement may be made by varying the intensity of the trace at definite time intervals, which may be done by applying a pulse or a square wave to the control grid of the cathode-ray tube. A positive pulse will increase the flow of electrons for a length of time equal to the duration of the pulse and will produce a more intense trace for that period. A negative pulse applied to the control grid of the cathode-ray tube will correspondingly cut off (blank) the beam for the same period of time and produce a dark spot on the trace. Modulation of the beam in this way is sometimes called "Z-axis modulation" because the control grid provides another axis for applying a third signal to the cathode-ray tube. Figure 6-12 shows a signal with timing markers applied to intensify the trace, and Fig. 6-13 shows the same signal with timing markers blanking the trace.

Single Sweep. For certain applications which do not repeat but occur only once under a given set of conditions, it is necessary to observe these conditions on a single sweep. Single sweep is desirable in studies of

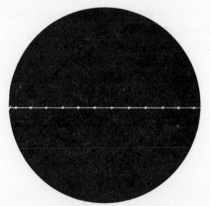

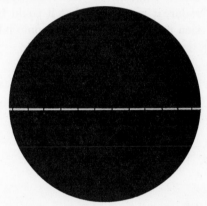

FIG. 6–12. Oscillogram of a horizontal trace with timing markers applied to intensify the trace.

FIG. 6–13. Oscillogram of a horizontal trace with timing markers applied to blank the trace.

pressure changes during detonations, voltage or current changes during welding operations, the operation of relays, and the testing of circuit breakers. The normal recurrent sweep for such studies has two major disadvantages. (1) The recurring base line is much more intense than the observed signal, since the base line occurs many times and the signal only once. (2) The signal being viewed occurs on an unpredictable portion of the screen, since the position of the spot at the time this type of signal occurs cannot be controlled. Single sweep causes the spot to sweep across the screen only once; thus, there is no base line to confuse the pattern. Furthermore, single sweeps may be triggered so that the desired waveform is obtained on the optimum viewing portion of the screen. Usually, cathode-ray tubes having long-persistance screens are employed with the single sweep so that the pattern may be viewed for a longer period of time.

Delay Networks. On occasions where the single sweep cannot be triggered except by the signal itself, it is common practice to connect a delay network in series with the signal before it is applied to the vertical amplifier. This procedure delays the signal sufficiently so that the sweep is started before the signal being observed is applied to the vertical deflection plates. Thus, the entire transient may be observed.

Repetitive Sweeps. The introduction of repetitive sweeps is a natural sequence to the single sweep. It is used for the observation of transient signals which occur at a definite repetition rate. The first important use of this type of sweep was in radar. Radar indicators employ sweep circuits that are triggered repetitively with every burst of r-f energy that is transmitted. After this type of sweep was developed and used for radar, it was found that it could be used for making innumerable precision measurements in electronic laboratories.

7 Power-Supply Circuits

Power Supply. The power supply of an oscilloscope is usually considerably more complex than the power supplies incorporated in most of the other electronic instruments. The average oscilloscope requires both high voltage and low voltage as well as special heater voltages. In addition, the rectified voltages must all be carefully filtered to eliminate ripple, which might cause spurious deflection of the beam of the cathode-ray tube.

Naturally, the design of the remaining circuits of the instrument determines the requirements of the power supply. For example, an oscilloscope containing a high-gain amplifier requires a B+ voltage, which is practically free of all ripple, for the plates of the amplifier tubes. An oscilloscope that operates the cathode-ray tube at high accelerating potentials, thus lowering the deflection sensitivity, requires the final amplifier stages to be operated at relatively high voltages.

Some oscilloscope designs demand that the power supply furnish both positive and negative low voltages as well as positive and negative high voltages.

Power Transformer. Most general-purpose oscilloscopes contain only one power transformer, which is usually designed with two primary windings and many secondaries, depending again on the requirements of the instrument. The design of the power transformer for oscilloscopes presents several factors in addition to normal transformer design. Its weight must be kept to a minimum, since most oscilloscopes are portable; it must be designed to operate at line frequencies as low as 40 c, which requires more core material, thereby increasing the weight; and the high voltages require additional insulation, again increasing the weight and size. Core material is also added to lower the leakage of magnetic flux.

No compromises may be tolerated on insulation or core material, but they are calculated very carefully with a suitable safety factor. The normal insulation between windings is sufficient for twice the peak-to-peak voltage plus 1,000. The weight factor is considered the least important of these three, since the slight difference in additional weight of core materials or insulation will not make the unit unwieldy.

The next factor in considering the power transformer is its location in the oscilloscope. The most important factor in locating the transformer is the effect of the magnetic field that surrounds the transformer on the beam of the cathode-ray tube. The transformer should be placed as far as possible from the cathode-ray tube and should be oriented in such a manner as to reduce this magnetic effect. As a result, the power transformer is usually located underneath the chassis and to the rear of the oscilloscope. The only other factor in the location of the power transformer is weight distribution for portability of the instrument, which can be counterbalanced by properly locating the carrying handle.

Primary Windings.   The primary windings of the power transformer are frequently designed for operation on either 115 or 230 volts. This is accomplished by winding two separate windings, each for operation on

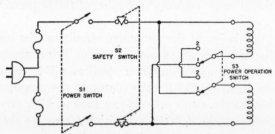

FIG. 7–1. Primary power circuit of an oscilloscope.

115 volts. The primary windings are connected to a double-pole double-throw switch as shown in Fig. 7-1. If the instrument is to be operated on 115 volts, the switch is thrown to position 1 and the two windings are connected in parallel. If, on the other hand, the instrument is to be operated on 230 volts, the switch is thrown to position 2, and the two windings are connected in series. The primary windings of the power transformer are usually surrounded by an electrostatic shield to prevent capacitive coupling between it and the high-voltage secondary winding. This shield is also shown in Fig. 7-1.

Furthermore, in the layout of the primary circuit of the transformer, it is good practice to include a safety switch. This safety switch is usually a double- (sometimes single-) pole single-throw switch of the momentary-close type. Power will pass through this switch only when pressure is applied to the switch button. When the pressure is released, the switch will open and no power can pass through the primary circuit of the transformer. This switch is usually mounted on the rear chassis of the oscilloscope so that, when the cabinet is in place and secured with screws, sufficient pressure is exerted on the switch button to keep it closed.

Since these screws must be removed before the chassis is removed from the cabinet, the pressure is released and the switch opens the primary circuit.

Transformer Secondary. The secondary windings of the power transformer will vary with the circuits employed in the instrument. In general, however, there must be a low-voltage winding (300 to 400 volts), which is center-tapped; a high-voltage winding (800 to 1,500 volts) for the operation of the cathode-ray tube, which is usually a single extension of the low-voltage winding; a separate filament winding for the cathode-ray tube, which must be electrostatically shielded; a heater winding for the low-voltage rectifier; a heater winding for the high-voltage rectifier;

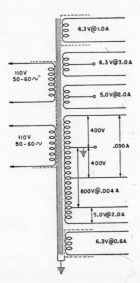

Fig. 7–2. Circuit of a typical power transformer for an oscilloscope.

a heater winding for the other tubes of the oscilloscope; and a separate heater winding for the regulator tubes if an electronic voltage regulator is employed. The current values of these windings vary, depending upon the number and type of tubes employed, but the high-voltage winding that supplies the cathode-ray tube need only furnish 2 or 3 ma. Figure 7-2 shows the schematic of a typical power transformer with the voltages indicated as well as the circuits that they supply.

Low-Voltage Power Supply. Low-voltage power supplies, as previously pointed out, vary in complexity depending upon the demands made upon them by the remaining circuits of the oscilloscope. Figure 7-3 shows the schematic of a simple low-voltage power supply. The primary circuit contains a power switch $S1$; a safety switch $S2$; and a fuse $F1$. The primary circuit will be open, and no current will flow under any of the following conditions: (1) the power switch is open; (2) the safety switch is open; (3) a short circuit in the primary or the secondary causes the fuse to "burn out."

The secondary circuit consists of two windings: a 700-volt winding, which is center-tapped, and a 5-volt filament winding for the rectifier tube. The rectifier is a type 80 full-wave rectifier, the plates of which are connected to the opposite ends of the 700-volt secondary winding. The center-tap of this winding is grounded to the chassis to give a voltage reference point.

As 115 volts alternating current is applied to the primary of the power transformer, an alternating voltage of 700 volts appears across the two

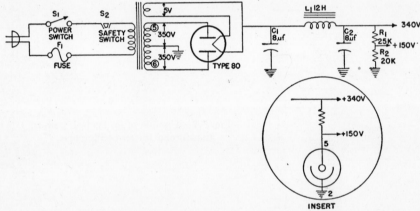

FIG. 7–3. Typical power-supply circuit for obtaining a low positive voltage.

terminals of the low-voltage secondary. Since the center tap is grounded, the voltage between terminal 5 and ground changes from +350 volts to 0 to −350 volts to 0 and back to +350 volts at the rate of 60 times per second. The voltage at terminal 6 likewise changes at the same rate. However, when terminal 5 is at a potential of +350 volts, terminal 6 is at a potential of −350 volts, and vice versa. Thus, it may be said that the voltage at terminal 5 is always 180 deg out of phase with the voltage at terminal 6.

Thus, when the transformer is connected to the rectifier plates, as shown in Fig.7-3, first one plate has a positive voltage applied to it, and then the other. Therefore, electrons flow from the cathode of the rectifier to the plate $P1$ when it is positive, and then from the cathode to the plate $P2$ when it is positive. Since the cathode is continually losing electrons, the voltage on the cathode is positive. Also, since the flow of electrons varies continuously, the voltage at the cathode is pulsating direct current.

This voltage is filtered by the capacitor input filter consisting of capacitor
C1, choke L1, and capacitor C2. The filter provides a rather constant
d-c output, which contains only a small percentage of ripple voltage.
The voltage-divider resistors R1 and R2 furnish positive voltage outputs
at two different voltage levels. These voltages can be changed by changing the values of the two resistors. Simple Ohms law calculations are
used to arrive at the desired values.

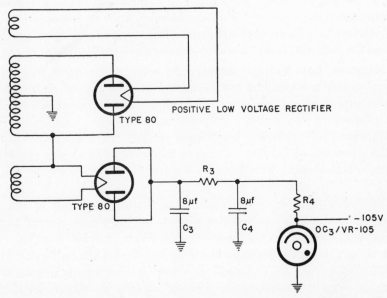

FIG. 7–4. Typical power-supply circuit for obtaining a low negative voltage.

Since some oscilloscope circuits, such as the time-base generator, produce signals that may feed back to other circuits through the power
supply, it is desirable for the power supply to have a low impedance to
ground for such signals. In the circuit of Fig. 7-3, it can readily be seen
that C2 offers a very low impedance to ground for any a-c signals attempting to pass from the +340-volt source to the +150-volt source, and
vice versa. However, if the +150-volt source is used to supply both the
time-base generator and the low-level stages of the amplifiers, the saw-
toothed signal may easily get into the signal being amplified. To overcome such a condition, all that is necessary is to connect another 8 μf
capacitor between +150 volts and ground.

If the +150-volt source is to be used to supply plate voltage to the
low-level amplifier stages, it might possibly contain too much ripple
voltage for this purpose. If such is the case, a gas-type voltage-regulator

tube, a VR-150, may be used in place of $R2$, as shown in the insert of Fig. 7-3. This tube contains an inert gas which ionizes when the voltage between its anode and its cathode is 150 volts. The characteristics of a gas regulator are such that it maintains, within limits, a constant potential across its electrodes irrespective of the current changes. Once the voltage is sufficient to "fire" this tube, it remains in a conducting state even though the voltage across its electrodes falls below the firing potential, again within limits. Such a device is highly suited as a regulator for the low-voltage circuits of an oscilloscope, since its response to voltage changes is almost instantaneous. This type of regulator presents a fixed d-c potential from a low-impedance source that is free of ripple.

Negative Low-Voltage Supply. In some oscilloscopes, it is necessary to obtain a negative low voltage. Since the current requirements of this supply are usually small, the voltage can be obtained from the same secondary that supplies the positive low voltage. Usually, too, the rectifier used is connected as a half-wave rectifier. Such a supply is shown in the schematic of Fig. 7-4. The type 80 rectifier can also be employed again in this supply. This filament winding is connected to one end of the low-voltage secondary winding.

As this winding becomes negative on the negative half of the a-c cycle, the cathode of the rectifier is made negative with respect to the plates, which are connected together. As a result, electrons flow from the cathode to the plates. Since no electrons flow during the half cycle when the cathode is positive, and since the plates are continually gaining electrons, a pulsating negative d-c voltage appears on the plates of the rectifier. This pulsating negative d-c voltage is filtered by the resistance-capacitance (RC) filter $C3$, $R3$, and $C4$. $R4$ serves as a limiting resistor, limiting the current through the VR tube. The VR tube again serves as a voltage-regulating device, providing a negative d-c potential of 105 volts from a low impedance.

Electronic Voltage Regulators. In cases where it is necessary to obtain more current than the inert-gas type of voltage regulator can handle and still maintain good voltage regulation from a low impedance, the electronic voltage regulator is employed. A typical example of this type of regulator circuit is shown in Fig. 7-5. The regulator tube in this diagram is $V1$, a 6L6. It is capable of handling about 45 ma. If more current is required, one or more of the same type of tube may be connected in parallel with $V1$, thus obtaining a total of 90 ma by the addition of one more tube or of 135 ma by the addition of two more tubes. Naturally, the power transformer must be capable of furnishing the additional current.

Connected in this manner, $V1$ may be regarded as a variable resistor or as a cathode follower. Low-value resistors $R2$, $R3$, and $R4$ are inserted in series with the screen, the grid, and the cathode, respectively, to prevent parasitic oscillations from occurring. The grid of the regulator tube is connected to the output of the two-stage amplifier, a dual triode $V2$ connected in cascade. The plate-load resistor $R1$ of this stage is large and is connected to the unregulated voltage to give the amplifier a maximum range. The VR tube $V3$ is connected to the cathode of the first amplifying stage to give a voltage reference point to the entire regulating circuit. $V3$ receives its firing voltage from B+ through $R5$ and keeps the first cathode (pin 3) of $V2$ at a constant voltage of +105 volts.

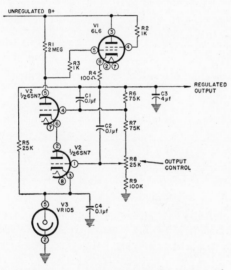

FIG. 7–5. Typical regulator circuit for regulating the output of a low-voltage positive power supply.

The output control $R8$ controls the output voltage. If this control is turned so that the arm of the potentiometer approaches $R9$, the output voltage *increases*. The action is as follows: as the arm of the potentiometer approaches $R9$, the grid (pin 1) of $V2$ is made more negative while its cathode (pin 3) remains at a constant potential. Thus, this section of $V2$ conducts less current than previously, raising the potential on the plate (pin 2). Since pin 2 is connected to the cathode (pin 6) of the second stage, the cathode voltage is also increased (made more positive). With its cathode more positive with respect to its grid (pin 4), which was not subjected to change, the second amplifier conducts less current, which causes a rise in the voltage on its plate (pin 5). An increase in voltage on the plate of the second amplifier also increases the positive voltage on the control grid (pin 5) of the regulator tube. The increase in voltage on the control grid of the regulator tube $V1$ causes it to conduct more current, thus *increasing* the output voltage at its cathode.

Moving the arm of the potentiometer in the opposite direction—toward $R7$—*decreases* the output voltage. This action places a higher positive voltage on the grid $P1$ of $V2$. Thus, the first amplifying stage conducts more current, lowering the voltage at its plate (pin 2) and correspondingly on the cathode (pin 6) of the second stage. A lower positive voltage on the cathode increases the current flowing through the second amplifying stage, which decreases the voltage at its plate (pin 5). This action results in the positive voltage at the control grid (pin 5) of the regulator tube $V1$ being reduced, thus decreasing the current flowing through $V1$. A decrease in current through $V1$ results in a *decrease* in the output voltage taken from its cathode.

The regulating action follows the same reasoning. If the output voltage rises a small amount because of increased line voltage or decrease in load, the increased voltage is applied to the grids (pins 1 and 4) of $V2$. The increased voltage on the grids causes more current to flow through $R1$ and the two tubes, decreasing the voltage on the plate (pin 5) on $V2$ and also on the grid (pin 5) of $V1$. This voltage produces a decreased current through $V1$, resulting in almost instantaneous compensation for the increased voltage. Compensation for rapid changes, such as hum or transients (line surges or signals returning to B+ from the sweep generator) is made, since the voltage change is impressed on both grids of the amplifier through the capacitors $C1$ and $C2$ instead of passing through the bleeder resistor. Thus, these sudden changes may be compensated as rapidly as they occur.

If the output voltage decreases a small amount because of increased load or decreased line voltage, the grids of the amplifiers are made more negative, with the result that less current is conducted through $R1$. With less current passing through $R1$, the grid of the regulator tube $V1$ becomes more positive, causing $V1$ to conduct more current and thus raising the output voltage taken from its cathode.

This circuit can never regulate perfectly because the controlling voltage comes from the output. It will, however, result in greatly improved regulation, since it reduces as much as 6 per cent hum to 0.05 per cent. It will maintain practically a constant output voltage as the line voltage varies between 100 and 130 volts.

The Negative High-Voltage Supply. Most oscilloscopes employ a negative high-voltage supply to operate the electrodes of the cathode-ray tube at a negative potential. As pointed out in an earlier chapter, this enables the accelerating electrode of the cathode-ray tube to be operated at or near ground potential, thus eliminating a defocusing action that occurs if the accelerating electrode is operated at a potential greatly different from that of the deflection plates. A typical example of a negative, high-voltage supply is shown in Fig. 7-6. The high-voltage winding of the transformer is merely an extension of one of the ends of the low-voltage winding. The cathode of the rectifier tube $V1$ is connected directly to the high-voltage winding. As this end of the winding swings negative with respect to ground, the cathode also swings negative with respect to ground. As a result, the cathode of $V1$ becomes negative with respect to the plate, and conduction takes place across the tube resulting in a high negative potential on the plate. Since this is a half-wave recti-

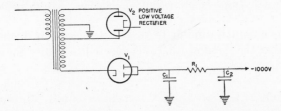

Fig. 7-6. Typical power-supply circuit for obtaining a high negative voltage.

fier, during the half of the cycle that drives the cathode of the rectifier positive the tube does not conduct, and no voltage appears on the plate. The result is a half-wave rectified voltage on the plate of $V1$.

The half-wave rectified voltage is usually filtered by means of an RC filter, which is also shown in Fig. 7-6. The capacitor $C1$ is in parallel with the high-voltage bleeder resistor $R1$, resulting in a long time constant for this RC combination. Capacitor $C2$ is also included in this network and is in parallel with $C1$, resulting in an even longer time constant. Consequently, these capacitors have time only to discharge a very small amount during the half cycle that $V1$ is not conducting, so that the resultant voltage is maintained at a high potential with a small percentage of ripple content.

The Positive High-Voltage Power Supply. Some oscilloscopes employ intensifier-type cathode-ray tubes, which require that a positive voltage be applied to the intensifier electrode. In some cases, the filtered but unregulated B+ voltage is applied to the intensifier to give an additional accelerating potential to the electron beam. Other oscilloscopes employ a high-voltage rectifier to rectify the positive peaks of the high-voltage winding and supply an intensifier voltage that is equal and opposite in polarity to the voltage applied to the cathode of the cathode-ray tube.

Figure 7-7 shows the connection of a rectifier for rectifying the positive peaks of the high-voltage winding to obtain a source of positive high

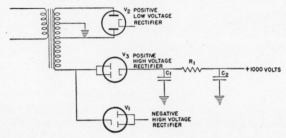

FIG. 7–7. Typical power-supply circuit for obtaining a high positive voltage.

voltage. This circuit is similar to that of the negative high-voltage circuit, except that the rectifier tube is connected to rectify the positive half of the cycle.

8 Amplifiers, Attenuators, and Positioning Circuits

Amplifiers. Since the cathode-ray tube is a relatively insensitive device, it has been found that the amplitudes of many signals are too small to be applied directly to the deflection plates of the cathode-ray tube and still achieve usable deflection. As a result, amplifiers are generally employed in both the vertical and horizontal channels, thus increasing the range of the amplitude of the input signals that may be displayed on the oscilloscope.

Since oscilloscopes generally use electrostatic deflection, resistance-coupled voltage amplifiers are usually employed because the current absorbed by the deflection plates of the cathode-ray tube is practically negligible. This type of amplifier is of low-cost construction and can be

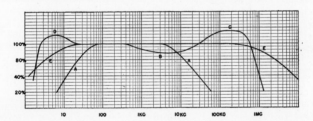

Fig. 8–1. Frequency response curves of several amplifiers plotted on a single graph.

compensated quite readily to increase its low- and high-frequency response. Also, resistance-coupled amplifiers can be designed to amplify signals over a wide range of frequencies, whereas impedance-coupled amplifiers are inherently frequency conscious.

Since the cathode-ray tube can be employed to view signals with a range of frequencies from very low to very high (from one cycle or even d-c to several hundred megacycles), it would be ideal if amplifiers could be designed to amplify this wide range of frequencies uniformly. At the present time, however, certain limitations in the various circuit components prevent the design of such an amplifier.

83

The frequency response of an amplifier is usually plotted in the form of a graph where the relative gain in percentage is plotted along the Y axis, and the frequency in sinusoidal cycles per second is plotted along the X axis. Such a graph is shown in Fig. 8-1. A good uncompensated amplifier response is shown on this graph by the curve marked A. This curve is practically flat (from 30 c to 30 kc); i.e., it amplifies the various frequencies within this range the same amount.

It is necessary for the user to know the frequency response of the amplifier in his oscilloscope, in order to interpret intelligently the patterns observed on the screen of the cathode-ray tube.

The frequency response of an amplifier is frequently determined by its ability to amplify a square wave. The square wave is introduced into the grid of the first amplifier stage, and it is observed again at the plate of that stage. If the square wave has been faithfully reproduced, it can

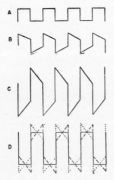

A. The original square-wave input.

B. The output from $R1$ $C1$ to the grid of $V1$ in Fig. 8-3.

C. The output at the plate of V1 without plate compensation.

D. Plate compensation produces the result shown by the broken line. This voltage superimposed on the saw-toothed top of the wave, dotted line, results in a good square wave.

FIG. 8–2.   The results obtained from the testing of an amplifier with a square-wave signal.

be said of the amplifier that its frequency response is flat (between the limits of $f/10$ and $10f$) when f is the square-wave frequency. A square wave is used for testing these amplifiers because the steep front of the wave gives an indication of the high frequency, or "transient response," and the flat top of the wave gives an indication of the low-frequency characteristics of the amplifier. The terms "high" and "low" frequency are, of course, in relation to the fundamental frequency of the square wave.

If the amplifier has poor low-frequency response to the fundamental square-wave frequency, the flat tops of the square wave will take on the saw-toothed appearance shown in Fig. 8-2b. This is due to the fact that the time constant $R1C1$ of Fig 8-3 is short. As a result, the capacitor, after it has been charged, immediately begins to discharge and in doing so, decreases the voltage being applied to the grid. Figure 8-2a shows the square wave applied to the input terminals of an amplifier, and Fig. 8-2b shows the effect of the short time constant $R1C1$ on this wave. Because the rising edge of the square wave drives the grid positive, more current flows in the plate of this tube, causing a drop in the voltage at the plate. Thus, the wave shown in Fig. 8-2c is amplified and in the opposite phase to that shown in Fig. 8-2b.

To overcome this deficiency in low-frequency response, it would seem to be necessary merely to increase the values of $C1$ and $R1$ to a point where their time constant was sufficient to prevent this discharge. However, to increase the low-frequency response below a frequency of 10 c by this method, the physical size of the capacitor becomes unreasonably large, since the grid resistor is limited by the grid current characteristics

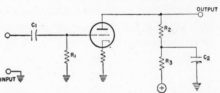

Fig. 8-3. A typical single-stage amplifier showing the use of plate compensation.

of the vacuum tube. Another factor governing the design of this section of the circuit is the fact that it is desirable to keep the time constant of $R1$ and $C1$ as small as possible, since this factor determines the time required for the amplifier to recover from the effects of a transient pulse of large amplitude. One method of obtaining good low-frequency response and still limiting the time constant of $C1$ and $R1$ is to employ plate-circuit compensation.

Low-Frequency Compensation. Plate compensation for the saw-toothed shape of the peaks of the square wave requires that the plate resistor $R2$ be proportioned into two separate resistors $R2$ and $R3$. $R2$ is large with respect to $R3$. The capacitor $C2$ is connected between the junction of these resistors and ground, as shown in Fig. 8-3. The new time constant $R2C2$ is responsible, in effect, for generating a counter saw-toothed voltage that is equal and opposite to that occurring on the plate of the vacuum tube.

When the signal voltage being applied to the grid begins to decrease, owing to the discharging of capacitor $C1$, the plate voltage starts to increase. However, the newly added capacitor $C2$, which has been discharged to the same potential as the plate, must be charged before the plate voltage is increased. Therefore, if the time constant $R2C2$ is made long enough, the plate voltage will not change appreciably during the flat top of the square wave. However, the falling edge of the square wave immediately decreases the current in the plate circuit of the tube, and both the plate and the capacitor reach the same relatively high potential. This potential is not as high as would be obtained by the plate alone

FIG. 8–4. The output of an amplifier having poor high-frequency response.

without $C2$. At this same time, the capacitor $C1$ is charged negatively. However, the capacitor $C1$ soon starts to discharge through $R1$, and the plate current begins to increase. This would normally cause the plate voltage to drop, but the capacitor $C2$, which is charged to the same potential as the plate, must also discharge. Since $C2$ must discharge through the long time constant $C2R2$, the plate voltage does not change appreciably during the flat top of the square wave. The square wave resulting from this action is shown in Fig. 8-2d superimposed on the uncompensated

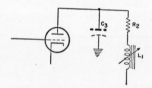

FIG. 8–5. Circuit for improving the high-frequency response of a given amplifier.

wave with the saw-toothed peaks. However, it should be remembered that the over-all gain of this stage has been decreased because of the addition of this new RC circuit $R2C2$. Unfortunately, the various compensating circuits employed to extend either or both the high or the low limits of an amplifier result in a decrease in the over-all gain of that amplifier. It necessitates an increase in the number of amplifier stages in order to achieve the same output voltage.

High-Frequency Compensation. If, in testing an amplifier with a square wave for its frequency limits, the square wave takes the shape shown in Fig. 8-4, the response of the amplifier to high frequencies, with respect to the fundamental frequency of the square wave, is poor. The reason that the amplifier response tapers off at high frequencies is the fact that the capacitances between the electrodes of the vacuum tubes, the stray circuit capacitances, and the capacitance of the various components with respect to ground effectively act to provide a shunt capacitance, which is represented in total by the capacitor $C3$ in the circuit of Fig. 8-5. If the frequency passing through the amplifiers is increased, the reactance of this capacitor is effectively decreased, thus shunting an appreciable portion of the high-frequency signal to ground. This high-frequency loss can be compensated by employing a small inductance in series with the plate load resistor. Since the inductive reactance of this coil increases with frequency, the total plate-load impedance also increases with frequency, and the normal loss in voltage output at the higher frequencies is automatically compensated. If the inductance applied at this point is too small, the result will be an effect of not giving

FIG. 8–6. Overpeaking of an amplifier results in an oscillation appearing on the top of the square wave.

sufficient compensation at low enough frequencies. Thus, a dip occurs near the center of the response curve as shown in curve *B* of Fig. 8-1. Too high an inductance applied at this point will result in overpeaking and a relatively sharp, high-frequency cutoff indicated by curve *C* in Fig. 8-1. Overpeaking also manifests itself by an oscillation that occurs on the flat top of the square wave at the leading edge. An example is shown in Fig. 8-6. Overcompensation for low-frequency response is

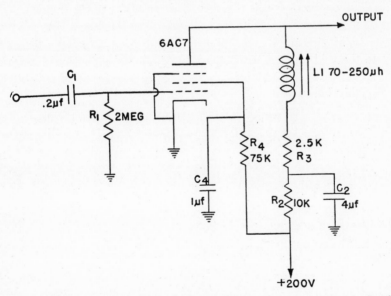

FIG. 8–7. Circuit of a single-stage amplifier whose frequency response is flat from 10c to 1 megacycle.

shown by curve *D* of Fig. 8-1. A typical example of a pentode amplifier whose frequency response is flat from 10 c to 1 megacycle is shown in the schematic of Fig. 8-7. Note that the plate circuit is compensated for both low and high frequencies. The time constant $R2C2$ increases the low-frequency response, and the inductance $L1$ in series with the plate-load resistors extends the high-frequency response. The response of this amplifier is shown by curve E of Fig. 8-1.

Direct-Coupled Amplifiers. Resistance-capacitance coupled amplifiers ordinarily employed in a cathode-ray oscilloscope will not pass d-c signals because of the inability of direct current to flow through a capacitor. In most cases, therefore, a-c signals superimposed upon a d-c potential are established on a new reference, corresponding to the average voltage of the a-c component. Since in some measurements it is desirable to view a signal and observe its d-c component as well as its a-c component, it is necessary to connect such signals directly to the plates of the cathode-ray tube. In some cases, however, direct-coupled amplifiers have been designed for use in oscilloscopes, but extending the frequency response from d-c potentials through high frequencies introduces a number of additional problems that are difficult to cope with. The Du Mont type 208-B utilizes both resistance-capacitance and direct-coupled amplifiers in both its vertical and horizontal channels. The vertical amplifier from this oscilloscope is shown in Fig. 8-8. This amplifier has a frequency response that is flat within ± 10 per cent from 2 to 100,000 c.

The input circuits and the first stage will be considered later. The input to the grid of $V2$ is from the arm of a $100K$ potentiometer which is connected to an 8-μf capacitor $C4$. The time constant of this circuit is reasonably long:

$$\frac{8 \times 100,000}{1,000,000} = 0.8 \text{ sec}$$

However, since this amplifier is flat to 2 c, it is still necessary to incorporate low-frequency compensation in the plate circuit. This is accomplished by $C7$ and $R7$ in the plate of $V2$ and again in the plate of $V3$ by $C8$ and $R10$. The inductances $L1$ and $L2$ are in series with the plate-load resistors of $V2$ and $V3$, respectively, to extend the high-frequency response. The output of $V3$ is impressed on the grid of $V4$ through capacitor $C10$, a 1-μf capacitor. The grid-return resistor for this tube is a 1-megohm resistor, which results in a time constant of 1 sec for the combination $C10$ and $R15$. Since $V4$ is a cathode follower, which is noted for having a wide frequency response, no compensation, either high or low, is required in this stage. From the cathode of $V4$, the signal is impressed upon the push-pull direct-coupled amplifiers $V5$ and $V6$, which are directly coupled to the deflection plates of the cathode-ray tube. Notice that the plate circuits of $V5$ and $V6$ both contain inductances $L3$

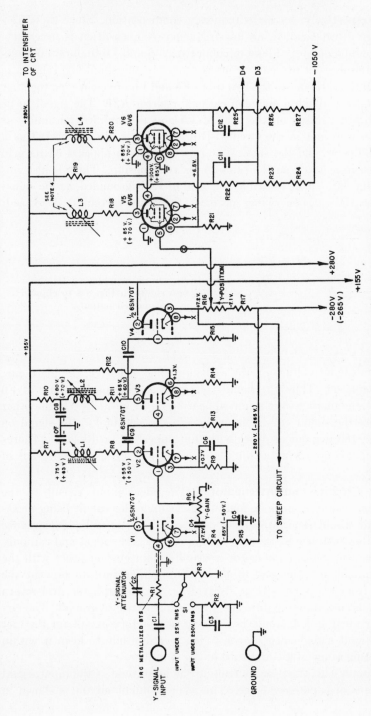

Fig. 8-8. Circuit of the vertical amplifier in a Du Mont Type 208-B Cathode-Ray Oscillograph. (*Courtesy, Allen B. Du Mont Laboratories, Inc.*)

and *L4*, respectively, for high-frequency compensation. Since these amplifiers are direct-coupled, no low-frequency compensation is necessary.

The method employed here in connecting *V5* and *V6* to obtain outputs that are 180 deg out of phase is interesting. In the simplified schematic of Fig. 8-9 the cathodes of the two tubes *V5* and *V6* are connected together and grounded through a common cathode resistor *R21*. The signal to be amplified is impressed on the grid of *V5* and is amplified normally, as though *V6* were not in the circuit. However, *V5* is also connected as a cathode follower, and the same signal as that which appears on its grid appears on its cathode in the same phase relationship. Thus, it also appears on the cathode of *V6*. Since the grid of *V6* is grounded, as the signal voltage on the cathode swings positive, the plate current is decreased;

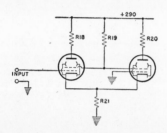

Fig. 8–9. Direct coupling of the last two stages shown in Fig. 8–8 to obtain a balanced output.

and, as the signal voltage on the cathode swings negative, the plate current is increased. Thus, the signal voltage appearing on the plate of *V6* is in the same phase as the signal appearing on its cathode. On the other hand, since the signal voltage is applied to the grid of *V5*, the signal on its plate is 180 deg out of phase with that appearing on its grid. Therefor, the signals appearing at the plates of *V5* and *V6* are 180 deg out of phase.

Input Circuits and Attenuators. The ideal input circuit to the oscilloscope would produce no loading effect upon the circuit being measured. This would require a circuit that exhibited no shunt capacitance and infinite resistance to ground. Such a circuit is the ideal and can only be approached. Since a capacitor is usually connected in series with the input terminal and the grid of the first amplifier tube to prevent the operator from applying a large d-c voltage to the grid, the grid-return resistor must be large to reduce the direct capacitance to ground. The circuit, shown in Fig. 8-7, would be entirely satisfactory except for the fact that the input signal must be controlled in amplitude to keep it within the operating range of the first tube of the amplifier.

The simplest method for controlling the amplitude of the input signal is by means of a potentiometer. This type of input circuit is shown in

Fig. 8-10. This is the type of input circuit usually employed in the lower-priced oscilloscopes. The signal is attenuated to the desired level by moving the arm of the potentiometer toward ground. This type of input attenuator is quite satisfactory for the kind of work usually assigned to a low-priced instrument. It is not satisfactory, however, for an instrument employed in precision measurement, or for one that has a wide-band amplifier, since it does not attenuate all frequencies uniformly.

Actually, when the arm of the potentiometer is in any position other than at the extreme ends, distributed capacitances exist between the arm and both ends of the potentiometer, as shown by the dotted capacitors in Fig. 8-10. Effectively, these capacitors provide a capacitance voltage

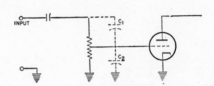

Fig. 8-10. Circuit showing the distributed capacitances in a simple potentiometer attenuator.

divider, which, because these capacitors are quite small, affects only the higher frequencies. This capacitance voltage divider is in parallel with the resistance voltage divider (the potentiometer). Since the ratio of $C1$ to $C2$ is essentially constant for any intermediate setting of the arm, the high frequencies are attenuated a definite amount regardless of the setting of the arm of the potentiometer, whereas the low frequencies are attenuated by an amount equal to the ratio between $R1$ and $R2$. Thus, the use of this type of input attenuator results in an over-all frequency-

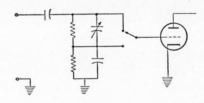

Fig. 8-11. Circuit of a stepped attenuator with fixed attenuation ratios.

response curve that is not flat but dependent upon the setting of the arm of the input potentiometer. At first glance it would seem that the frequency discrimination produced by such an attenuator could be lessened by the use of a low-resistance potentiometer. Such an arrangement would be feasible except for the fact that this circuit is the input circuit, and the loading produced on the circuit under test would be excessive.

Careful inspection of this type of attenuator, however, led to the development of the stepped attenuator. It was found that at one intermediate setting of the potentiometer the over-all frequency response of this system was the same as when the potentiometer was set to provide maximum signal. This setting is the point where the ratio of $R1$ to $R2$ attenuates the signal to the same level as that produced by the ratio of $C1$ to $C2$. At this setting all signals are attenuated equally and the over-all frequency response is maintained. This fact is utilized in the design of compensated stepped attenuators, such as the one shown in Fig. 8-11. Capacitors are actually connected in the circuit so that they are in parallel with the distributed capacitances, and the resistors used are of fixed values. This scheme provides for at least one capacitor to be adjustable,

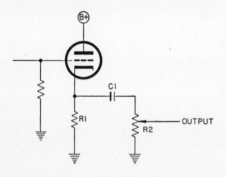

Fig. 8–12. A cathode-follower input circuit with a low impedance gain control.

so that compensation may be made for minor differences in distributed capacitance. The resistors used are held to close tolerance. This circuit proves to be a very satisfactory means of attenuating the signal, but a large number of steps would be required if it were to provide useful attenuation over a wide range. Consequently, other means of producing continuous attenuation were sought and found.

One of the most common methods employs a cathode follower for the input stage of the amplifier. The cathode follower reproduces the same signal on its cathode as that which appears on its grid over a wide range without frequency discrimination and reproduces it across a low impedance. No gain in amplitude is produced by this stage; as a matter of fact, there is a slight loss, but the advantage of absence of frequency discrimination makes it worth while. The circuit of the cathode-follower continuous attenuator is shown in Fig. 8-12. When $R1$ and $R2$ are low-value resistors, the distributed capacitances have a negligible effect even at frequencies as high as several megacycles. The capacitance $C1$ is used as a blocking capacitor to prevent the direct current that appears on the cathode from being applied to the grid of the next stage. It is a large-value capacitance to offer negligible impedance to the low frequencies being amplified.

When the cathode-follower continuous-attenuator circuit is used for continuous attenuation and a stepped attenuator is employed in the grid circuit of the cathode follower, a wide range of amplitudes of input signals may be handled without frequency discrimination. In Fig. 8-8 it can be seen that this amplifier employs a cathode follower for continuous attenuation and that a stepped attenuator is employed in the grid circuit utilizing the full input signal in the 1:1 position and attenuating it to one tenth in the 10:1 position.

Positioning Circuits. The circuit for positioning the beam of the cathode-ray tube so that the pattern will fall in the desired position on the screen depends upon the type of deflection used and on the type of

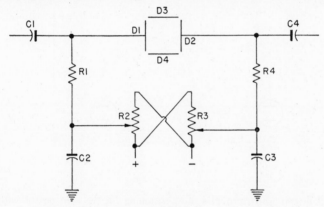

Fig. 8-13. A circuit for providing a-c positioning of the spot on the cathode-ray tube screen.

amplifiers. Actually, the fundamental principle of all positioning circuits is the same, viz., to establish a controllable d-c potential on each pair of deflection plates upon which the signal to be observed may be superimposed.

Actually, there are two types of positioning circuits in common use at this writing. They are called "a-c positioning" and "d-c positioning" circuits. These names are not indicative of voltage employed to position the beam, but rather of the action of the electron beam when subjected to these two types of circuits.

The circuit used for a-c positioning of the electron beam is shown in Fig. 8-13. A dual potentiometer, i.e., two potentiometers on a single shaft, is connected so that each potentiometer has a positive voltage applied to one end and a negative voltage applied to the other end. Furthermore, these voltages are so connected that turning the common shaft causes the arm of one potentiometer to approach its positive voltage and the arm of the other potentiometer to approach its negative voltage. These potentiometers are usually large-value resistors, varying in different circuits from about 250,000 ohms to several megohms, and both are of the same value.

Thus, if the arms are set at the mid-position, both potentiometers are at the point of zero voltage, and the beam is centered on the screen of the cathode-ray tube. Moving the shaft of $R6$ toward the negative voltage causes the shaft of $R7$ to move toward the positive voltage. Thus, $D1$

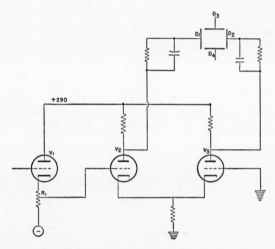

Fig. 8–14. A circuit which provides d-c positioning for the spot on the cathode-ray tube screen.

becomes negatively charged and $D2$ becomes positively charged to an equal positive voltage. As a result, $D1$ repels the electron beam, and $D2$ attracts the beam. Moving the shaft of the potentiometer in the other direction causes the arm of $R6$ to approach the positive voltage and the arm of $R7$ to approach the negative voltage. This charges $D1$ positively and $D2$ negatively so that the electron beam is moved toward $D1$. The capacitors $C5$ and $C8$ are connected to the plate circuits of the tubes supplying push-pull deflection to this pair of plates and permit the signals from these tubes to be superimposed upon the d-c potentials applied to the deflection plates. The capacitors $C6$ and $C7$ are by-pass capacitors to prevent the signal voltage from getting into the power supply. The resistors $R5$ and $R8$ are large-value resistors to maintain a high input impedance to the deflection plates and to ensure good low-frequency response. For oscilloscopes employing single-ended deflection, this same type of circuit is used, except that in these units one deflection plate is connected directly to ground. If this plate is $D2$, then $C7$, $C8$, $R7$, and $R8$ are deleted from the circuit.

The type of positioning just described is called "a-c positioning" because of the sluggish response of the electron beam to movement of the positioning controls. This sluggishness is due to the large time constants $C5R5$ and $C8R8$. The capacitors $C5$ and $C8$ must charge or discharge to the new potential caused by a change in setting of the positioning controls before the charge appears on the deflection plates.

Another method of positioning the electron beam is called "d-c positioning." This method is usually used when the final amplifier stage is a push-pull stage and is direct-coupled to the deflection plates. As shown previously in Fig. 8-8 and in a simplified version in Fig. 8-14, a cathode follower is often employed to drive the final push-pull amplifier. If the cathode resistor is a potentiometer and one end is returned to a source of negative voltage instead of to ground, the arm of the potentiometer can pick off either a positive or a negative d-c potential, since the cathode end of the potentiometer is always positive. This d-c potential, upon which is superimposed the alternating signal voltage, is placed on the grid of the final stage. The circuit is so designed that when the arm of $R1$ is set to the zero voltage point, the deflection plates $D1$ and $D2$ are at ground potential. If the voltage selected by the potentiometer $R1$ is changed from the zero voltage point to a positive voltage, $V2$ conducts more current, so that the resulting d-c voltage applied to the deflection plate $D1$ is negative. Furthermore, the cathode of $V2$ is now more positive than it was previously and so is the cathode of $V3$. Then, since $V3$ is a grounded-grid amplifier, $V3$ conducts less current than previously and the resulting d-c voltage applied to the deflection plate $D2$ is positive. Thus, the electron beam of the cathode-ray tube is moved in the direction of $D2$, since it is repelled by $D1$ and attracted by $D2$. If a negative voltage is chosen by the arm of the potentiometer $R1$, the reverse is true, and $D1$ becomes positively charged while $D2$ becomes negatively charged. The only advantage of d-c positioning over a-c positioning is that there is no evidence of sluggishness on the part of the electron beam when the positioning control is turned.

9 Time-Base Circuits

The Linear Time Base. As previously stated in Chapter 6, the most commonly used time base is the linear time base, which results from the application of a saw-toothed wave to the horizontal deflection plates of the cathode-ray tube. A mechanical means of generating this saw-toothed wave was discussed in Chap. 6. This method obviously has many limitations, but it provided a satisfactory analogy for that chapter. The saw-toothed wave actually used as the time base of the oscilloscope is identical with the one previously discussed, but it is generated by an electronic circuit.

To obtain a saw-toothed wave by electronic means, the charging action of a capacitor is utilized. If a voltage is applied to a capacitor, the charge increases exponentially with time, as shown by the curve in Fig. 9-1. The

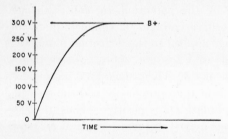

Fig. 9-1. Graph showing the charging action of a capacitor.

presence of a resistor between the capacitor and the charging voltage naturally increases the time required for the capacitor to charge to any given voltage, thus changing the slope of the curve. The actual time required for a capacitor C to charge through a resistor R to about two thirds of the supply voltage is equal to the product of $C \times R$, where C is expressed in farads and R is expressed in ohms. When the capacitor is fully charged, the time required for it to discharge to about one third its original value is also equal to $C \times R$. This value is referred to as the "time constant" of the RC circuit.

Essentially, a time base, or saw-toothed, generator consists of a gas tube, such as a neon lamp or any other gas diode, such as a voltage-regulator tube. The circuit of a simplified time base generator is shown in

Fig. 9-2. The capacitor $C1$ is connected in parallel with the gas diode $V1$. The plate of $V1$ and one side of the capacitor are connected through the fixed resistor $R1$ and the variable resistor $R2$ to a source of positive voltage. When voltage is applied to the circuit, the capacitor $C1$ charges through $R1$ and $R2$, preventing the plate of the tube from immediately attaining the same potential as the power supply. When the capacitor $C1$

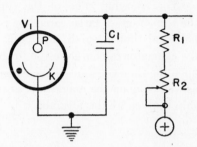

Fɪɢ. 9–2. Circuit of a simplified linear
time-base generator.

and likewise the plate of $V1$ reach the breakdown, or firing, potential of $V1$, the gas in the tube ionizes and the tube conducts. Since the impedance of $V1$ is practically zero when it is conducting, the capacitor discharges rapidly until its potential reaches the extinction potential of the tube. At this point, the potential across the tube is no longer high enough to maintain the gas in an ionized state, and the tube ceases to conduct. The capacitor again begins to charge through the resistors $R1$ and $R2$. The charge builds up again on $C1$ until the firing potential is reached and $V1$ again conducts. This cycle is repeated until the source of positive voltage is removed.

Fɪɢ. 9–3. The waveform resulting from the charging and discharging action of the capacitor in a time-base generator.

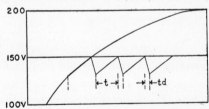

The wave form resulting from the charging and discharging action is shown in Fig. 9-3. Because the charging curve of the capacitor is exponential in nature, only a small portion of the curve is actually used, as is also shown in Fig. 9-3. This small portion is chosen in the straight portion of the curve, and the B+ supply is of sufficiently high potential that the difference in potential between the firing and the extinction potentials is only about 10 per cent of the supply voltage. Both of these design features make for a sweep voltage that is linear. The time required for the capacitor to charge to the firing potential of the tube is represented by the letter

T. This time will vary, depending upon the setting of the variable resistor *R2*. When *R2* is set to a greater resistance, the time *T* will be longer. When *R2* is set to a lower resistance, the time *T* will be shorter. The time shown in Fig. 9-3 as T_d is the discharge time, the time required for the capacitor to discharge through *V1*. The resistor *R1* is included in the circuit to limit the current flowing through *V1* when it is conducting.

The charging time of the capacitor also varies with the value of the capacitor—a large capacitor requires more time to charge to a given potential than a small capacitor. Actually, then, the time required for the capacitor to charge to the firing potential of the tube *V1* is dependent upon the time constant of the capacitor *C1* and the resistances *R1* and *R2*, as well as upon the magnitude of the supply voltage. The exact relationship is given by the formula

$$E_c = E_b \left(1 - e^{\frac{-t}{RC}} \right)$$

where E_c = capacitor voltage at time *T*;
  E_b = supply voltage;
  e = base of the natural logarithms;
  t = elapsed time in seconds;
  R = resistance in ohms;
  C = capacitance in farads.

From this relationship the formula for the frequency of a complete oscillation (charging time plus discharge time) may be developed. The formula is approximate, but it is close enough for all practical purposes.

$$f = \frac{E_b}{RC} \left(\frac{1}{E_f - E_x} \right)$$

where f = frequency of oscillation;
  E_f = potential at which the tube fires;
  E_x = potential at which the tube ceases to fire (extinction potential).

The preceding discussion covers the fundamentals of circuit operation. An example of a complete time base generator as it is employed in an oscilloscope is shown in Fig. 9-4. The tube employed is a type 884 gas triode, sometimes referred to as a "thyratron," and contains a heater that heats the cathode to the temperature at which it gives off electrons. The tube operates much the same as a cold-cathode gas diode; when the potential between the cathode and the grid is sufficient to cause the gas to ionize, the tube fires. This tube, however, contains a grid that is capable of controlling the operation of the tube. When the grid is positive, the tube will fire before the normal firing potential is reached. If the grid is made negative, the plate must charge to a potential that is higher than normal before the tube can fire.

This circuit operates precisely the same as the one previously described with a few added features. The switch $S2$ selects one of the capacitors, $C2$ through $C6$, depending upon the frequency desired. This capacitor is charged by the current from B+ passing through $R3$ and $R4$. When the capacitor is charged to the firing potential of the tube, the gas

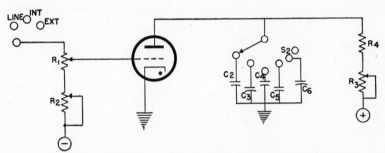

Fig. 9–4. Circuit of a typical linear time-base generator.

ionizes and the capacitor discharges through the tube. When the extinction potential is reached, the tube no longer conducts and the capacitor begins to charge again.

The fixed bias on this tube is controlled by the potentiometer $R2$. This adjustment is usually made at the factory and is, in reality, a calibration control. The frequency of the sweep generator is determined by the setting of $S2$ and $R3$. The switch $S2$ selects the capacitor to be charged, and the setting of the potentiometer $R3$ governs the rate at which the capacitor is charged. Thus, there are two operating controls of the sweep generator: the COARSE FREQUENCY SELECTOR (the switch $S2$) and the FINE FREQUENCY control (the potentiometer $R3$).

The grid is connected so that it may receive a synchronizing signal to synchronize the action of the time-base generator to that of the signal being observed. Nearly all oscilloscopes have provision for this signal to be derived from either the signal passing through the vertical amplifier or a separately furnished synchronizing signal from an external source. This signal is selected by the operator by means of the SYNCHRONIZING SIGNAL SELECTOR switch $S1$. A third source of synchronizing signal is sometimes made available. This third signal is the power-line frequency, which is obtained from one of the windings of the power transformer. The potentiometer $R1$ provides a continuously variable control, the

SYNCHRONIZING-SIGNAL AMPLITUDE control, for varying the amplitude of the synchronizing signal applied to the grid. Correct usage of the controls calls for the operator to adjust the sweep frequency as closely as possible with both the COARSE and the FINE FREQUENCY controls and with $R1$ set to receive minimum synchronizing signal, and then to turn $R1$, the SYNCHRONIZING-SIGNAL AMPLITUDE control, until the pattern is synchronized on the screen. Only as little synchronizing signal as is necessary should be applied to the grid, otherwise the linearity of the sweep voltage will be destroyed.

The gas triode serves extremely well as a time-base generator for frequencies between 2 and 50,000 c. At frequencies higher than 50 kc, the deionization time of the gas triode becomes too large a part of the total sweep cycle, and the signal becomes distorted because part of it is dis-

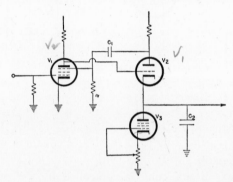

Fig. 9–5. Circuit of a high-vacuum time-base generator.

played on the returning sweep. Therefore, oscilloscopes requiring the use of higher-frequency time bases must resort to a different type of time-base generator tube. High-vacuum tubes are usually used for time-base generators that are required to deliver sweep frequencies higher than 50 kc. These tubes are frequently referred to as "hard" tubes, and gas-filled tubes are called "soft" tubes.

High-Vacuum Time-Base Generators. Many circuits have been designed to utilize a high-vacuum tube to produce a saw-toothed output. Earlier circuits were usually relaxation oscillators, but recent developments have leaned toward circuits employing multivibrators. A typical example of such a circuit is shown in Fig. 9-5. In this circuit, the triode $V1$ and the pentode $V2$ are connected as an unbalanced multivibrator. In addition, the pentode $V3$ is connected as a constant-current device and is in series with $V1$. The tubes $V1$ and $V3$ are normally conducting with the cathode of $V1$ and the plate of $V3$ at the same potential. Since the capacitor $C2$ is connected to the junction of these two electrodes of the two different tubes, the capacitor is also charged to the same potential. The circuit constants of $V1$ and $V2$ are so chosen that the multivibrator action causes a positive pulse to appear at the plate of $V2$ and the grid of $V1$, since these are connected. When this positive pulse is applied to the grid of $V1$, it conducts more current, thus raising the potential of the cathode and thereby increasing the charge on the capacitor $C2$. The capacitor $C2$ charges above its normal value throughout the duration of the pulse, since $V3$ is connected to pass only a constant current. After the pulse has been removed from the grid of $V1$, $V2$ is cut off, because of the high positive charge remaining on its cathode, and the capacitor $C2$ discharges through the constant-current pentode $V3$. Since the discharge is constant, a linear saw-toothed waveform appears at the plate of $V3$. As soon as $C2$ has discharged to its normal value, the cathode of $V1$ returns to its normal voltage, and the cycle is repeated. Careful selection of all components for the correct value permits the design of a linear sweep of very high speed. It is the normal practice with this type of sweep to connect the capacitor $C2$ into the circuit by means of a multiple switch, such as that used with the ordinary gas-filled tube, so that various capacitors can be switched in to permit the frequency to be varied over several ranges. The fine adjustment of frequency is controlled by the setting of the potentiometer $R1$ in the grid and cathode circuit of $V3$. This potentiometer permits the bias on $V3$ to be controlled so that the tube will conduct more or less current, therefore, discharging $C2$ more or less rapidly.

Single-Sweep Time-Base Generators. A single sweep of the beam of the cathode-ray tube may be generated by either a gas-triode or a high-vacuum sweep generator. It has been found that the high-vacuum tube results in a circuit that gives the better performance, but many instruments of the gas-triode type are still in use.

The gas-triode circuit for generating a single sweep uses the same circuit as the gas-triode, recurrent-sweep circuit with the addition of one other tube, a diode. The basic circuit is shown in Fig. 9-6. The plate of the diode $V2$ is connected to the plate of the gas triode. The cathode of the diode is connected to the arm of the potentiometer $R3$, which is connected between B+ and ground. If the arm of the potentiometer is set so that the voltage on the cathode of $V2$ is less than the voltage on its plate, conduction will occur across the diode. Thus, if the voltage on the cathode is set just below the plate voltage, the diode will conduct before the voltage on the plate of the gas triode $V1$ builds up sufficiently to ionize the gas, and the tube will not fire.

The sweep is initiated by a positive synchronizing pulse applied to the

42682

grid of the gas triode. This positive pulse drives the grid in a positive direction enabling the tube to ionize at a potential that is lower than the potential established by the diode. The capacitor $C1$ then discharges through the gas triode until the extinction potential is reached. At this time, the capacitor begins to charge again. The single-sweep cycle is complete when the capacitor is charged to the potential at which the diode begins to conduct again, and no further sweep will occur until another positive pulse is applied to the grid of the gas triode.

With this type of single-sweep circuit, the return trace occurs first, followed by the linear sweep. Therefore, in the untriggered state, the spot formed by the beam of the cathode-ray tube rests at the right edge of the screen. As the discharge occurs through the gas triode, the spot

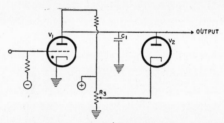

Fig. 9–6. A gas-triode circuit for generating a single sweep.

moves rapidly to the left side of the screen; and when the discharge ceases and the capacitor again begins to charge, the spot begins its linear sweep from left to right. When the capacitor has been charged to the limit established by the diode, the spot is in its rest position at the right side of the screen.

This type of sweep may be synchronized or, as in this case, started by either an external or an internal signal. If an internal signal is used, the signal passing through the vertical amplifier is displayed on the screen before the return trace has occurred and thus before the sweep is started. As a result, the early part of the transient signal cannot be observed. To observe this part of the signal, the sweep must be synchronized or triggered from an external source which occurs far enough ahead of the signal to cause the return trace to occur and the sweep to start before the signal being observed reaches the vertical deflection plates of the cathode-ray tube.

A single sweep design is very easily accomplished when a high-vacuum time-base generator is used. In the same circuit as that shown in Fig. 9-5, it is only necessary to maintain a sufficient positive bias on the grid of $V2$ in order to stop the continuous operation. As it is desired, the sweep voltage may be triggered (initiated) by applying a negative pulse or a negative triggering voltage to the grid of $V2$. This pulse must be sufficient to swing the grid negative enough so that the multivibrator action is started. The pulse should be sufficiently sharp so that only one sweep will occur. Although the return trace of this hard-tube single-sweep circuit still occurs before the linear sweep, the time for the return trace, as well as the time for the linear sweep, may be considerably shorter than that of a gas-tube circuit simply because of the relatively long time required to ionize and deionize the gas within the gas tube.

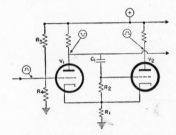

Fig. 9–7. A typical gate-generator circuit.

The Trigger Circuit. It was mentioned previously in Chap. 6, that a number of phenomena have recently been devised which require repetitive sweeps that are not necessarily continuous. The sweeps occur again and again at regular intervals with a definite repetition rate. An example of this type of circuit is the radar transmitter. Since it is desirable to view the reflected radio wave from the target picked up by the radar transmitter, and to know certain things about that target—for instance, its range—it is sometimes desirable to use a triggered sweep circuit. This circuit is usually triggered at a definite repetition rate.

For generating a driven sweep, sometimes called "triggered sweep," or "slave sweep," it is necessary to use a circuit known as a "gate generator." Figure 9-7 shows a typical cathode-coupled, multivibrator type of gate generator. $V1$ and $V2$ are two triodes whose cathodes are connected through a common cathode resistor $R1$. Since the grid of $V2$ is connected to its cathode through the resistor $R2$, $V2$ is normally conducting because its bias is zero volts. Not only is $V2$ conducting, but it is conducting a rather heavy current. Thus, the voltage on its cathode is at a relatively high positive potential. Since the cathode of $V1$ is connected to the cathode of $V2$, it is maintained at the same potential. A definite positive potential is maintained on the grid of $V1$ through the resistors $R3$ and $R4$, but this is not sufficient to permit $V1$ to conduct. The normal condition, then, of the two tubes of the multivibrator is $V2$ conducting and $V1$ not conducting. If a positive trigger pulse is applied to the grid of $V1$

with sufficient amplitude to cause $V1$ to conduct, a negative square wave will appear at the plate of $V1$ and will be impressed on the grid of $V2$ through the capacitor $C1$. This negative square wave is sufficient at least to reduce the conduction through $V2$ and causes the plate voltage to rise, forming a positive square wave on the plate of $V2$. Both of these waves are known as "gates." The time constant $R2C1$ will determine the time that $V2$ is cut off and therefore will determine the width of the gates, that is, the length of time over which the gates extend.

Figure 9-8 shows how a gate may be used to generate a saw-toothed voltage for the time-base generator. The exact circuit of Fig. 9-7 has been duplicated with the addition of $V3$ and $V4$. $V3$ and $V4$ effectively make up a bleeder circuit from B+ to ground. Both of these tubes are normally con-

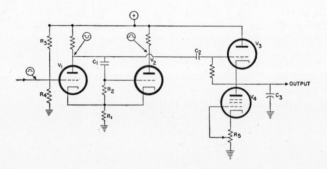

FIG. 9-8. A high-vacuum circuit for generating a driven sweep.

ducting and are connected in series. V3 is connected as a normal triode, and $V4$ is connected as a constant-current pentode. The cathode of $V3$ and the plate of $V4$ are connected, with the capacitor $C3$ also connected at this junction. Since a constant current is normally flowing through these tubes, the capacitor $C3$ is charged to a definite positive potential. If the negative gate from the multivibrator-gate generator is impressed upon the grid of $V3$, it will cut off $V3$ and enable the capacitor $C3$ to discharge through the constant-current pentode $V4$. The capacitor $C3$ will continue to discharge through $V4$ as long as the negative gate is impressed upon the grid of $V3$, keeping it cut off. Therefore, the circuit constants of the multivibrator and the value of the capacitor $C3$ determine the length of the sweep.

It will be noted that in this type of sweep circuit, the linear sweep occurs first and the return trace occurs after the linear sweep has been triggered. Therefore, the spot on the cathode-ray tube normally rests at the left edge of the screen. With this type of circuit, the cathode-ray tube can be blanked out completely while the beam rests on the left edge of the tube screen. The beam may be turned on by capacitively coupling the positive gate from the plate of $V2$ to the grid of the cathode-ray tube. This positive gate overcomes the normal bias on the cathode-ray tube and turns on the trace only during the period of the sweep.

Other Time Bases. Occasions often arise where a linear time base is not necessary for making certain types of measurements. As pointed out in an earlier chapter, provision is usually made in the oscilloscope so that the linear time-base generator may be switched off and an external signal may be injected into the horizontal channel of the oscilloscope by means of the horizontal channel input terminal. Some oscilloscopes have other types of time bases built in as part of the actual circuit. However,

Fig. 9–9. The voltage of a sine wave varies most rapidly and also most uniformly between the point A and B and the points C and D.

these are usually special instruments. A sinusoidal time base is frequently used for certain applications. In some cases, it is used because it is more practical, but it is used most often because a sine wave is usually readily available. This saves the cost and trouble of incorporating a linear time-base generator.

In the drawing of the sine wave in Fig. 9-9 it can readily be seen that the voltage varies most rapidly and, at the same time, most uniformly between the points A and B and the points C and D; whereas at the peaks above and below these portions, the voltage varies only slightly and not at all uniformly. Thus, if this voltage is applied to the horizontal deflection plates of a cathode-ray tube, the spot moves from one side of the screen to the other and back again to the first side. At the ends of the trace, the spot travels quite slowly and not at all linearly; while near the center of the screen, the spot moves quite rapidly and very nearly linearly with respect to time. This central portion of the trace can be made even more nearly linear through expanding the trace by advancing the horizontal gain control and using only the central portion for viewing the pattern. The addition of a simple phase-shifting network that is capable of shifting the phase of the sine wave through 180 deg will enable the operator to place any portion of the desired vertical signal on the linear section of the trace. The major objection to this type of trace for normal oscilloscopic use is that the return trace takes just as long as the forward trace. A continuous oscillation will appear then on both traces, and the pattern observed will be unintelligible. However, this type of time base can be used for the study of noncontinuous signals (transients). Also, if the sine wave producing the horizontal deflection, or a portion of it, is also impressed upon the grid of the cathode-ray tube, the negative half of the cycle will blank the beam and thus blank out the return trace. To prevent the fluctuation in intensity that will occur during the positive half cycle, a diode may be connected to the grid to prevent the grid from rising above a fixed voltage.

Another method of distinguishing the two traces is to separate them slightly to form an elliptical trace. This separation may be accomplished by feeding the sine wave through another phase-shifting network and

FIG. 9–10. A drawing of a sine wave displayed on an elliptical sweep.

applying its output to the vertical deflection plates. The signal to be observed is merely superimposed upon this voltage. A drawing of a pattern appearing on an elliptical trace is shown in Fig. 9-10. If the phase is shifted exactly 90 deg by this second phase shifter, a circular trace will result. A signal that is then superimposed on the vertical deflection plates will appear as a radial deflection; i.e., deflection occurs along the radii of the circle. Such a device is employed most frequently in studies of rotary motion where the deflection produced is a function of rotation. An example of the use of this type of time base is in the study of explosions occurring within each of the cylinders of a gasoline engine.

Intensity Modulation. As stated previously in Chap. 6, it is sometimes necessary or useful to apply to the cathode-ray tube an intensifying pulse or possibly a blanking pulse, which, respectively, intensifies or blanks out the beam of the cathode-ray tube at definite specified intervals. This pulse is usually applied to the grid of the cathode-ray tube so that a positive pulse intensifies the beam and the negative pulse blanks the beam. In cases where the pulse is applied to the cathode, the reverse is true.

In the general-purpose oscilloscope, the discharge of the capacitor in the sweep generator is sometimes used to blank the beam on its return trace. Since this is effectively a negative pulse, a small capacitor coupled between the plate of the thyratron and the grid of the cathode-ray tube will transmit a negative pulse to the grid and blank the beam during the return-trace time. Such an application is shown in Fig. 9-11.

Intensity modulation is also frequently used to record precise time intervals. In such cases, an oscillator at a given frequency—the frequency

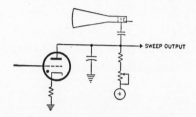

FIG. 9–11. Circuit for obtaining return-trace blanking from a linear time-base generator.

SWEEP OUTPUT

of the time intervals required—is fed directly to the grid of the cathode-ray tube. In order that the markers may be sharp, it is necessary to convert these oscillations into pulses so that the markers show up as definite changes in intensity on the trace of the cathode-ray tube. With the usual general-purpose oscilloscope, the intensity markers will probably shift,

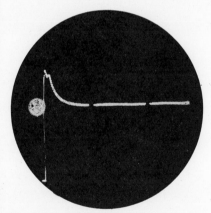

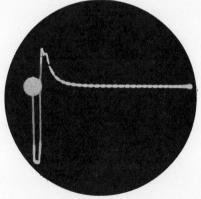

FIG. 9–12. Oscillogram showing the use of a triggered sweep and intensity markers. Markers are at 100 microsecond intervals.

FIG. 9–13. Oscillogram showing the use of a triggered sweep and intensity markers. Markers are at 10 microsecond intervals.

or rather, be seen to move along the trace that is being measured. The circuits of the oscilloscope are such, however, that it is highly improbable that the markers as well as the signal being viewed can both be synchronized to the frequency of the time-base generator. In most cases where it is necessary to make precise measurements of time, a specialized oscilloscope is used. This oscilloscope usually contains a driven sweep from which a pulse may also be derived to drive the marker oscillator. Thus, since the marker oscillator is triggered at the same time as the sweep, the markers that appear on the trace are synchronized automatically with the sweep. Also, since the sweep can be synchronized to the signal, all three items—the sweep, the markers, and the signal being observed—are in synchronism. An illustration of the use of a triggered sweep and markers to measure the duration of a pulse appears in Fig. 9-12. This figure shows blanking markers at 100-microsecond intervals. Fig. 9-13 shows the same situation except that the markers appear at intervals of 10 microseconds.

10 Operation of the Oscilloscope

Introduction. The individual who undertakes to use an oscilloscope for the first time is probably perplexed at the number of controls that appear on the front panel. Actually, there are only about ten on a general-purpose oscilloscope, each control serving a specific objective. Of these ten controls, no more than four or five are varied in the more general uses of the instrument. Furthermore, there is reassurance for the individual who has purchased an oscilloscope in the fact that the more controls there are available on the front panel, the more versatile is his instrument.

This chapter is written to guide the user in learning exactly what effect is produced on the beam of the cathode-ray tube by each control. For continuity, the text will center about the instrument shown in Fig. 10-1 with its list of controls appearing in tabular form in Table 10-1. However, in order that this book may be as helpful as possible, Table 10-1 also provides a list of the exact names of the comparable controls as they appear on the front panels of several other popular general-purpose models.

Operating Controls. The controls that appear on the front panel of the oscilloscope fall into two major types: potentiometers and switches. Also appearing on the front panel of the general-purpose oscilloscope are a number of binding posts, or jacks, to which connections may be made in the course of using the instrument for testing purposes. Potentiometers are those controls which operate in a manner similar to the volume control of a radio. They may be rotated smoothly and may be set in any position. The maximum setting of these controls is in the extreme clockwise position and the minimum setting is in the extreme counterclockwise position.

Two major types of switches are generally used in oscilloscopes, viz., the toggle switch and the rotary switch. The toggle switch is commonly known for its leverlike handle which may be in one position or the other. If this switch is used as a power switch, it is standard practice for the handle to be up when the power is on. When the toggle switch is used for other purposes, the position of the handle points to the lettering on the front panel that describes that position. The rotary switch has a knob similar to that used on potentiometers and is rotated in steps. The num-

FIG. 10-1. Front panel of a general-purpose cathode-ray oscilloscope. (*Courtesy,*
Allen B. Du Mont Laboratories, Inc.)

ber of these steps or positions may vary from two to twelve depending upon its use. Figure 10-2 shows sketches of these three types of controls. It should also be pointed out at this time that another type of rotary switch is sometimes connected on the back of the intensity potentiometer so that when the intensity is turned up, the power is turned on simultaneously. This type of switch is also frequently employed on the sound volume controls of radios.

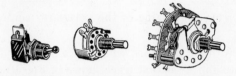

Fig. 10–2.   Drawing showing a toggle switch, a potentiometer and a rotary switch (reading from left to right).

Warning

Because of the high potentials (a minimum of 1,000 volts) used in the circuits thereof, never operate an oscilloscope with its case removed.

Since the easiest way to learn is to learn by doing, a step-by-step procedure is given in the following paragraph for learning to use the controls of an oscilloscope.

Step 1.   Set both the INTENSITY and FOCUS controls at approximately their mid-positions.

Step 2.   Set the Y POSITION and X POSITION controls at their mid-positions.

Step 3.   Set the Y GAIN control at minimum.

FIG. 10–3.   Trace out of focus.   FIG. 10–4.   Trace in focus.

Step 4.   Set the FINE FREQUENCY and SYNC SIGNAL AMPLITUDE controls at their minimum position.

Step 5.   Set the COARSE FREQUENCY switch between 150 and 500.

Step 6.   Set the SYNC SIGNAL SELECTOR switch at INT.

Step 7.   Set the BEAM switch to the ON position.

Step 8.   Set the X GAIN control at about 30.

Step 9.   Turn the POWER switch to the ON position.

After about ½ min, a line should appear across the face of the screen of the cathode-ray tube. If it does not, take the next step.

Step 10.   Increase the setting of the INTENSITY control until the line does appear.

The chances are that the trace which does appear on the screen will be out of focus and appear as that trace shown in Fig. 10-3.

FIG. 10–5. Trace positioned too far to the right side of the screen.

FIG. 10–6. Trace positioned too high on the screen.

Step 11.   Increase the setting of the FOCUS control to obtain a fine clear trace with fine edges and with equal thickness throughout its length.

After this adjustment has been made, the operator may find that the intensity of the trace is too bright. If this is true, then—

Step 12.   Reduce the setting of the INTENSITY control until the trace can be seen clearly without undue brightness as well as without its being so dim that it strains the eyes to observe it.

Step 13.   Readjust the FOCUS control to obtain again a clearly defined trace.

Figure 10-4 shows a well-focused trace, which is adjusted to the proper length on the screen. *Notice that for every setting of the intensity control, there is an optimum setting for focus.*

Step 14.   If the ends of the trace cannot be seen, the x GAIN control is set too high and should be reduced until both ends are visible.

Positioning Controls.   The next controls that the operator should try to use are the Y POSITION and X POSITION controls. The Y POSITION control moves the trace vertically, either up or down (usually a clockwise movement of the knob moves the trace up, and a counterclockwise motion moves it down). The trace will move as the control is turned and thus may be located at the top or the bottom of the screen of the cathode-ray tube, or at any point in between.

Step 1.   Turn the x POSITION control to the right and follow the movement of the trace.

Step 2.   Position the trace in the approximate position of the trace shown in Fig. 10-5.

FIG. 10–7.   Trace positioned too far to the left of the screen.

FIG. 10–8.   Trace positioned too far downward on the screen.

Step 3.   Turn the Y POSITION control to locate the trace in the approximate position shown in Fig. 10-6.

The x POSITION control moves the trace horizontally either left or right. The action is similar to that of the Y POSITION control except for the plane in which the trace moves. For practice —

Step 4.   Position the trace in the approximate position shown in Fig. 10-7.

Step 5.   Position the trace in the approximate position shown in Fig. 10-8.

By using a combination of these two controls, the trace may be located anywhere on the screen of the cathode-ray tube. In the majority of cases, it is desirable to have the trace centered on the screen of the cathode-ray tube. To obtain the true center horizontally —

Step 6. Position the trace by noting the distance between each edge of the trace and the edge of the screen on each side of the tube.

Figure 10-9 shows a trace centered both vertically and horizontally on the screen. Vertical centering is easily obtained merely by noting that the trace falls along the center line of the calibrated scale which is over the face of the cathode-ray tube. If the trace is not long enough, merely increase the setting of the x GAIN control until the trace is just a short distance from the edge of the screen on each side of the tube. Figure 10-9 also shows the approximate length of the trace as compared with the diameter of the tube.

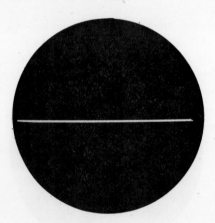

FIG. 10–9. Properly focused and centered trace about optimum length.

Coarse Frequency and Fine Frequency Controls. To understand the function of these controls —

Step 1. Turn the FINE FREQUENCY control to the minimum setting, the extreme counterclockwise position.

Step 2. Turn the COARSE FREQUENCY control to the OFF position, but do not leave it in this position longer than ½ min.

Step 3. Turn the COARSE FREQUENCY control one step in a clockwise direction as soon as the spot has been observed.

Caution

If the spot is left in one position for a longer period of time than about ½ min, it may burn the screen of the tube, rendering that particular portion of the screen useless for future observation. In most cases this is not too serious, but if too many spots occur on the screen, they become a nuisance. A trace of excessively high intensity will also burn the screen of the tube if it is left in one position for a period of from 3 to 5 min. Therefore, if it is desirable to leave the oscilloscope operating for a period of time with a fixed trace appearing on the screen, decrease the intensity.

The spot that was observed when the COARSE FREQUENCY switch was turned off is caused by the electron beam striking the face of the tube. The trace that appears on the screen when the COARSE FREQUENCY switch is rotated clockwise is due to that spot moving so rapidly across the face of the tube that it is impossible for the eye to detect it as a single spot. The persistence of the eye causes the moving spot to blend into a solid straight line, provided that the spot is moving rapidly enough. This is analogous to the spinning airplane propeller, which cannot be identified as a propeller but rather as a large circular blur. The persistence of the screen is another factor that makes the moving spot seem like a fixed line. To prove this —

Step 4. Turn the COARSE FREQUENCY switch off again and turn the X POSITION control rapidly back and forth with the hand.

If the movement of the spot is observed carefully, it will be noticed that the circular spot appears to have a tail as it is moving. This is due to the persistence of the screen. Specifically, this is referred to as phosphorescence, the phenomenon that causes the screen to give off light *after* it has been excited by the electron beam. A more complete discussion of persistence in screens is given in Chap. 5.

Step 5. Turn the COARSE FREQUENCY control to give the lowest sweep frequency.

Step 6. Turn the FINE FREQUENCY control to its minimum setting.

Some instruments have sweep frequencies that are slow enough in this position to permit the viewer to see the spot move across the screen. In such a case, it will be noted that the spot starts at the left side of the screen and moves slowly across to the right. As it completes its journey across to the right side of the screen, it will be seen to start again almost immediately at the left side of the screen. In other instruments, which do not have quite that low a sweep frequency, a flickering line will be observed at the lowest setting of the two frequency controls. This is due to the fact that the speed of the spot, plus the persistence of the screen, is not sufficient to cause the motion to blend into a fixed image.

Step 7. Gradually increase the setting of the FINE FREQUENCY control.

In instruments having slow sweeps, the spot first blends into a flickering trace as the frequency is increased. As the FINE FREQUENCY control is advanced farther, the rate of flicker increases until a solid, unflickering straight line finally appears on the screen. This latter condition is the only one that can be observed with oscilloscopes whose sweep frequency does not go below 10 c.

Reading the Coarse Frequency Control. On the instrument in Fig. 10-1, the switch position falls between two numbers. For instance, in the figure, the COARSE FREQUENCY control is set on the line between the numbers 150 and 500. This indicates that for this setting of the COARSE FREQUENCY switch, the FINE FREQUENCY control has a range of 150 to 500 c; that is, it can vary the movement of the spot across the screen from 150 to 500 times each second. If the COARSE FREQUENCY control were set on the line between **8** and 40, the FINE FREQUENCY control would have a range of 8 to 40 c. The abbreviation K used on the markings of the COARSE FREQUENCY switch represents 1,000. Thus, 2K, 8K, 25K, and 50K represent, respectively, 2,000, 8,000, 25,000, and 50,000 c. Thus, by reading the setting of these two controls, the frequency with which the spot sweeps across the screen may be approximated. Do not depend on this, however, for an accurate measurement of frequency. Actually in the production testing of oscilloscopes, the only checks of sweep frequency

FIG. 10–10. When the X-GAIN control is at zero only a spot will appear at the center of the screen.

that are made are the low frequency of the slowest coarse position and the high frequency of the highest coarse position. The other ranges usually overlap slightly for operating convenience and are checked for overlap.

Other oscilloscopes have two numbers printed at the various positions of the COARSE FREQUENCY switch, e.g., 10-100, 90-900, and so on. These markings also indicate the range of the FINE FREQUENCY control when the COARSE FREQUENCY switch is in that particular position, i.e., from 10 to 100 c and from 90 to 900 c, respectively.

X-Gain Control. The X-GAIN control was used in preceding steps for adjusting the length of the line generated by the sweep generator. When this control is at zero, a spot will appear at the center of the screen (Fig. 10-10). As the control is advanced toward maximum, the length of the horizontal trace is simultaneously increased. Further use of this control will be discussed later.

The Test-Signal Binding Post. This binding post is connected internally to a low-voltage winding of the power transformer (usually about 6 volts) so that an alternating current voltage at power-line frequency is available to the operator for testing purposes.

Displaying a Pattern on the Screen. To display a pattern on the screen of the oscilloscope:

Step 1. Set the COARSE FREQUENCY control to the 40/150 position.

Step 2. Adjust the X GAIN control so that the trace covers about three fourths of the width of the cathode-ray tube.

Step 3. Connect a wire from the TEST SIGNAL binding post to the SIGNAL INPUT binding post on the left side of the panel (the operator's left).

Step 4. Advance the setting of the Y GAIN control from minimum until the deflection produced covers one half to three fourths of the screen.

A pattern will be seen on the screen; but it will not be discernible because of the rapid, apparently random, motion of the pattern.

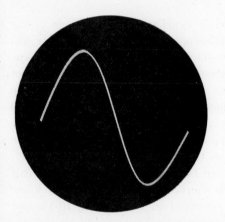 

FIG. 10–11a. A 60-c a-c wave synchro-nized on a 60-c sweep.

FIG. 10–11b. A 60-c a-c wave on a sweep frequency which is close to 60 c.

Step 5. Be sure the COARSE FREQUENCY control has been set to 40/150. (On other instruments to the range which includes 60 c.)

Step 6. Set the SYNC SIGNAL AMPLITUDE control to its minimum posi-tion.

Step 7. Set the SYNC SIGNAL SELECTOR switch to LINE FREQ.

(In other instruments without a LINE FREQUENCY position, set the SYNC SIGNAL SELECTOR switch to INTERNAL.)

Step 8. Advance the FINE FREQUENCY control until a single wave of the power-line frequency (60 c) can be seen moving across the screen.

Step 9. Minimize the motion of this wave by carefully adjusting the FINE FREQUENCY control.

Step 10.   Advance the SYNC SIGNAL AMPLITUDE control until the wave "locks in" and is thus stationary on the screen of the tube as shown in Fig. 10-11*a*. Figure 10-11*b* shows the pattern on the screen before the wave "locks in."

Note

Setting the SYNC SIGNAL AMPLITUDE control too high will distort the pattern being observed. Therefore good operating procedure calls for stopping the pattern as closely as possible with the FINE FREQUENCY control and adding just enough synchronizing signal with the SYNC SIGNAL AMPLITUDE control to stop any motion. A condition showing distortion caused by too high a setting of the SYNC SIGNAL AMPLITUDE control is shown in Fig. 10-12.

For oscilloscopes with no test signal connection, use the secondary of a filament transformer (from 2.5 to 12 volts) as the input to the oscilloscope. Connect one of the secondary leads to the Y SIGNAL INPUT binding post and the other to the GND binding post immediately below it. It is not necessary to use the GND post if a test signal is provided by the instrument as the internal connections to the chassis establish a common ground.

The foregoing procedure resulted in synchronizing one cycle of the sine wave on the screen of the oscilloscope. Therefore, the sweep frequency is exactly equal to the power-line frequency, which, in this case, is 60 c. If, by turning the FINE FREQUENCY control in the direction of lower frequency, two complete sine waves appear on the screen, the sweep frequency is then half of the line frequency, or 30 c. The operator should practice using the COARSE FREQUENCY and FINE FREQUENCY controls by adjusting the sweep frequency from 60 c to 30 to 20 to 15 and observe that 1, 2, 3, or 4 complete cycles of the 60-c sine wave, respectively, appear on the screen. To obtain sweep frequencies below 40 c with this instrument, it is necessary to switch the COARSE FREQUENCY to a lower position. These conditions may be observed in Figs. 10-13, 10-14, and 10-15, respectively. Each of these figures can be duplicated by the following procedure:

Step 1.   Turn the SYNC SIGNAL AMPLITUDE control to minimum.

Step 2.   Obtain the desired number of cycles and stop the wave as nearly as possible with the FINE FREQUENCY control.

Step 3.   Increase the SYNC SIGNAL AMPLITUDE control just enough to lock in the pattern.

It will be noted that when the frequency of the time-base generator is close to the frequency of the wave under observation, or a submultiple of that frequency, the pattern will drift across the screen either from left to right or from right to left. The operator will also notice that by changing the setting of the FINE FREQUENCY control, he can pass through the point of exact frequency and thus the pattern will change its direction;

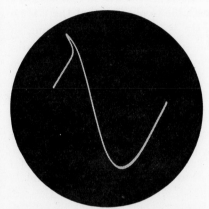

FIG. 10–12. A 60-c a-c wave on a 60-c sweep frequency with too much synchronizing voltage applied. (SYNC SIGNAL AMPLITUDE control set too high.)

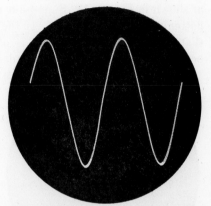

FIG. 10–13. A 60-c a-c wave synchronized on a 30-c sweep.

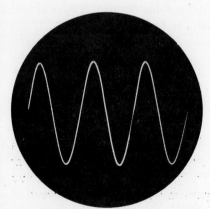

FIG. 10–14. A 60-c a-c wave synchronized on a 20-c sweep.

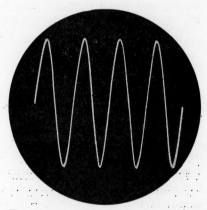

FIG. 10–15. A 60-c a-c wave synchronized on a 15-c sweep.

that is, if it were drifting from right to left and gradually slowing down as the operator rotated the FINE FREQUENCY control counterclockwise, he would see the wave continuously becoming slower until he had passed a certain point, and the pattern would then drift from left to right.

Additional Uses of the X-Gain Control. Consider the same wave as shown in Fig. 10-13. Suppose it is desirable to observe that there is no flattening of the top peaks. If the X GAIN is increased to maximum, so that the horizontal deflection is off the screen, this wave has actually been magnified until it is spread out over many times the size of the

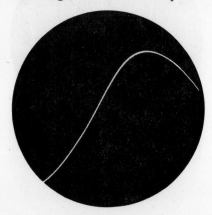

FIG. 10–16. A 60-c a-c wave expanded by increasing the X-GAIN control.

screen, and small portions may be observed for details. The wave of Fig. 10-13 magnified by the X GAIN control is shown in Fig. 10-16. If the portion of the wave that is desired for observation should be off the screen because of this expansion of the horizontal axis, it can probably be brought back by turning the X POSITION control to the right or left. If, as may occur in special cases, this is of no assistance, the X GAIN control will have to be decreased or the SYNC SIGNAL AMPLITUDE control turned down so that the pattern drifts slowly across the screen.

Y-Gain Control. The Y GAIN control can also be used to magnify a pattern up to the point where the signal overloads the amplifiers, and the Y POSITION control is used to bring the correct portion of the pattern onto the screen. Correct expansion of the pattern with the Y GAIN control is shown in Fig. 10-17, while Fig. 10-18 shows too high an input voltage resulting in the overloading of the amplifiers within the oscilloscope. Figure 10-18 thus illustrates a distorted wave, which is the result of incorrect operation of the oscilloscope.

Note

It is extremely important that the operator remember that too much vertical gain or too great an input signal may overload the amplifiers and thus result in a pattern that does not correctly represent the wave under observation.

Sync Signal Selector Switch. One control that has not yet been described is the SYNC SIGNAL SELECTOR switch. In the instrument under discussion here, this switch has three positions: INTERNAL, EXTERNAL, and LINE FREQ. However, some instruments may have only INTERNAL and EXTERNAL.

The INTERNAL position is convenient in that a portion of the signal being directed through the vertical deflection amplifiers is furnished to the sweep generator to synchronize the horizontal motion of the electron beam with that of the vertical motion. Thus, the wave under study may be made stationary by properly setting the SYNC SIGNAL AMPLITUDE control. The disadvantage of using internal synchronization is that every time it

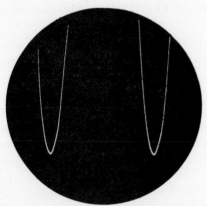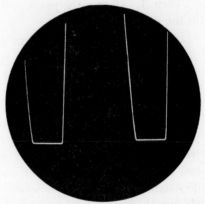

FIG. 10–17. A 60-c a-c wave synchronized on a 30-c sweep expanded by increasing the Y-GAIN control.

FIG. 10–18. Same as Fig. 10–17 but Y-GAIN control was increased so much that the amplifiers have been overloaded.

becomes necessary to change the Y-GAIN control, the SYNC SIGNAL AMPLITUDE control must be reset because these controls react inherently on each other when the SYNC SIGNAL SELECTOR switch is set in this position.

To illustrate this point:

Step 1. Set the SYNC SIGNAL SELECTOR switch to INTERNAL and obtain the pattern shown in Fig. 10-13.

Step 2. Set the Y GAIN control to obtain a vertical deflection of about three inches.

Step 3. Gradually decrease the setting of the Y GAIN control and notice that the pattern jumps out of synchronization. In order to obtain again a stationary pattern, it will be necessary to increase the setting of either the Y GAIN or the SYNC SIGNAL AMPLITUDE controls.

The EXTERNAL position is used when the operator is observing different amplitudes of the same signal to avoid changing the setting of the SYNC

SIGNAL AMPLITUDE control each time a signal of different amplitude is to be observed. To make use of this position, it is necessary to connect a lead from a constant signal source to the EXTERNAL SYNC SIGNAL binding post to provide the sweep generator with a constant synchronizing voltage. The pattern will remain synchronized when the SYNC SIGNAL SELECTOR switch is in this position irrespective of the amplitude of vertical deflection. To prove this:

Step 1.   Set the SYNC SIGNAL SELECTOR switch to EXTERNAL, and make the connections necessary to obtain the pattern shown in Fig. 10-13.

Step 2.   Connect an additional wire from the TEST SIGNAL binding post to the EXTERNAL SYNC SIGNAL binding post.

Step 3.   Obtain the pattern of Fig. 10-13 synchronized on the screen in the usual manner.

Step 4.   Reduce the Y GAIN control until the pattern is no longer visible on the screen. Increase its setting and notice that the pattern remains stationary regardless of vertical amplitude.

The LINE FREQ position of the SYNC SIGNAL SELECTOR switch on this and many other types of oscilloscopes provides an internal connection of the line frequency to the sweep generator for synchronizing signals whose frequencies are the same as, or are whole number multiples of, the line frequency. This position is just an added convenience to save the time and trouble of making another connection to the oscilloscope. It may be duplicated, in instruments which do not have this switch position, by placing the switch in the EXTERNAL position and connecting a wire from the TEST SIGNAL binding post to the EXTERNAL SYNC SIGNAL binding post.

Beam Switch.   The BEAM switch is another added convenience for the operator. In performing experiments with the oscilloscope, it is frequently desirable to leave everything operating for a period of time and to take readings only occasionally. To leave the oscilloscope with a pattern on the screen for a long time might result in burning the screen of the cathode-ray tube. To turn the oscilloscope off each time would require the operator to wait for the oscilloscope to warm up every time he wished to view the pattern. Of course, the INTENSITY control could be turned down, but then it would have to be reset for every reading. Instead, the BEAM switch automatically cuts off the beam of the cathode-ray tube, and a mere flick of the switch returns the instrument to immediate operating condition.

Limitations of the Oscilloscope.   There is practically no limit to the number of different kinds of signals that may be viewed on the screen of a cathode-ray tube. As pointed out earlier, these signals may be the result of any variable that may be converted into a corresponding variable voltage. However, just as a voltmeter has limitations as to the magnitudes of the voltages it can measure, so does the oscilloscope. If a signal is so weak that the amplifiers cannot amplify it sufficiently to produce a deflection of sufficient amplitude to be readable, this oscilloscope pattern cannot be relied upon. If necessary, however, such signals can always be amplified before they are applied to the input terminals of the oscilloscope. Occasionally, too, a signal voltage is too large to be applied to the input terminals. In such cases, the signal must be attenuated before it is applied to the input terminals.

Another limitation of the oscilloscope is the frequency range of its amplifiers. If the frequency of the signal to be studied is above or below the frequency limits of the amplifier, that signal will not be faithfully reproduced by the amplifier, and inaccurate conclusions may be made from such observations. In order to observe such a signal (if it has sufficient amplitude), it must be connected directly to the deflection plates of the cathode-ray tube. Every standard cathode-ray tube will reproduce signals faithfully within a frequency range from 0 c to about 200 megacycles. Thus, the only frequency limitation for the cathode-ray tube itself is at very high frequencies. To ensure that the voltage and frequency limits of a given oscilloscope are not exceeded, the instruction book for that instrument should be consulted.

TABLE 10-1

OSCILLOSCOPE CONTROLS AND THEIR FUNCTIONS

Model	Controls bias on CRT, thus regulating intensity of fluorescent spot	Controls volt. applied to focusing electrode of CRT, thus focusing fluorescent spot	Controls d-c-volt. applied to vert. deflec. plates changing vert. position of spot or trace	Controls d-c volt. applied to hor. deflec. plates, changing hor. position of spot or trace
Du Mont 208-B	Intensity	Focus	Y position	X position
Du Mont 164-E	Intensity	Focus	V position	H position
Du Mont 224-A	Intensity	Focus	Y position	X position
Du Mont 241	Intensity	Focus	Y position	X position
Du Mont 274	Intensity	Focus	Vertical position	Horizontal position
Sylvania 131	Intensity	Focus	Vertical centering	Horizontal centering
Sylvania 132	Intensity	Focus	Vertical centering	Horizontal centering
Hickok 195	Intensity	Focus	Positioning	Positioning
*Hickok 305; 505	Intensity	Focus	Positioning	Positioning
Supreme 546-A	Intensity	Focus	Vert. position	Hor. position
Electr. Dev. Lab. 41; 49	Intensity	Focus	Vertical centering	Horizontal centering
G.E. Cro-3A	Intensity	Focus	Vert. centering	Hor. centering
G.E. Cro-5A	Intensity	Focus	Vert. centering	Hor. centering
Waterman S10A	Intensity	Focus	....	....
R.C.A. 155-C	Intensity	Focus	Ver. centering	Hor. centering
R.C.A. 158	Intensity	Focus	Centering	Centering
R.C.A. 160-B	Intensity	Focus	Centering	Centering

* Also contains controls for an internal signal generator.
Note: The use of parentheses indicates that the control is there, but it is not specifically marked, although it may be indicated by the panel layout.

TABLE 10-1—(Continued)

OSCILLOSCOPE CONTROLS AND THEIR FUNCTIONS

Varies d-c resist. in plate circuit of thyraton, thereby varying time of sweep	Varies capac. used in sweep gen.	Controls ampl. of signal passing through vert. (or Y axis) amplifier	Controls ampl. of signal passing through hor. (or X axis) amplifier	Controls ampl. of synchronizing signal applied to sweep gen.
Fine frequency	Coarse frequency	(Y axis) gain	(X axis) gain	Sync. signal amplitude
Sweep vernier	Sweep range	V gain	H gain	Sync.
Freq. vernier	Freq. range	Y gain	X gain	Sync. Signal
Frequency vernier	Frequency range	Y gain	X gain	Synchronizing Signal
Fine frequency	Coarse frequency	Vertical amp.	Horizontal amp.	Sync. amp.
Fine frequency	Coarse frequency	Vert. gain	Hor. gain	Sync. amplitude
Fine frequency	Coarse frequency	Vert. gain	Hor. gain	Sync. amplitude
Vernier	Steps	Vertical gain	Horizontal gain	Locking
Vernier	Steps	Gain	Gain	Locking
Fine freq.	Sweep freq.	Vert. gain	Hor. gain	Sync. control
Sweep vernier	Sweep range	Gain	Gain	Synchronization
Fine freq.	Coarse freq.	Vertical gain	Horizontal gain	Sweep sync.
Fine freq.	Coarse freq.	Gain	Gain	Sync.
Frequency	Range	V. gain	H. gain	....
Frequency	Range	Ver. gain	Hor. gain	Sync. adjust.
Frequency	Range	Gain	Gain	Sync.
Frequency	Range	Gain	Gain	Sync.

* Also contains controls for an internal signal generator.
Note: The use of parentheses indicates that the control is there, but it is not specifically marked, although it may be indicated by the panel layout.

TABLE 10-1—(Continued)

OSCILLOSCOPE CONTROLS AND THEIR FUNCTIONS

Model	Controls ampl. of signal passing through intensity modulation (or Z axis) amplifier	Selects desired sync. signal.	Applies primary volt. to power trans.	Cuts off beam of CRT	Attenuates vert. signal prior to its being applied to vert. amplifier
Du Mont 208-B	…………	Sync. signal selector	Power	Beam	(Y attenuator)
Du Mont 164-E	…………	Sync.	(On intensity control)	…………	…………………
Du Mont 224-A	…………	Sync. selector	Power	…………	(Y attenuation)
Du Mont 241	Z gain	Synchronizing selector	Power	…………	(Y attenuation)
Du Mont 274	…………	Sync. selector	(On intensity control)	…………	…………………
Sylvania 131	…………	Sync. selector	(On intensity control)	…………	…………………
Sylvania 132	…………	Sync. selector	Off-on	…………	…………………
Hickok 195	…………	…………………	(On intensity control)	…………	…………………
*Hickok 305; 505	…………	Sync.	(On intensity control)	…………	…………………
Supreme 546-A	…………	(Ext. syn.— int. syn.)	(On intensity control)	…………	…………………
Electr. Dev. Lab. 41; 49	…………	Synchronization	(On intensity control)	…………	…………………
G.E. Cro-3A	…………	Synchronizing	(On intensity control)	…………	(Vertical Amplifier)
G.E. Cro-5A	…………	Sync. Select.	(On intensity control)	…………	(Y attenuator)
Waterman S10A	…………	Connection	(On intensity control)	…………	…………………
R.C.A. 155-C	…………	Sync. selector	(On intensity control)	…………	…………………
R.C.A. 158	…………	Timing sync.	(On intensity control)	…………	Attenuator
R.C.A. 160-B	…………	Timing sync.	(On intensity control)	…………	Amplifier

* Also contains controls for an internal signal generator.
Note: The use of parentheses indicates that the control is there, but it is not specifically marked, although it may be indicated by the panel layout.

TABLE 10-1—(Continued)

OSCILLOSCOPE CONTROLS AND THEIR FUNCTIONS

Applies signal to vert. amplifier or directly to vert. deflec. plates	Permits direct coupling or capacitive coupling to the deflec. plates of CRT.	Selects an ext. Z axis signal or int. signal for return-trace blanking	Connects the sweep gen. or an ext. signal for horizontal deflection	Attenuates hor. signal prior to its being applied to hor. amplifier
....	....	....	....	....
....	....	....	(Hor. input)	....
(Y input)	⎧ Deflection plates connections	....	....	X attenuation
....	⎩	Z signal selec.	....	X attenuation
Vertical input	....	....	....	....
....	....	....	....	....
....	....	....	....	....
(Amp. in- amp. out) Selector	....	....	(Hor. input)	....
....	....	....	Selector	....
....	....	....	(Ext. sweep- int. sweep)	....
....	....	....	(Horizontal amplifier)	....
....	....	....	(On sync. select)	....
....	....	....	....	....
....	....	....	(Hor. input)	....
....	....	....	(Same as Timing sync.)	....
....	....	....	....	....

* Also contains controls for an internal signal generator.

Note: The use of parentheses indicates that the control is there, but it is not specifically marked, although it may be indicated by the panel layout.

TABLE 10-1—(Continued)

OSCILLOSCOPE CONTROLS AND THEIR FUNCTIONS

Model	Term. for applying input signal to vert. amplifier	Term. for applying input signal to hor. amplifier	Output a-c signal usually of line freq. for use as test signal	Term. for applying an ext. synchron. signal
Du Mont 208-B	Y signal input	X signal input	Test signal	External sync. signal
Du Mont 164-E	V	H	Test signal	Ext. sync.
Du Mont 224-A	Y signal input	X signal input	60-c signal	External sync. signal
Du Mont 241	Y signal input	X signal input	60-c signal	Ext. sync. input
Du Mont 274	Vertical input	Horizontal input	Test signal	Ext. sync.
Sylvania 131	Vert. input	Hor. input	6.3 v. a-c	Ext. sync.
Sylvania 132	Vert. input	Hor. input	6.3 v. a-c	Ext. sync.
Hickok 195	Vertical input	Horizontal input	....	Ext. sync.
*Hickok 305; 505	Input	Input	....	Ext. sync.
Supreme 546-A	Vert.	Hor.	....	Ext. syn.
Electr. Dev. Lab. 41; 49	Vert. input	Hor. input	6 v. a-c	Ext. sync.
G.E. Cro-3A	Vert. input	Hor. input	....	Ext. syn. input
G.E. Cro-5A	Vert. input	Hor. input	....	Ext. sync.
Waterman S10A	Vertical	Hor./sync.	....	....
R.C.A. 155-C	Ver. amp. input	Hor. amp. input	6 v. a-c	Ext. sync.
R.C.A. 158	(Probe connection)	High	....	Sync.
R.C.A. 160-B	Cap grid	Cap grid	....	Sync.

* Also contains controls for an internal signal generator.
Note: The use of parentheses indicates that the control is there, but it is not specifically marked, although it may be indicated by the panel layout.

TABLE 10-1—(Continued)

OSCILLOSCOPE CONTROLS AND THEIR FUNCTIONS

Term for applying signal to deflect.-plate pair D1D2	Term for applying signal to deflect.-plate pair D3D4	Term. for applying intensity modulat. signa!	Term for obtaining sync. signal from within oscill.	Term for connecting grounds of various units together to ensure common ref. pt. for all signals
....	....	....	....	2 gnd.
....	....	....	....	2 gnd.
D1D2	D3D4	Int. mod.	....	3 gnd.
....	....	Z input	....	3 gnd.
....	....	Intensity mod.	....	2 gnd.
....	....	....	....	2 gnd.
....	....	....	....	2 gnd.
....	....	....	Int. syn.	2 gnd.
....	....	Z axis input	....	4 gnd.
Plate	Plate	....	....	2 gnd.
....	....	....	....	3 gnd.
....	....	....	....	2 gnd.
....	....	....	....	3 gnd.
....	....	....	....	2 gnd.
....	....	....	....	4 gnd.
....	....	....	....	2 gnd.
....	....	....	....	2 gnd.

* Also contains controls for an internal signal generator.

Note: The use of parentheses indicates that the control is there, but it is not specifically marked, although it may be indicated by the panel layout.

II Interpretation of Basic Patterns

Introduction. Any instrument or measuring device is only of value insofar as its operator can interpret the readings obtained therefrom. For instance, the graph obtained from an electrocardiograph means nothing to the layman because he has had no training or experience in using such an instrument. To the trained technician, however, it tells a complete story.

Likewise, with the oscilloscope, the patterns that appear on the screen mean nothing unless they are properly interpreted. It should be remembered that an oscilloscope is nothing more than a voltmeter that indicates the peak-to-peak voltage of a-c signals and also displays their waveform.

D-C Voltage. The effects produced on the beam of the cathode-ray tube by d-c voltages applied to the deflection plates were fully discussed in Chap. 4. Summarizing this discussion, it may be said that d-c voltages applied directly to the deflection plates of a cathode-ray tube merely affect the position of the electron beam for as long a period of time as that voltage is applied. Since, by definition, an oscilloscope is a device for viewing oscillations or variations, it is of little value in viewing d-c signals. A plain, ordinary voltmeter should be used to measure d-c signals, unless it is desirable to observe a d-c signal that has an a-c signal superimposed upon it.

A-C Signals. Figure 11-1 shows the effect produced on the beam of the cathode-ray tube when three a-c signals of the same amplitude but different waveform are applied to the vertical deflection plates without any voltage being applied to the horizontal deflection plates.

Note
For convenience in seeing the cause of the deflection, the wave causing the vertical deflection has been drawn at the side of the circle representing the tube screen. As the voltage of the wave swings upward from zero, the beam is deflected upward from zero an equal amount. As the voltage of the wave swings downward from zero, the beam swings downward from zero an equal amount.

Since the signal is applied only to the vertical deflection plates, the beam traces a vertical straight line on the face of the cathode-ray tube irrespective of the frequency or shape of the wave. As a result, it is impossible to determine the waveform or the frequency of the signal producing the vertical deflection by studying the pattern on the cathode-ray tube. The only characteristic of the signal that can be determined by such an observation is its relative voltage. (As mentioned previously, the

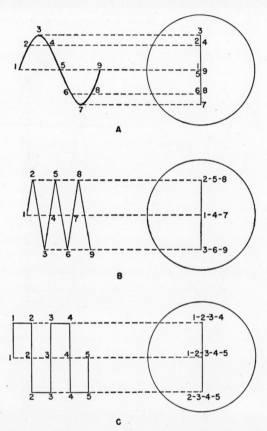

Fig. 11–1. The effect produced on the beam of the cathode-ray tube when three a-c signals of the same amplitude, but different waveforms, are applied to the vertical deflection plates without any voltage being applied to the horizontal deflection plates.

inertialess characteristic of the electron beam enables it to indicate the peak-to-peak voltage of the signal.)

The relative peak-to-peak voltages of the sine waves in Fig. 11-2 can be readily determined from the deflection which they produce in the examples *a*, *b*, and *c*. The deflection produced in *a* is three times that of *c*, and the deflection produced in *b* is two times that of *c*. Therefore, the relative voltages of *a*, *b*, and *c* equal, respectively, 3*c*, 2*c*, and *c*. Knowing the value of any one of these signals, the exact voltage of the other two can readily be calculated.

By the same token, if the three signals of Fig. 11-1 were applied to the horizontal deflection plates and no signal to the vertical plates, they would produce a horizontal trace which would also be only an indication of voltage. If the three sine waves of Fig. 11-2 were applied to the horizontal deflection plates in the same manner, they would indicate three different amplitudes that would still bear the same relationship to each other.

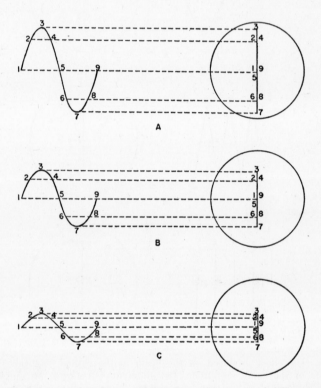

FIG. 11–2. The effect produced by applying three sine waves of different amplitudes to the vertical deflection plates with no voltage applied to the horizontal deflection **plates.**

Sweep Voltage Applied to the Horizontal Plates.   Since most patterns that appear on the cathode-ray tube show the voltage variations in a given signal with respect to time, that is the next logical step in the discussion. A simple method for seeing the effect of two such a-c signals acting simultaneously on the beam of the cathode-ray tube is to represent the two signals graphically and observe the instantaneous voltages of each.

Figure 11-3 shows a sine wave being applied to the vertical deflection plates of a cathode-ray tube and a saw-toothed wave of exactly the same frequency being applied to the horizontal plates. The graph of the sine wave is drawn on the side of the circle that represents the screen of the cathode-ray tube, and the saw-toothed wave is drawn beneath the circle. This form of graphic representation shows most clearly the effect that would be produced by each wave and does *not* in any way indicate the plate to which the waveform is applied.

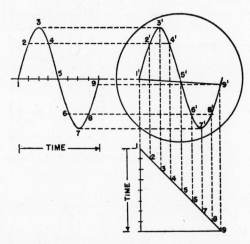

FIG. 11-3. A projection drawing showing an a-c signal applied to the vertical deflection plates and a sweep signal of the same frequency applied to the horizontal deflection plates.

Vertical dotted lines are drawn from equal time intervals along each wave to show the voltage applied to deflect the beam in that plane at each interval of time. Time 1 on the sine wave occurs at the same instant as time 1 on the saw-toothed wave; time 2 on the sine occurs at the same instant as time 2 on the saw-toothed wave; and so on. If the voltage at each of these instants is projected to the circle representing the screen of the cathode-ray tube, the point at which the projection of point 1 on the sine wave intersects the projection of point 1 on the saw-toothed wave will be point 1'. This will be the position of the beam at that instant. The projection of point 2 on the sine wave will intersect the projection of point 2 on the saw-toothed wave at point 2'. This, in turn, represents the position of the beam at instant 2. If this is repeated for each of the nine points on the two waves, each of these points will be plotted on the screen of the cathode-ray tube. Connecting these points results in the pattern as it actually appears. Of course, to accomplish an exact pattern, many more than nine points should be taken; but this is enough to give an approximate representation of the pattern that occurs under these conditions.

Figure 11-4 is a similar projection drawing of the same frequency sine wave as that employed in Fig. 11-3 except that its voltage is much less.

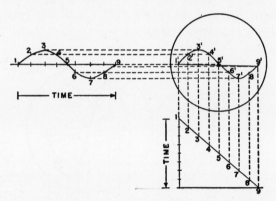

Fɪɢ. 11–4. Same as Fig. 11–3 except that the voltage of the sine wave is much less.

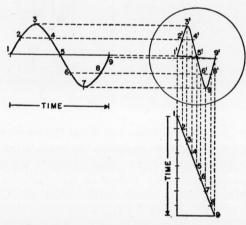

Fɪɢ. 11–5. Same as Fig. 11–3 except that the voltage of the saw-toothed wave is much less.

This drawing, using a saw-toothed wave of the same frequency and same voltage, shows the resulting pattern on the screen.

Figure 11-5 shows the same sine wave that appeared in Fig. 11-3 again applied to the vertical deflection plates and the same frequency saw-toothed wave of lesser amplitude applied to the horizontal deflection plates. The pattern resulting on the screen is still a sine wave, but it has less breadth than when previously presented.

Figure 11-6 shows a sine wave, of twice the frequency of that in Fig. 11-3, being applied to the vertical deflection plates. The saw-toothed wave applied to the horizontal deflection plates is similar in amplitude and frequency to that used in Fig. 11-5. Since, in this case, the frequency of the saw-toothed wave is one half the frequency of the sine wave on the vertical deflection plates, two complete sine waves appear on the screen of the cathode-ray tube.

A saw-toothed wave is applied to the vertical deflection plates, and another saw-toothed wave of one third the frequency is applied to the horizontal plates, as shown in Fig. 11-7. The result is that three complete

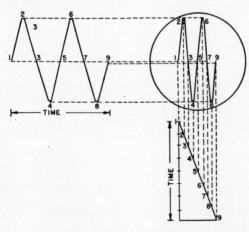

Fig. 11–6.   A projection drawing similar to Fig. 11–3 except that the sine wave is twice the original frequency.

cycles of the saw-toothed wave applied to the vertical plates appear on the screen of the cathode-ray tube.

Figure 11-8 shows a square wave applied to the vertical deflection plates whose frequency is twice that of the saw-toothed wave applied to the horizontal deflection plates. The resultant pattern consists of two cycles of the square wave, which are displayed on the screen.

In viewing Figs. 11-6 and 11-8, each of which displays two complete cycles of the wave applied to the vertical deflection plates, it should be kept in mind that as the horizontal saw-toothed wave sweeps the beam across the screen once, the wave on the vertical plate has swept the beam through two complete cycles vertically. On the next horizontal sweep,

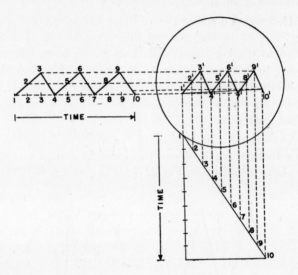

FIG. 11–7. A projection drawing showing a saw-toothed wave applied to the vertical deflection plates and another saw-toothed wave of one-third the frequency applied to the horizontal plates.

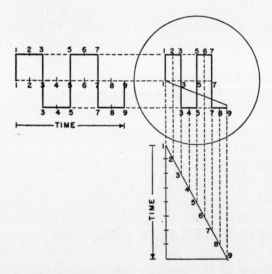

FIG. 11–8. A projection drawing showing a square wave applied to the vertical deflection plates and a saw-toothed wave of one half the frequency applied to the horizontal deflection plates.

the next two cycles of the waveform applied to the vertical plates will be displayed. On the horizontal sweep following that, the next two cycles will be displayed, and so on, so that every cycle of the wave applied to the vertical deflection plates will be displayed.

In Fig. 11-7 every cycle of the wave applied to the vertical deflection plates is also displayed, but in this case, three complete cycles are displayed for every one cycle of the saw-toothed wave applied to the horizontal deflection plates.

Lissajous Figures. Lissajous figures are named in honor of the French scientist by the same name who first obtained these figures geometrically and optically. They illustrate one of the earliest uses to which the cathode-ray tube was put. Lissajous patterns are used to determine the frequency of an unknown signal by comparing it with the frequency of a known signal.* The usual practice is for the known signal to be applied to the horizontal channel of the oscilloscope and the unknown frequency to the vertical channel.

As an example of a Lissajous figure, suppose a 60-c signal (from the TEST SIGNAL output terminal) is applied to the horizontal channel of an oscilloscope, and an audio oscillator whose output is set at 120 cycles is applied to the vertical channel. The pattern appearing on the screen of the cathode-ray tube is shown in Fig. 11-9. This figure also shows the reason that such a pattern results on the screen, since it is a projection drawing like those used earlier in this chapter. Points 1 to 17 are taken at the same time intervals on each wave and are projected to the circle representing the cathode-ray tube screen. Point 1 of each wave intersects at point 1', and points 2 at 2', and so on, resulting for this example in 17 points from which the Lissajous figure is produced. In this case, the ratio of the frequency applied to the vertical channel to the frequency applied to the horizontal channel is as 2 is to 1.

Figure 11-10 shows the Lissajous pattern obtained when the frequency applied to the vertical channel is three times the frequency applied to the horizontal channel. It should be remembered that these patterns rarely, if ever, stand absolutely still on the screen. Instead, they appear to rotate on the axis to which the higher frequency is applied. This is always the case unless the signals themselves have been synchronized before they are applied to the respective inputs of the oscilloscope. As a result, Fig. 11-10 will appear as shown in the projection drawing only for brief instants when cycles of both waves start simultaneously. More often than

---

* The Lissajous figures shown in this chapter are the result of comparisons between *sine* waves of different frequencies. Wave shapes other than sine waves can be compared in the same manner, but their interpretations are much more difficult and their frequencies are usually measured by different methods.

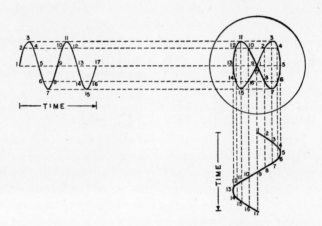

FIG. 11–9. A projection drawing showing the Lissajous figure obtained when a sine wave of $2x$ frequency is applied to the vertical deflection plates and a sine wave of x frequency is applied to the horizontal deflection plates.

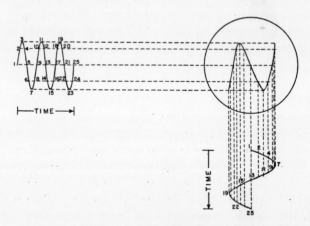

FIG. 11–10. A projection drawing of a Lissajous figure obtained when a sine wave of $3x$ frequency is applied to the vertical deflection plates and another sine wave of x frequency is applied to the horizontal deflection plates.

not, this pattern will appear with three distinct loops, as shown in the oscillogram in Fig. 11-11.

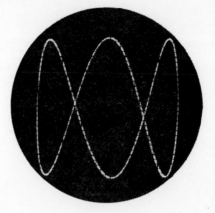

Fig. 11–11. Oscillogram showing the pattern obtained on the screen when a sine wave of $3x$ frequency is applied to the vertical deflection plates and a sine wave of x frequency is applied to the horizontal deflection plates.

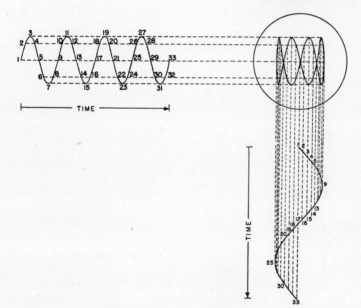

Fig. 11–12. A projection drawing showing a sine wave of $4x$ frequency applied to the vertical deflection plates and a sine wave of x frequency applied to the horizontal deflection plates.

Figure 11-12 is another projection drawing showing a frequency applied to the vertical channel which is four times the frequency applied to the horizontal channel. Figure 11-13, on the other hand, shows the Lissajous figure that results when the channels are reversed, i.e., when the frequency applied to the *horizontal* channel is four times the frequency applied to the vertical channel.

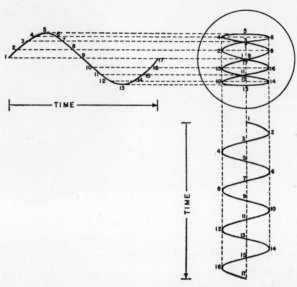

FIG. 11–13. A projection drawing showing a sine wave of x frequency applied to the vertical deflection plates and a sine wave of $4x$ frequency applied to the horizontal deflection plates.

The rule for determining the frequency ratio from a Lissajous pattern is very simple and easily applied. Imagine a horizontal line AB, as shown in Fig. 11-14, and the vertical line AC. There are five loops tangent to AB and three loops tangent to AC. The ratio of the frequency applied to the

FIG. 11–14. Determining frequency relationships from a Lissajous figure.

$$\frac{\text{Frequency applied to the vertical channel}}{\text{Frequency applied to the horizontal channel}} = \frac{\text{number of loops tangent to a horizontal line}}{\text{number of loops tangent to a vertical line}}$$

vertical channel to the frequency applied to the horizontal channel is as 5:3. The following general rule may be stated: The frequency applied to the vertical channel is to the frequency applied to the horizontal channel as the number of loops tangent to an imaginary horizontal line is to the number of loops tangent to an imaginary vertical line. Mathematically, it is represented as shown above, opposite Fig. 11-14.

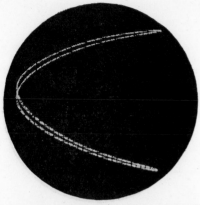

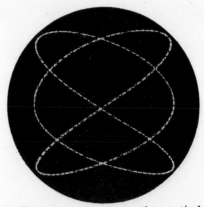

a. Frequency applied to the vertical channel is to the frequency applied to the horizontal channel as one is to two.

b. Frequency applied to the vertical channel is to the frequency applied to the horizontal channel as two is to three.

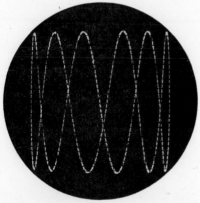

c. Frequency applied to the vertical channel is to the frequency applied to the horizontal channel as six is to one.

d. Frequency applied to the vertical channel is to the frequency applied to the horizontal channel as one is to two.

Fig. 11–15. Oscillograms of various Lissajous figures.

Figure 11-15 shows a number of different Lissajous patterns photographed from the screen of a cathode-ray tube. Each is labeled with the ratio of the frequency that is applied to the vertical channel to the frequency that is applied to the horizontal channel.

Phase Differences. When the Lissajour pattern of two signals of the same frequency is observed, the pattern will appear as one of the illustrations shown in Fig. 11-16. If the frequencies of the two signals are

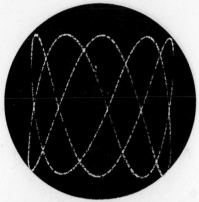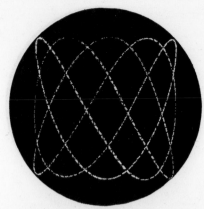

e. Frequency applied to the vertical channel is to the frequency applied to the horizontal channel as five is to two.

f. Frequency applied to the vertical channel is to the frequency applied to the horizontal channel as five is to three.

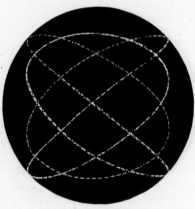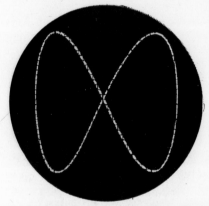

g. Frequency applied to the vertical channel is to the frequency applied to the horizontal channel as three is to four.

h. Frequency applied to the vertical channel is to the frequency applied to the horizontal channel as two is to one.

Fig. 11–15. (*Continued*).

slightly different, the pattern will change continuously, varying from one of these illustrations to the next, passing through the complete cycle, and continuing again.

If, however, the two frequencies are exactly the same, their phase relationship with respect to each other may be determined. The series of projection drawings in Figs. 11-17 through 11-20 show the resultant patterns that appear when the frequency of the wave applied to the hori-

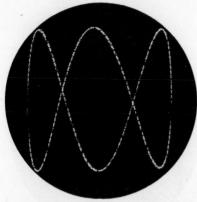

i. Frequency applied to the vertical channel is to the frequency applied to the horizontal channel as three is to one.

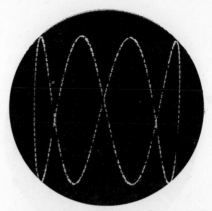

j. Frequency applied to the vertical channel is to the frequency applied to the horizontal channel as four is to one.

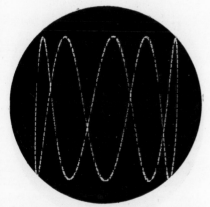

k. Frequency applied to the vertical channel is to the frequency applied to the horizontal channel as five is to one.

l. Frequency applied to the vertical channel is to the frequency applied to the horizontal channel as three is to two.

Fig. 11–15. (*Continued*).

zontal channel is first in phase with the frequency applied to the vertical channel and then 90 deg, 180 deg, and 270 deg out of phase with it. At any phase difference of angles other than 90 deg, 180 deg, and 270 deg, the pattern is an ellipse, as can be determined also by projection drawings. The photographs of Fig. 11-16 show examples of these ellipses.

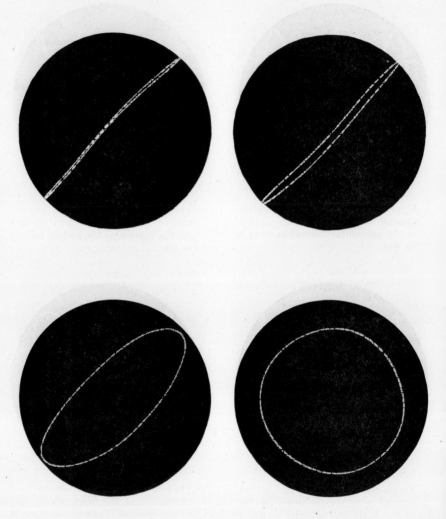

FIG. 11–16. Oscillograms showing shifting of phase from zero to 180° of two sine waves having the same frequency.

Note

There are two important considerations that enter into the display of phase-difference patterns through the amplifiers of an oscilloscope. The first is that the amplifiers must contain the same number of amplifying stages. For example, if the vertical amplifier has three amplifying stages and the horizontal amplifier only two, two signals that are actually in phase will result in a pattern that indicates they are 180 deg out of phase. To ascertain whether your oscilloscope will result in correct

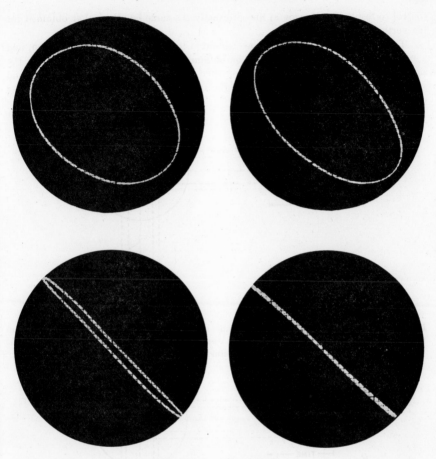

Fɪɢ. 11–16. (*Continued*).

readings for phase difference, connect the test signal to both amplifier inputs. The resultant pattern on the screen should be a straight line from the upper right side of the screen to the lower left side, because the signal applied to the two inputs is certainly in phase with itself. If an ellipse is obtained, it indicates a difference in the phase-shift characteristics in the amplifiers of the oscilloscope. Such amplifiers could not be used for phase-shift measurements. If the pattern extends from the upper left to the lower right the amplifiers already represent a 180-deg phase shift. This should be taken into account when making measurements of phase difference, or, to be safe, the signal inputs should be connected directly to the deflection plates.

The second consideration, if the amplifiers are used, is that both amplifiers should be calibrated to result in exactly the same deflection on the screen. To accomplish this, connect the signal to the vertical amplifier, and with no signal applied to the horizontal channel, set the vertical gain control to result in a deflection of about 3 in. Remove the signal from the vertical input connection, and apply the signal for the horizontal channel to the horizontal input. Set the horizontal gain control to result in a horizontal line of exactly the same length as that obtained for the vertical channel (3 in.).

Thus, the two amplifiers are now calibrated to result in the same deflection, and a true phase-difference pattern may be obtained. In case the operator couples the signals directly to the deflection plates, equal deflection on both the horizontal and vertical channels must be adjusted by the output controls of the oscillators under examination.

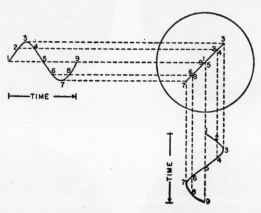

Fig. 11–17. Projection drawing of a sine wave applied to the vertical deflection plates and a sine wave of exactly the same frequency applied to the horizontal deflection plates.

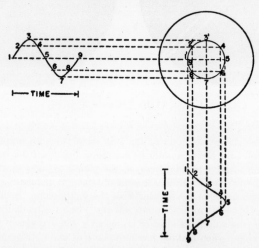

Fig. 11–18. Projection drawing showing a sine wave applied to the vertical deflection plates and a sine wave exactly the same frequency but 90 deg out of phase applied to the horizontal deflection plates.

Phase differences can also be accurately determined on an oscilloscope in the following manner. Using the calibrated scale of the oscilloscope,

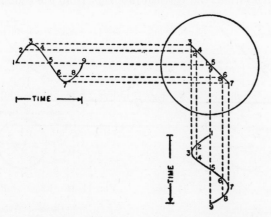

Fig. 11–19. Projection drawing showing a sine wave applied to the vertical deflection plates and a sine wave of exactly the same frequency but 180 deg out of phase applied to the horizontal deflection plates.

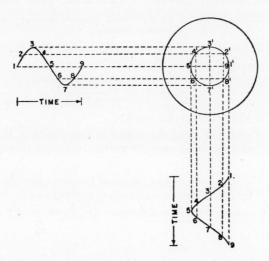

Fig. 11–20. Projection drawing showing a sine wave applied to the vertical deflection plates and a sine wave exactly the same frequency but 270 deg out of phase applied to the horizontal deflection plates.

determine the points at which the pattern crosses the horizontal and vertical axes of the scale. The sine of the phase-difference angle is then equal to the distance of the vertical intercept from the center of the screen

Fig. 11–21. Phase difference 0 deg.   Fig. 11–22. Phase difference 30 deg.

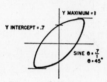

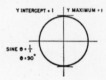

Fig. 11–23. Phase difference 45 deg.   Fig. 11–24. Phase difference 90 deg.

Fig. 11–25. Phase difference 120 deg.   Fig. 11–26. Phase difference 135 deg.

Figs. 11–21 to 11–26. Examples of measuring phase-difference angles of various Lissajous patterns.

divided by the distance of the maximum vertical deflection from the center of the screen. Mathematically,

$$\text{where:} \qquad \text{sine } \theta = \frac{y \text{ intercept}}{y \text{ maximum}}.$$

where θ = phase difference angle;

y intercept   = distance from the center of the screen to the point where the ellipse crosses the vertical axis (as measured in tenths of an inch);

y maximum   = distance from the center of the screen to the highest point on the ellipse (as measured in tenths of an inch).

Examples of measuring phase-difference angles are shown in Figs. 11-21 through 11-26.

12 Auxiliary Equipment

Calibrated Scales. The calibrated scales used in conjunction with oscilloscopes would probably be more correctly classified as accessories, but their use is worthy of separate mention. The calibrated scale, an example of which is shown in Fig. 12-1, may be permanently mounted in front of the cathode-ray tube screen, or it may be removable. These scales are usually calibrated in inches and tenths of an inch and provide a convenient means for relative measurement of voltage.

Alternating-current voltages as indicated by a-c voltmeters are root-mean-square (rms) values of voltage. Since a-c voltages are continually varying from zero voltage to a peak or maximum value, the only way

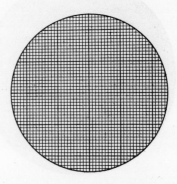

Fig. 12–1. A standard calibrated scale for a 5-in. cathode-ray tube divided into tenths of an inch.

they can be measured with a meter is by the effect which that voltage will produce in terms of power or work accomplished. This value is called the "effective voltage" or the "root-mean-square" voltage. The effective value of a pure sine wave is equal to 0.707 times the peak voltage.

The electron beam of the cathode-ray tube in the oscilloscope, on the other hand, is inertialess and responds to all the instantaneous values of a-c voltage. Therefore, the oscilloscope measures the peak voltage or the peak-to-peak voltage of any a-c signal. Figure 12-2 is a drawing of a sine wave showing the values referred to by the three terms. Two voltages can be compared, and their ratio will still be the same whether the effective voltages, the peak voltages, or the peak-to-peak voltages are used for comparison.

As an example of the use of the calibrated scale in measuring voltages, the two illustrations in Figs. 12-3 and 12-4 are given for reference. Figure

FIG. 12–2. Analysis of a sine wave showing rms, peak, and peak-to-peak voltages.

12-3 shows a sine wave producing a peak-to-peak deflection of 2.4 in., and Fig. 12-4 shows another sine wave producing a peak-to-peak deflection of 0.8 in. with the same setting of the VERTICAL GAIN control. From this observation it can be concluded that the voltage of Fig. 12-3 is three times that of Fig. 12-4. Thus, if the value of Fig. 12-4 has been previously measured and is known to be 6.3 volts (rms), then the value of Fig. 12-3 is 6.3 times 3, or 18.9 volts (rms).

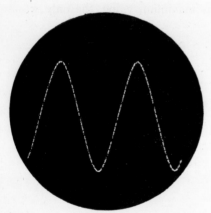

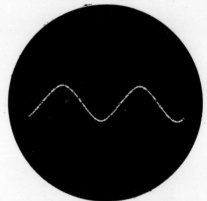

FIG. 12–3. Oscillogram of a sine wave having a peak-to-peak amplitude of 2.4 in. as measured with a calibrated scale.

FIG. 12–4. Oscillogram of a sine wave having a peak-to-peak amplitude of 0.8 in. as measured with a calibrated scale.

Other calibrated scales are available for measurements on the cathode-ray tube of the oscilloscope. For example, a scale may be obtained for measuring the logarithmic decrement of damped oscillations and there is a polar coordinate scale for measurements of angular displacement.

Voltage Calibrator.   In laboratory work with an oscilloscope, it frequently becomes necessary to measure the actual peak voltage of a signal under observation on the screen of the oscilloscope. One device for such measurement is the Du Mont type 264-A (Fig. 12-5). The circuit of this device (Fig. 12-6) consists merely of a power supply that furnishes positive and negative voltages to bias two diode clippers to a voltage level of approximately 75 volts each. Both of these diodes are connected to a sine-wave output (approximately 300 volts) of the power transformer,

Fig. 12-5. Photograph of the front panel of the Du Mont Type 264-A Voltage Calibrator.

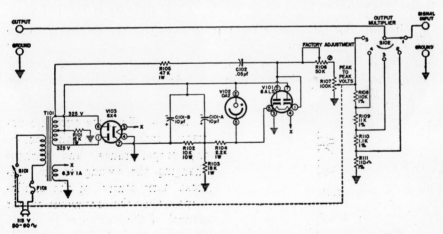

Fig. 12-6. Schematic of circuit of the Du Mont Type 264-A Voltage Calibrator.

but one of the diodes is connected to clip the negative peaks of the sine wave while the other is connected to clip the positive peaks. Therefore, the wave form of the output voltage is essentially a square wave. The output is adjusted to exactly 100 volts peak-to-peak, and connected to a decimal-multiplier-type attentuator to obtain four ranges of voltage for the continuous accentuator: 0 to 100 volts, 0 to 10 volts, 0 to 1 volt, and 0 to 0.1 volt.

The use of this instrument is quite simple.

Step 1. Connect the signal to be measured to the input terminals of the calibrator and connect the output terminals of the calibrator to the VERTICAL INPUT terminals of the oscilloscope.

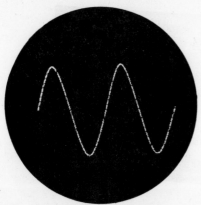 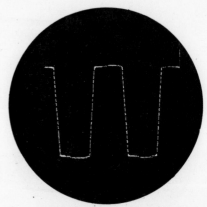

FIG. 12–7. Oscillogram of a sine wave whose peak-to-peak voltage is to be measured.

FIG. 12–8. Oscillogram of the square-wave output of the voltage calibrator adjusted to the same amplitude as that of the wave in Fig. 12–7.

Step 2. Set the OUTPUT MULTIPLIER switch of the calibrator to the SIGNAL OUTPUT position.

Step 3. Synchronize the signal to be measured on the screen of the oscilloscope and note the peak-to-peak deflection which it produces (see Fig. 12-7).

FIG. 12–9. Cross-sectional drawing of the front panel of an oscilloscope having vertical calibration jacks.

Step 4. Turn the OUTPUT MULTIPLIER switch of the calibrator to the proper range, and without changing the setting of the VERTICAL GAIN control of the oscilloscope, adjust the continuous-output control of the calibrator to obtain the same peak-to-peak amplitude as the signal being measured (see Fig. 12-8).

Step 5. Read the calibrated dial of the continuous-output control and multiply by the setting of the OUTPUT MULTIPLIER to obtain the peak-to-peak signal voltage.

Another means of measuring the voltage of a signal can easily be built into any oscilloscope. However, this method is only satisfactory for measuring the voltage of signals applied directly to the deflection plates.

Step 1.   Drill two holes in a convenient position on the front panel of the oscilloscope near the VERTICAL POSITIONING controls.

Step 2.   Mount a tip jack, or a similar type of insulated jack, in each of these holes, connecting each jack to the arm of one of the two dual potentiometers that make up the VERTICAL POSITIONING control.

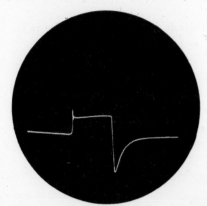
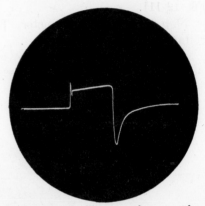

FIG. 12–10. Oscillogram of a pulse whose leading edge is to be measured with the voltage calibration jacks. The vertical positioning control has been adjusted to produce a 0-volt reading on the voltmeter.

FIG. 12–11. Oscillogram of same pulse appearing in Fig. 12–10 with the base line moved upward to measure the amplitude of the leading edge of the pulse.

Note

If a single potentiometer is used for vertical positioning, connect one jack to the arm of the potentiometer and the other to ground.

Figure 12-9 is a drawing showing the side view of a front panel of an oscilloscope with the connections made. These jacks can be used to accommodate a voltmeter for measuring a vertical deflection in accordance with the following procedure:

Step 1.   Synchronize the signal to be measured on the screen of the oscilloscope.

Note

This signal must be capacitively or directly coupled to the vertical deflection plates, not through the vertical amplifier.

Step 2.   Plug the leads from a high-impedance d-c voltmeter (preferably 20,000 ohms per volt) into these jacks.

Note

The meter should be set to its highest voltage range because the polarity of the voltage may be opposite to that of the meter.

Step 3.   Adjust the VERTICAL POSITIONING control until the meter reads zero; change the scale on the meter to the 250-volt scale, and reset to zero if necessary.

Step 4.   Note the location of the peak of the signal on the calibrated scale or mark the face of the tube with ink or with a china marker (see Fig. 12-10).

Step 5.   Remove the signal so that the base line is visible and turn the VERTICAL POSITIONING control until the base line is on the mark that indicates the position previously reached by the peak of the signal (see Fig. 12-11).

Step 6.   Read the voltmeter. This voltage is equivalent to the peak voltage of the signal.

Fɪɢ. 12–12.   Du Mont Type 271-A Oscillograph-Record Camera.

Filters.   Several different-colored filters may be obtained and used between the calibrated scale and the face of the tube for filtering out any light other than the color of the filter. Such filters increase the contrast of the luminescent screen and relieve eyestrain if considerable visual observation is necessary. An amber filter is particularly helpful when a P7 type of screen is used for visual observation. The initial flash of light from this screen is blue-white, which is very hard on the eyes if a filter is not employed.

Camera for Photographing Patterns.   The normal recurrent patterns appearing on the screen of a cathode-ray tube may be photographed with nearly any kind of camera in a darkened room by even an average amateur photographer. Undoubtedly, some work will be spoiled and much time will be wasted until all the details have been worked out. For the photography of nonrecurrent phenomena, such as high-speed transients, however, the problem becomes more complex.

To simplify the problem of photography of patterns on the oscilloscope, there is a camera that is especially adapted for such work. This camera is the Du Mont type 271-A (Fig. 12-12). It consists of nothing more than a metal tube with a 35-mm camera mounted in the end that fits over the bezel of the cathode-ray tube. The camera itself contains a fixed-focus lens with an aperture of $f/3.5$ and shutter speed of 1/30 sec, as well as time and bulb. A "peep-hole" can be opened in the end of the light shield to enable the operator to see the pattern on the screen. This device permits a novice to photograph patterns appearing on the cathode-ray tube under any conditions of ambient light or cramped quarters with a minimum of preparation. A more complete discussion of photographing patterns from the screen of an oscilloscope is given in Chap. 20.

Microphones. For converting sound waves into electrical energy so that they may be viewed on the oscilloscope, it is necessary to use a microphone. For best results with an oscilloscope, the microphone should have a high output impedance and a flat frequency response over the range of frequencies where it is to be used. The required directional response of the microphone will depend upon the application for which it is to be used.

The selection of the proper transducer for a specific problem is extremely important. Due care and consideration should be given to the nature of the problem and the factors to be measured. This same consideration should be given to the selection of all transducers as well as microphones. For example, a microphone which is to be used to determine the location and nature of noises in machinery should have a unidirectional response, whereas one used in determining the acoustical properties of a room should have an omnidirectional response.

Vibration Pickup. A vibration pickup is necessary for the conversion of mechanical vibrations into electrical voltages which may be studied by an oscilloscope. Both the waveform and the frequency of vibrations may be determined by the oscilloscope for such applications as motor balancing and the effects of machinery vibrations on building structure.

Pressure Pickup. For the study of pressure within a closed cylinder by means of an oscilloscope, a pressure pickup is necessary to convert varying pressures into electrical voltages. The pressure pickup finds its chief application in the study of compression and detonation within the cylinder of gasoline and Diesel engines.

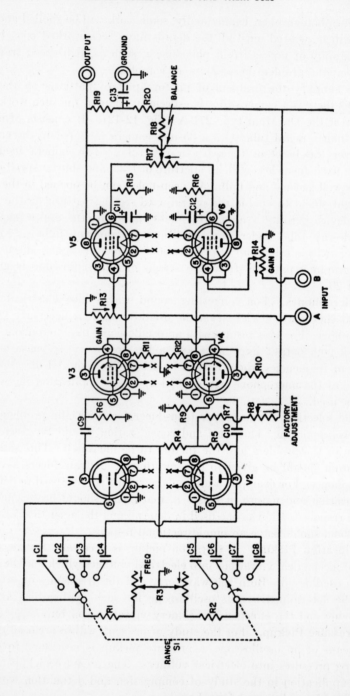

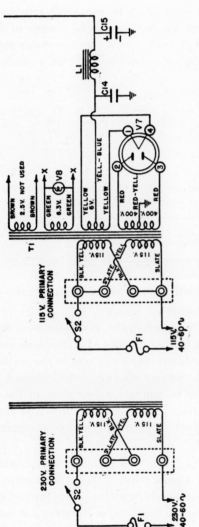

Fig. 12-15. Schematic of the Du Mont Type 185-A Electronic Switch and Square-Wave Generator. This is a multivibrator type of square-wave generator. $V1$ and $V2$ are the multivibrators and $V3$ and $V4$ serve as cathode followers. The tubes $V5$ and $V6$ are amplifiers for two external signals connected with a common output. The square waves generated in the multivibrators are connected to the cathodes of $V5$ and $V6$ through the cathode followers $V3$ and $V4$ automatically switching the amplifiers on and off. If the two gain controls $R13$ and $R14$ are turned off and the baselines are displaced, the output of the switch is a square wave.

Photocells.   The function of the photocell is to convert light energy into electrical energy so that it may be studied on the oscilloscope. As is true of microphones, a number of different sizes and types of photocells are available for different applications. The type of measurements to be made must be considered before the photocell is selected.

Strain Gauges.   Stress and strain may be converted into equivalent electrical potentials for study on the oscilloscope by means of a strain gauge. The strain gauge is bonded firmly to the member under stress and changes its resistance as the member is deformed. Thus, a small current

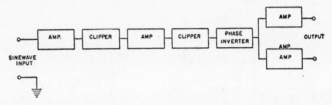

Fɪɢ. 12–13. Block diagram of one type of square-wave generator.

Fɪɢ. 12–14. Block diagram of a multivibrator-type square-wave generator.

passing through the strain gauge will vary as the resistance varies causing a change in potential across the gauge.

Square-Wave Generator.   A square-wave generator is a valuab'e auxiliary instrument for use with the oscilloscope. Its chief uses are in the testing of amplifiers and in furnishing timing markers to the oscilloscope, as will be explained in Chap. 13. Square waves may be obtained by two different methods. One method is to generate a sine wave of the desired frequency and by successive stages of high-gain amplifiers and clippers a square-wave output results. A block diagram of this type of square-wave generator is shown in Fig. 12-13.

The other type of square-wave generator employs a multivibrator circuit that generates essentially a square wave. This approximate square wave is then fed to a clipper stage which furnishes a true square wave to the output stage. A block diagram of this type of square-wave generator is shown in Fig. 12-14.

Electronic Switch.   An electronic switch is another handy auxiliary instrument for use with the oscilloscope when it is desirable to display two signals on the screen simultaneously. The electronic switch offers a means of comparing the amplitude, wave shape, and phase of the two signals.

Additional examples of the use of an electronic switch are given in Chap. 18.

The schematic of the Du Mont type 185-A electronic switch is shown in Fig. 12-15. The circuit contains a conventional multivibrator, consisting of $V1$ and $V2$, whose output is essentially a square wave. The output of the multivibrator is taken from the plate of each tube and impressed upon the grids of the two cathode-follower isolating stages $V3$ and $V4$. These stages are in turn coupled to the cathodes of the two output stages.

Since the output from each plate of the multivibrator tubes is 180 deg out of phase with the opposite plate, this phase relationship is maintained

FIG. 12–16. Drawing showing the action of an electronic switch in displaying two signals simultaneously.

throughout. Thus, the square waves applied to the output stages are 180 deg out of phase with each other, and the stages are biased on and off alternately. Each of the signals to be viewed simultaneously is impressed on the grid of one of these stages. The resulting output signal, owing to the switching effect, is a small portion of the first signal followed by a small portion of the second signal, which in turn is followed by the next

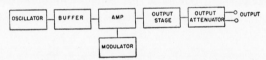

FIG. 12–17. Block diagram of a typical r-f signal generator.

portion of the first signal and so on. This action is shown in the drawing of Fig. 12-16. The two signals are separated when there is a difference in potential between the screen grids of the two amplifying stages.

The A-F Signal Generator. An a-f signal generator is a valuable auxiliary instrument for measurements on audio amplifiers and for frequency comparisons by means of Lissajous figures. This instrument should have a sine-wave output, and it is not uncommon for such a signal generator to have a frequency range from 10 c to 200 kc. An audio-signal generator is also very useful for classroom demonstration with an oscilloscope.

The a-f signal generator is very often nothing more than an R-C oscillator followed by suitable amplifier stages.

The R-F Signal Generator. The r-f signal generator is another practical instrument for use with the oscilloscope. It may serve as a secondary frequency standard, if it is accurately calibrated, for use in servicing television receivers. If it contains an accurate output attenuator and provision for modulating the r-f signal with an audio frequency, it may be used to measure receiver sensitivity, attenuation of the sound traps in the video-i-f section of a receiver, and the limiting action of the limiters in FM receivers. Furthermore, it will be very useful in classroom demonstrations. These uses are explained more fully in Chaps. 14, 15, and 16.

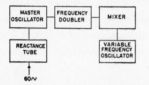

Fig. 12–18. Block diagram of a typical frequency-modulated signal generator.

This type of signal generator is essentially a low-power radio transmitter with a wide frequency range which is obtained by switching oscillator coils. Tuning throughout the range of each oscillator coil is usually accomplished by a variable capacitor. A block diagram of a typical r-f signal generator is shown in Fig. 12-17.

Frequency-Modulated Signal Generator. A frequency-modulated type of signal generator is necessary for obtaining response curves for the alignment of tuned circuits with an oscilloscope. One of the better types of f-m signal generators will serve for all three major kinds of receivers—a-m, f-m, and television; but most servicemen will have two instruments, one for work on a-m and f-m receivers and another for television receivers.

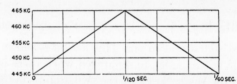

Fig. 12–19. Graph showing the varying frequency of the output of a frequency-modulated signal generator.

The circuits for this type of signal generator are all essentially the same, although they may differ in frequency, and the television type may be more elaborate.

A 60-c signal (the power-line frequency) is applied to a reactance tube, which, in turn, varies the frequency of the master oscillator, as may be seen in the block diagram in Fig. 12-18. The frequency-modulated output of the master oscillator is then doubled in frequency by a frequency-doubler stage. The output of the frequency-doubler stage is coupled to one control grid of a mixer, and the output of the tunable-frequency oscillator is applied to the other control grid. The tunable-frequency oscillator beats against the frequency-modulated oscillator, thereby furnishing the desired output frequency. The extent to which the frequency of the master oscillator is varied in frequency, i.e., the frequencies through which it is swept, is controlled by the amplitude of the 60-c voltage applied to the reactance tube.

In some of the older types of FM signal generators the reactance tube is replaced by a variable capacitor, which is rotated by a small synchronous motor rotating at 3,600 rpm. The 3,600 rpm of the motor corresponds to the 60-c frequency applied to the grid of the reactance tube in the newer types. Since both the rotating capacitor and the reactance tube cause the frequency of the master oscillator to be constantly changing, these devises became known as "wobbulators." Later, this term was applied to this type of signal generator as a whole, and it became known as a "wobbulated signal generator," or simply a "wobbulator."

The output of this signal generator is a signal whose frequency changes linearly throughout a definite frequency range at a definite speed. The frequency completes one excursion, or sweep, from minimum frequency to maximum and back to minimum again in 1/60 sec. Thus, it is said that the sweep frequency of this generator is 60 c. The graph of Fig. 12-19 shows how the frequency varies with respect to time when the instrument is set to adjust the i-f stages of an a-m receiver.

13 Typical Applications in the Electronics Industry

Introduction. Since the oscilloscope is an electronic instrument, it is only natural that its uses in the electronic field would be exceedingly numerous both in the manufacturing and in the engineering and research phases of the industry. It is impossible for this chapter to include all the uses to which an oscilloscope has ever been put, but it does survey many of the more common applications, which will undoubtedly suggest a great many others to the reader. Chapters 14 through 17 are devoted entirely to alignment and servicing techniques on various types of receivers. These techniques were originally developed for the testing and alignment of receivers on the production line and are, of course, still used for that purpose. However, these techniques have developed into rather elaborate procedures, which require separate treatment.

The oscilloscope is used in the engineering and research laboratories in many ways, but one of its chief uses is to study, check, and measure the characteristics of circuit designs and improvements.

Measuring the Gain of an Audio Amplifier. As a particular example of the use of an oscilloscope in studying circuits, the audio amplifier, which is one of the most familiar circuits, is taken as representative.

The voltage gain of an amplifier stage is not only important from a design standpoint, but the absence of gain in a given amplifier stage may well indicate trouble to the serviceman. The following is a step-by-step procedure for measuring the approximate gain of an amplifier stage:

Step 1.　Connect a sine-wave signal between the grid and ground of the amplifier stage.

Step 2.　Connect the VERTICAL INPUT terminals of the oscilloscope between the plate of the amplifier and ground.

Step 3.　Adjust the VERTICAL GAIN control of the oscilloscope to result in as large an amplitude as is readable.

Step 4.　Synchronize two or more cycles of the signal on the screen and inspect the waveform for distortion.

Note

Either the signal applied to the grid of the stage being studied or the signal to the vertical amplifiers of the oscilloscope may be too large, and one or the other

162

may be overloaded. If overloading is evident, reduce the input signal to the amplifier because any overloaded condition will interfere with the measurement.

Step 5. Measure the peak-to-peak amplitude in tenths of an inch with the calibrated scale.

Step 6. Without changing the setting of the VERTICAL GAIN control of the oscilloscope, remove the oscilloscope lead from the plate circuit and connect it to the grid of the same stage.

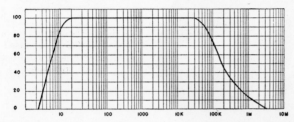

Fig. 13–1. Graph of the frequency response of a typical amplifier.

Step 7. Measure the peak-to-peak voltage of the input voltage, the signal now appearing on the screen, in tenths of an inch.

Step 8. Substitute these two values in the following equation to determine the voltage gain of the stage:

$$\text{Voltage gain} = \frac{\text{output voltage}}{\text{input voltage}}$$

Note

The accuracy of this measurement is sufficient for most purposes. Occasionally, however, the gain of a single stage may be so great that a calibrated attenuator of 10:1 or more will have to be inserted between the connection to the plate of the stage and the oscilloscope in order to obtain a pattern on the screen that can be measured. If such is the case, the deflection produced by the signal measured at the plate must be multiplied by 10 in order to obtain the correct value of output voltage.

Measuring the Frequency Response of Audio Amplifiers. The frequency response of an amplifier is that continuous range of sine-wave frequencies which is amplified. As an example, a typical frequency response curve is given in Fig. 13-1. This shows that the amplifier will amplify all the frequencies between 2 c and 4 mc. However, the *uniform* frequency response (within ±10 per cent) only from 10 c to 60 kc.

Amplifiers in the vertical and horizontal channels of oscilloscopes are designed to have a frequency response curve that is flat over a wide range of frequencies to permit their use in a wide variety of applications. The frequency response of audio amplifiers used in radio receivers and record players, however, need not be particularly broad since the human ear can distinguish sounds of frequencies only between 16 and about 18,000 c. While it is true that some individuals can distinguish sounds up to 23,000 or 25,000 c, they are the exception rather than the rule. In general, audio amplifiers having a response curve that is flat within ± 10 per cent from 60 c to 10,000 c is considered excellent, and, even then, tone controls are

Fig. 13–2 Oscillogram of a sweep-frequency transcription passed through an amplifier with nearly uniform frequency response.

made available, so that the response may be changed to appeal to the irregularities in the hearing range of different individuals.

One method for checking the frequency response of an amplifier is given in Chap. 18. However, this method is not too convenient or economical for such rapid checks as may be required on the production line. Another method is to employ a sweep-frequency generator, which sweeps through the desired frequency range.*

Still another method employs a Sweep-Frequency Transcription† which is a record on which the range of audio frequencies from 60 to 10,000 c has been recorded. The change in frequency from the low end tc the high end varies logarithmically, and one complete sweep through the frequency range requires 1/20 sec. The recording transmits a synchronizing pulse at the start of each sweep frequency for synchronizing the sweep of the oscilloscope. The output of this recording is shown in Fig. 13-2.

This Sweep-Frequency Transcription can be employed for either laboratory, transmitting-station, or production testing. But it requires the use of a pickup head that has a frequency response better than the frequency response of the recording, so that no distortion is introduced by the pickup head itself. One other precaution must be taken in the use of this transcription. This is to make sure that the frequency response of the vertical amplifier in the oscilloscope is flat throughout a wider range

* One such generator is manufactured by the Clough Brengle Co., Chicago, Ill.
† Manufactured by the Clarkstan Corporation, Los Angeles, Calif.

than the Sweep-Frequency Transcription. If it is not, the vertical amplifier will falsify the results.

In addition to checking the flat response of an amplifier, the device can also be used to check the action of tone controls, as shown in Fig.

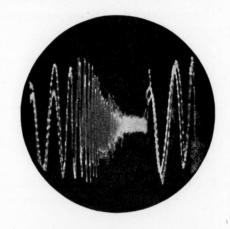

Fig. 13-3. A sweep-frequency transcription indicating the low frequencies of an amplifier accentuated by the tone control.

13-3 and 13-4. Figure 13-3 shows the low frequencies of an amplifier attenuated by the tone control, and Fig. 13-4 shows the high frequencies attenuated.

Fig. 13-4. A sweep-frequency transcription indicating the middle and high frequencies of an amplifier accentuated by the tone control.

Still another method of checking the frequency response of an amplifier is by means of a square wave. This method has already been discussed in Chap. 8. However, it should be noted here that square-wave testing can be applied only to resistance-coupled amplifiers, since the self-inductance characteristics of transformers prevent a faithful reproduction of a square wave.

Checking for Distortion in Audio Amplifiers. Distortion is some-times very difficult to identify when a sine wave is used to test audio amplifiers. However, an electronic switch offers a means of identifying distortion in a sine-wave signal. A portion of the input signal to one amplifier stage is also used as the input to one of the channels of an electronic switch. The output signal of the next amplifier stage is coupled

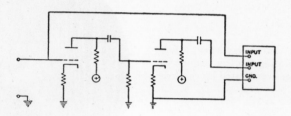

FIG. 13–5. Drawing showing the connections of an electronic switch to the circuit of a resistance-coupled amplifier to compare input and output signals.

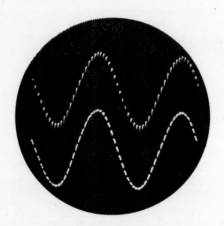

FIG. 13–6. Oscillogram showing the comparison of input and output signals in the amplifier of Fig. 13–5.

to the other channel, as shown in Fig. 13-5, and both signals are viewed simultaneously on the screen of the oscilloscope (Fig. 13-6). Both signals are adjusted to the same amplitude by the gain controls of the electronic switch and are then superimposed on each other (Fig. 13-7a). Figure 13-7b shows the two traces superimposed, but the signals are of unequal amplitude. If there is any distortion in the output signal, it becomes immediately noticeable when the two signals are superimposed. Distortion is evident in the output signal, as shown in Fig. 13-8.

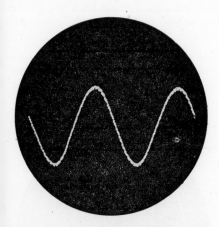

Fig. 13–7a. Oscillogram showing the waves of Fig. 13–6 having the same amplitude and superimposed.

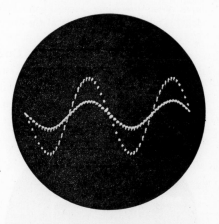

Fig. 13–7b. Same as Fig. 13–7a except the two waves do not have the same amplitude.

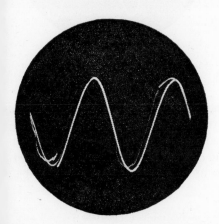

Fig. 13–8. Oscillogram of input and output waveforms showing distortion in the output waveform.

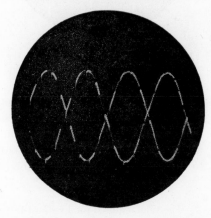

Fig. 13–9. Oscillogram showing the phase reversal of a sine wave as it passes through a single-stage amplifier.

Note

The output signal which is compared with the input signal is taken from the output of the second stage because the output from the same stage as the input is 180 deg out of phase with the input signal. The output from the second stage has been subjected to another phase reversal of 180 deg and is then in phase with the input of the preceding stage. Figure 13-9 shows the phase reversal when the output signal is taken from the plate of the same stage as that to which the input is applied.

Testing Other Electronic Circuits. Of course, the oscilloscope is not limited to the testing of audio amplifiers, but may be used to examine the waveforms of any electronic circuit. For example, in Fig. 13-10 the oscillogram obtained on the screen of the oscilloscope shows the output

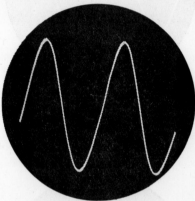

Fig. 13–10. Oscillogram showing the output of a blocking oscillator.

Fig. 13–11. Oscillogram showing two cycles of a 100-*kc* sine wave.

of a blocking oscillator that is operating at the frequency of 100 kc. Figure 13-11 shows the 100 kc sine wave that is used to trigger this blocking-oscillator circuit. In the particular device from which these wave forms were obtained, the output of the blocking oscillator is used to furnish timing markers at intervals of 10 μsec to a cathode-ray tube.

Note

The time required for 1 c of a 1-megacycle oscillation is 1/1,000,000 sec, or 1 μsec. The time required for 1 c of a 100-kc oscillation, which is one tenth the frequency of 1 megacycle, is ten times as long, or 10 μsec. Therefore, the time between pulses of the blocking oscillator, which is triggered by a 100-kc sine wave, is 10 μsec.

The 100-kc pulses from the blocking oscillator are also fed to a divider circuit which first divides the frequency by five to 20 kc and divides it again by two resulting in pulses at 10-kc intervals. These pulses represent time intervals of 100 μsec, and they, too, may be applied to the

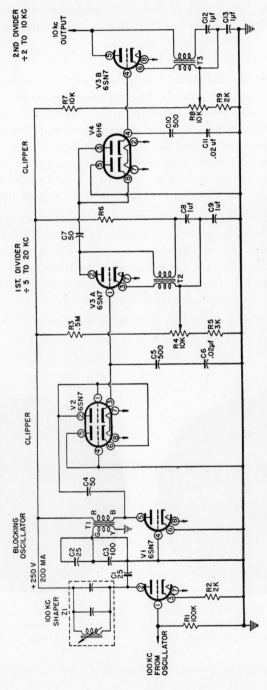

FIG. 13-12. Schematic of a blocking oscillator and frequency-divider circuits.

cathode-ray tube. Figure 13-12 shows a simplified version of the circuit, and Fig. 13-13 shows the oscillogram of the voltage on the grid of the first divider.

Note that the first divider tube is so biased that the capacitor in its grid circuit must be charged by five pulses from the blocking oscillator before the tube conducts, thus dividing the frequency by five. The charge on the grid after each pulse is indicated by the flat, steplike portion of the trace. Figure 13-14 shows the tube incorrectly biased to the extent that six pulses are required before the tube conducts, and Fig. 13-15 shows the bias control set too low and only four steps are seen. Figure 13-16 shows the action on the grid of the next divider stage. Since this stage divides by 2, only two pulses are required before the stage fires.

Among other applications, frequency-divider circuits are also used in television synchronizing-signal generators. In this case, the frequency of 15,750 c is divided down to 30 c in divisions by 7, 5, 5, and 3. A display of the divider circuits in a television synchronizing-signal generator is shown in Fig. 13-17. These circuits are monitored continuously, so that any error can be located and corrected immediately.

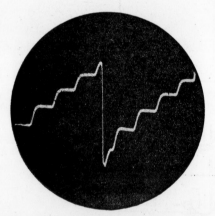 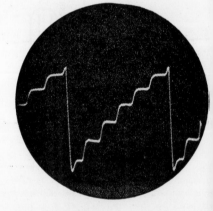

Fɪɢ. 13–13. Oscillogram of the voltage on the grid of frequency-divider stage showing division by five.

Fɪɢ. 13–14. Oscillogram of the voltage on the grid of a frequency-divider stage showing division by six.

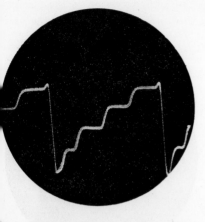

FIG. 13–15. Oscillogram of the voltage on the grid of a frequency-divider stage showing division by four.

FIG. 13–16. Oscillogram of the voltage on the grid of a frequency-divider stage showing division by two.

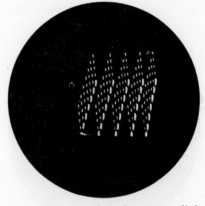

FIG. 13–17a. Oscillogram showing the division of frequency in a television synchronizing-signal generator showing division by five in each of the five steps and also division by three in each of the groups of steps.

FIG. 13–17b. Further frequency division by five as indicated by the dots in each of the vertical lines, and division by seven as indicated by the seven lines, and further division by five more as indicated by the five patterns.

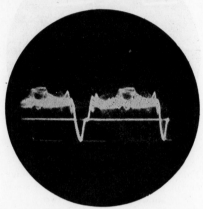

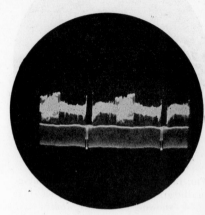

Fig. 13–18. Oscillogram showing the waveforms of two horizontal lines of a television picture.

Fig. 13–19. Oscillgram showingo the waveforms of two complete fields of a television picture.

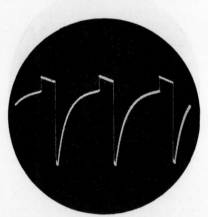

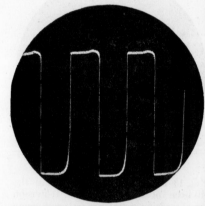

Fig. 13–20. Oscillogram showing the waveform at the grid of $V1$ in the circuit of Fig. 12–15.

Fig. 13–21. Oscillogram showing the waveform at the plate of $V1$ in the circuit of Fig. 12–15.

Also in television transmission, the video signal is monitored continuously by two oscilloscopes. One of these oscilloscopes is set at a sweep frequency of 15,750 c, so that every scanning line is monitored, and the other is set at a sweep frequency of 30 c, so that each frame is monitored. Figure 13-18 shows the signal on the oscilloscope of two horizontal lines from a television picture, and Fig. 13-19 shows the signal of one complete frame of a television picture.

A multivibrator circuit may also be investigated to show the waveforms that occur in different parts of the circuit. For instance, the waveform at the grid of $V1$ in the circuit in Fig. 12-15 is shown in Fig. 13-20, and the waveform at the plate of the same tube is shown in Fig. 13-21.

The differentiation of a square wave is another interesting circuit that can be observed on an oscilloscope. Figure 13-22 shows a 10 kc square wave which is the input signal to the differentiation circuit of Fig. 13-23. The output of this circuit is the waveform shown in Fig. 13-24a. When the value of $C1$ is changed from 1,100 $\mu\mu$f to 250 $\mu\mu$f, the output waveform is changed to that shown in Fig. 13-24b.

These are just a few of the many electronic circuits which are in use today and which can be adjusted, checked, studied, and serviced only with the oscilloscope. The high frequencies and/or the complexities of

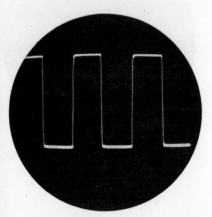

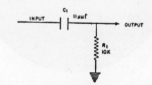

Fig. 13–23. Schematic of a differentiating circuit.

Fig. 13–22. Oscillogram of a 10 kc square wave.

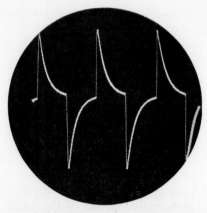

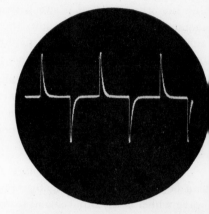

Fig. 13–24a. Oscillogram showing the differentiation of a 10 *kc* square wave when the value of *C*1 in Fig. 13–25 is 1100 μμf. and *R*1 is 10 *k*.

Fig. 13–24b. Oscillogram showing differentiation of a 10 *kc* square wave when the value of *C*1 in Fig. 13–23 is 250 μμf. and the value of *R*1 is 10 *k*.

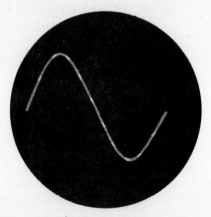

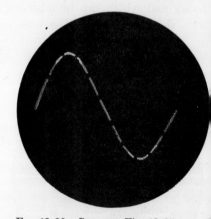

Fig. 13–25. Oscillogram showing 1000-microsecond pulses applied through the *Z* axis to a 100 cycle sine wave showing intensity markers.

Fig. 13–26. Same as Fig. 13–25 except showing blanking markers.

the waveforms in many of the circuits in common use today demand the use of the oscilloscope.

The Precision Measurement of Time. The oscilloscope is frequently used for the precise measurement of time in such applications as Radar and Loran and for other devices in the field of electronics, as well as for measurements in the field of nuclear physics.

In making such measurements, the timing markers are frequently applied to the grid or to the cathode of the cathode-ray tube to intensify or blank the beam. These markers really form another axis, which is available for applying a signal to the cathode-ray tube, and which is referred to as the "Z axis." The application of 1,000-μsec (1-msec) positive pulses

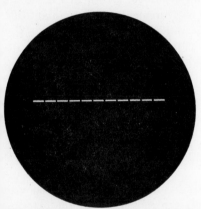

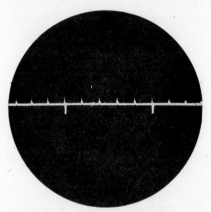

FIG. 13–27. Oscillogram showing 1000-μsec markers used to blank the trace when the sweep frequency is 100 c.

FIG. 13–28. Oscillogram showing markers applied to a trace as vertical deflections.

to the Z axis (the grid of the cathode-ray tube) of a general-purpose oscilloscope displaying 1 of a 100-c sine wave is shown in Fig. 13-25. The use of negative pulses applied to the grid is shown in Fig. 13-26. Also, either polarity of these pulses may still be applied when no signal is applied to the vertical deflection plates. Figure 13-27 shows this condition when blanking (negative) pulses are applied to the grid of the cathode-ray tube.

Radar-range oscilloscopes and A oscilloscopes frequently use this same principle to measure time and, therefore, distance along the trace, although they may apply the signal to the vertical deflection plates to achieve small vertical deflections. Figure 13-28 indicates this latter method. The distance between each of the small positive "pips" in this illustration represents 2,000 yd while the distance between the negative "pips" represents 10,000 yd.

For more accurate measurements of time, more elaborate oscilloscopes must be employed. Such instruments contain their own timing circuits, which are triggered by the sweep circuit of the oscilloscope to ensure synchronization at all times. Frequently, too, the signals that are to be measured are of the transient type and are also triggered by the sweep circuit to maintain synchronization. On the other hand, recurrent signals can be viewed by using a portion of the signal to trigger a driven sweep circuit, which, in turn, triggers the timing circuits. An illustration of this type of measurement is given in Fig. 9-12.

Use as a Null Indicator.   Among the more general uses of the oscilloscope is as a null indicator. Bridges for the measurement of inductance and capacitance, e.g., the General Radio type 650, shown in Fig. 13-29, must employ an a-c signal for accurate measurements of these quantities. Balance of such bridges is indicated by obtaining the minimum a-c signal. The point of minimum signal is called the "null point," and the means for detecting the null point is called the "null detector," or "null indicator."

The null point on such bridges may be indicated by earphones, a meter, or other device, but an oscilloscope is by far the most sensitive and, therefore, the most accurate of all the null-indicating devices.

The procedure for using the oscilloscope as a null indicator with this type of bridge is as follows:

Step 1.   Connect the VERTICAL INPUT terminals of the oscilloscope to the terminals provided on the bridge for the connection of the external null indicator.

Step 2.   Adjust the COARSE FREQUENCY and FINE FREQUENCY controls to result in a sweep frequency that is about one tenth of the frequency of the a-c source.

Step 3.   Connect the unknown quantity to the correct terminals of the bridge and turn the bridge signal source to ON.

Step 4.   Set the VERTICAL GAIN control to obtain a signal of large amplitude on the screen of the oscilloscope.

Step 5.   Set the HORIZONTAL GAIN control to any convenient horizontal deflection.

In some bridge measurements, harmonic frequencies are generated and the oscilloscope provides a convenient method of distinguishing between desired and undesired frequencies when obtaining bridge balance.

Step 6.   Adjust the bridge controls to obtain balance, which is indicated by a minimum deflection on the screen.

Step 7.   Increase the setting of the VERTICAL GAIN control as the balance point is approached so that enough vertical deflection is available to show a positive indication of the exact null point.

Fig. 13–29. General Radio Type 650 Impedance Bridge. (*Courtesy, General Radio Company.*)

Note

If harmonics are not present, the HORIZONTAL GAIN control may be set to zero. Under these conditions the pattern is just a vertical line which decreases in length as the balance point of the bridge is approached. Another method is to set the sweep frequency of the oscilloscope to the maximum sweep frequency available, resulting in a raster appearing on the screen of the oscilloscope. The null point is again indicated by the minimum vertical deflection. Figures 13-30, 13-31, and 13-32 indicate null points obtained with each of these methods.

Testing Potentiometers for Noise. The production testing of potentiometers for noise may be accomplished very quickly with an oscilloscope. The simple circuit is shown in Fig. 13-33. The potentiometer is held so that its three terminals contact the points A, B, and C. The point

B, which connects with the arm of the potentiometer, is connected to the VERTICAL INPUT terminal of the oscilloscope with either point *A* or point *C* furnishing the reference voltage to the other input terminal. Using the

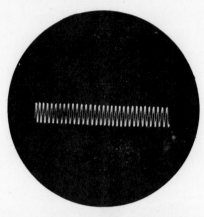

FIG. 13–30.   Oscillogram showing a null point obtained using a sweep signal with the sine wave synchronized.

FIG. 13–31.   Same as Fig. 13–30 without using a sweep signal.

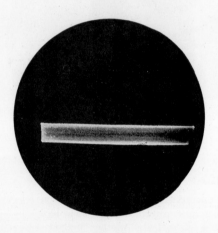

FIG. 13–32.   Same as Fig. 13–30 but using a sweep frequency much higher than the normal a-c source.

vertical amplifier and no sweep voltage, a rapid rotation, back and forth, of the potentiometer arm results in a vertical line on the oscilloscope. If the noise generated in the potentiometer is low, the vertical line will be smooth and even, as shown in Fig. 13-34. A noisy potentiometer will result in a vertical line that appears granulated (Fig. 13-35).

Testing Transformers for Continuity and Voltage Output.   For the production testing of transformers, a circuit similar to that shown in Fig.

13-36 can be constructed. The resistors between the various secondary windings and ground are merely voltage dividers, so that the a-c signal appearing on the screen of the oscilloscope is the same amplitude for all windings. Thus, the operator merely connects the transformer leads to

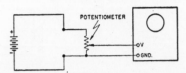

FIG. 13–33. Circuit for testing potentiometers for noise.

the proper terminals, turns on the primary power, and rotates the switch to check each winding in turn. A short circuit in some of the turns in one of the windings is indicated by a reduced vertical deflection, whereas an open circuit gives no vertical deflection.

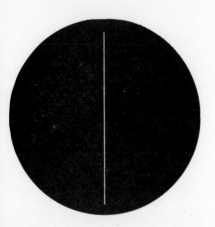

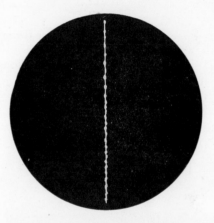

FIG. 13–34. Oscillogram obtained from the circuit of Fig 13–33 with the potentiometer exhibiting no appreciable noise characteristic.

FIG. 13–35. Same as Fig. 13–34 except that potentiometer is noisy.

Production Alignment of I-F and Discriminator Transformers. For the alignment of i-f transformers on the production line of transformer manufacturers, a typical i-f stage followed by a detector may be supplied to each operator. The i-f signal from a signal generator may be supplied to each test position through a distribution amplifier. The operator merely connects the transformer to be aligned into the circuit and tunes it to the proper bandwidth and amplitude, using the indication on an oscilloscope as a guide to tuning. (The adjustment of i-f transformers is given in complete detail in Chaps. 14, 15, and 16.)

For aligning discriminator transformers, the procedure is similar to that given in Chap. 15. In this case, however, the test bench must be supplied with a discriminator circuit for the connection of the discriminator transformer.

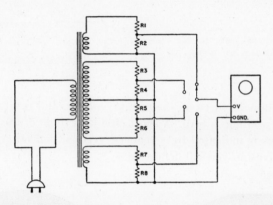

Fɪɢ. 13–36.   Circuit for the production testing of transformers.

Other Production Applications.   The oscilloscope also finds many uses in the production line of the manufacturers of peaking coils, vibrators, dynamotors, transformers of all types, and many other components for the electronic field. In addition, the manufacturers of electronic instruments and equipment usually employ the oscilloscope in the final testing of the various products.

14 Servicing A-M Radio Receivers

Introduction. A radio serviceman would find himself very much at a loss if he did not have a voltmeter to aid him in solving his servicing problem. Actually, the serviceman who has not yet learned the application of an oscilloscope to radio servicing is severely hampered.

Since an oscilloscope is in reality a voltmeter, which not only indicates voltage, but also indicates the waveform of that voltage, such a device is the answer to many problems in radio servicing. Some of the uses to which an oscilloscope may be put in the field of radio servicing are as an output meter, a distortion meter, a device for signal tracing to locate

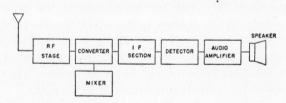

Fig. 14–1. Block diagram of a typical a-m superhetrodyne receiver.

trouble, and a frequency-measuring device. In addition, the oscilloscope is invaluable in checking the fidelity of audio amplifiers, the correct tuning of i-f amplifiers, and the proper adjustment of the local oscillator and the r-f section of the receiver.

The Superheterodyne Receiver. The normal a-m superheterodyne receiver may be divided into six main sections, or blocks, as illustrated in Fig. 14-1. These sections are, starting with the antenna, the r-f stage, the local oscillator, the converter (sometimes called the "first detector"), the i-f section, the detector, and the audio amplifier. In some of the lower-priced receivers, no r-f stage is employed, and the antenna is inductively coupled into the grid of the converter stage.

The function of the r-f (radio frequency) stage is to tune and amplify the desired radio frequency. The grid circuit of the converter stage is tuned simultaneously to the same radio frequency as the r-f stage, while another r-f signal from the local oscillator is impressed on another grid of this same tube. The resulting signal at the plate of the converter tube is the difference in frequency between the r-f signal coming from the r-f stage and the r-f signal coming from the local-oscillator stage. This difference in frequency is called the "intermediate frequency," which is often abbreviated "IF" or i-f.

Since the signal from the local oscillator is unmodulated, the i-f signal is modulated with the same signal as the original r-f carrier. After the modulated i-f signal has been amplified by the i-f amplifiers, the audio modulation is separated from the signal by the detector. The detector, in turn, transmits the audio signal to the audio amplifiers which amplify it sufficiently to drive the loudspeaker.

Of course, the number of stages in any of the general sections of the superheterodyne receiver will vary with the different models, but the circuits are all essentially the same.

Accepted Practice of Radio Servicing. Of course, all radio service-men have their own method for determining the cause of the trouble in a radio receiver. It is customary to check tubes, and quite frequently from previous experience with particular models, the radio serviceman can put his finger on the trouble immediately. However, when all else fails, it is necessary to make tests throughout the receiver to locate the fault. The accepted practice is to start with the audio end of the receiver and from this end work back through to the r-f section. Thus, the following text discusses the various procedures in that order.

The Use of the Oscilloscope in the Audio Stage. For locating trouble in the audio stage, the oscilloscope is connected across the speaker output leads. In most oscilloscopes, a convenient 60-c test signal is available on the front terminal. This 60-c sine-wave voltage may be used as the input to the grid of the first audio stage. A simple setup is shown in Fig. 14-2, which is the schematic of an audio amplifier. The 60-c source that is used as the input to the first audio stage can be obtained from either the front panel of the oscilloscope or from the filament winding of any transformer. This voltage should probably not exceed 3 or 6 volts, depending upon the amplifier, and 1 volt is usually sufficient. With the connections made in accordance with this setup, it will immediately become evident whether or not the audio stages of the receiver are capable of passing a signal. If they are, a 60-c wave will be observed on the screen of the oscilloscope. This procedure should be followed:

Step 1.   Set the VERTICAL POSITIONING and HORIZONTAL POSITIONING controls to result in a pattern that will appear near the center of the cathode-ray tube screen.

Step 2.   Set the INTENSITY and FOCUS controls to result in a trace of the desired intensity and optimum focus.

Step 3.   Set the HORIZONTAL AMPLITUDE control to result in a horizontal trace that ends approximately ¼ to ½ in. from each side of the screen.

Step 4.   Set the SYNC AMPLITUDE control at 0 and the SYNC SIGNAL SELECTOR switch to LINE FREQUENCY or INT, whichever is available.

Step 5.   Set the COARSE FREQUENCY and FINE FREQUENCY control to result in a sweep of less than 60 c.

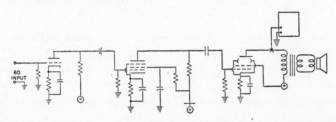

FIG. 14–2.   Circuit of a typical audio amplifier in an a-m receiver.

Step 6.   Set the VERTICAL GAIN control to about one tenth of its full clockwise rotation.

Step 7.   Connect the low-voltage 60-c source to the grid of the first audio stage and the ground lead from that source to the ground of the circuit being tested.

Step 8.   Connect the VERTICAL INPUT terminals of the oscilloscope to one of the output leads of the speaker transformer, and connect the GROUND terminal of the oscilloscope to ground of the receiver. (The lead from the VERTICAL INPUT terminal for this type of work can be an ordinary voltmeter type of probe with an insulated handle, so that it may be moved about readily without any chance of shock when it is connected to points of high voltage.)

Step 9.   Turn the power to all units to ON.

If the audio stages of this receiver are operating correctly, a 60-c wave will be observed on the screen of the oscilloscope. It may be necessary to adjust both the COARSE FREQUENCY and FINE FREQUENCY controls and the SYNC AMPLITUDE in order to stop the motion of this wave. Also, it will probably be necessary to increase or decrease the setting of the VERTICAL GAIN control to obtain a usable amplitude of the 60-c wave.

Step 10.   If no signal is observed, the lead to the oscilloscope should be removed from the output lead of the speaker transformer and connected to the plate of the output stage to determine whether or not a signal is present.

Step 11.   If no signal is observed here, the grid of this stage should be checked.

Step 12.   If no signal is observed here then the plate of the preceding stage must be checked.

When the 60-c test signal is finally observed, the trouble will thus be localized. Once the trouble has been localized, it is a simple matter for the serviceman to find the defective component by voltage and resistance measurements and correct the trouble. For example, the 60-c signal may

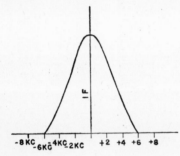

FIG. 14–3. Frequency-response curve of a single-peaked i-f transformer (properly tuned).

appear at the plate of one stage and not at the grid of the next stage simply because the coupling capacitor between the two stages is open. A signal may appear at the grid of a tube and not at the plate of the same tube, even though the tube may be good. This condition may be caused by an open or a shorted plate resistor. A shorted coupling capacitor is indicated by B+ being applied to the grid of the next stage. Other tests on the audio amplifier are given in Chaps. 8, 13, and 18. In these chapters sawtoothed wave testing of amplifiers, square-wave testing of amplifiers, and locating the cause of distortion are fully explained.

The I-F Amplifiers of an A-M Superheterodne Receiver.   Between each of the i-f stages and between the converter stage and the first i-f stage are located i-f transformers. Each of these transformers consists of two tuned circuits—one in the plate circuit of the preceding tube, and the other in the grid circuit of the following tube. These transformers are tuned by small ceramic capacitors to the intermediate frequency. In the lower-priced receivers, these transformers are peaked at the intermediate frequency, and the frequency response tapers off very rapidly on either side. Such transformers have what is known as "narrow bandwidth." The frequency response of such a transformer is shown in Fig. 14-3. The bandwidth of this transformer is approximately 5 kc, that is, 2.5 kc either side of the mid-frequency. The bandwidth of an i-f response curve is usually taken at a level of seven tenths of the peak value.

On the other hand, a good i-f transformer results in a wider-band i-f response curve, such as that shown in Fig. 14-4. This curve is double-peaked, which tends to broaden the over-all frequency response. Thus,

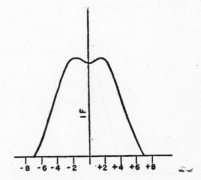

Fig. 14-4. Frequency-response curve of a double-peaked i-f transformer (properly tuned).

instead of having a bandwidth of 5 kc, this transformer has a bandwidth of about 8 kc, 4 kc either side of the mid-frequency.

Importance of Bandwidth in I-F Transformers. Although the r-f signal that is received by an a-m broadcast receiver is amplitude-modulated, sideband frequencies also are present above and below the r-f carrier. These sidebands are calculated quite simply. If f_c is the carrier frequency and f_m is the modulating frequency, the upper sideband is equal to $f_c + f_m$, and the lower sideband equals $f_c - f_m$.

Since most of the audio energy in the r-f signal is in the sidebands, they must pass through the i-f stages of the receiver in order to result in good tone response in the receiver. As a result, a receiver whose bandwidth is only 4 kc, that is, 2 kc either side of the carrier frequency, will only reproduce audio signals up to 2 kc because the sidebands produced by the higher frequencies cannot pass through the i-f stages. On the other hand, broad-band i-f stages with bandwidths of 8 kc, that is, 4 kc either side of the carrier frequency, will reproduce audio signals up to 4 kc.

In aligning the i-f stages of a receiver, many servicemen use the ear method to determine the proper tuning; that is, they adjust the capacitors in the i-f transformers until the loudest signal is transmitted. For the alignment of low-priced receivers with a single-peaked i-f transformer, this method may be satisfactory. However, a good receiver must have its i-f transformers tuned properly in order to present the wide range of audio frequencies to the audio amplifier and maintain its reputation for high-fidelity reproduction of sound.

In adjusting the double-peaked high-fidelity i-f transformers by the ear method, the normal shape of the response curve is distorted when it is adjusted to obtain the loudest signal, and one of the two peaks is increased considerably, so that the curve resembles the curve of Fig. 14-5. Note that this virtually reduces to zero the ability of this stage to pass the lower sideband. It is also quite possible that the stage may be tuned

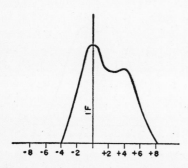

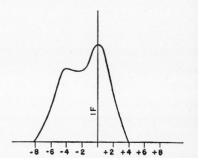

Fig. 14–5. Frequency-response curve of a double-peaked i-f transformer peaked with the broadest bandwidth on the high-frequency side.

Fig. 14–6. Frequency-response curve of a double-peaked i-f transformer peaked with the broadest bandwidth on the low-frequency side.

to the other side, so that the curve resembles that in Fig. 14-6. In this situation, the upper sideband will not be allowed to pass through the stage.

It is therefore easy to see that in tuning i-f stages by ear, one stage can easily be peaked and cut off most of the lower sidebands and the next stage can be peaked to cut off the upper sidebands. Thus, the result is an over-all i-f response curve that is narrow, and the high fidelity of the i-f amplifier stages is destroyed. The use of an oscilloscope in aligning i-f stages prevents such an occurrence, since the response curve is presented visually on the screen.

Aligning the I-F Stages.   The only additional equipment necessary for i-f alignment with an oscilloscope is a frequency-modulated signal generator. As explained in Chap. 12, Auxiliary Equipment, this signal generator may be frequency-modulated with a reactance tube or a rotating variable capacitor. Irrespective of the method employed in the signal generator for achieving frequency modulation, the end result is the same as far as the serviceman is concerned. With the frequency of

:he signal generator set to the i-f frequency, usually 456 kc, the reactance :ube or the rotating capacitor varies the center frequency plus and minus 10 kc or more. Thus, the output frequency of the signal generator varies from 446 to 466 kc when the signal generator is set to 456 kc. If the output frequency is assumed to start at 446 kc, the reactance tube will increase this frequency at a linear rate until the frequency of 466 kc is reached. At this point, the reactance tube has reached its minimum capacitance and begins to increase. Therefore, the frequency change is in the opposite direction, viz., from 466 kc to 446 kc. This change is considered as one cycle of wobbulation. A graph showing the change in the frequency of the output of a frequency-modulated signal generator is shown in Fig. 12-19. Another requirement of the vertical amplifier is that it must have sufficient gain to produce a good-sized pattern on the screen of the oscilloscope. For a-m servicing a vertical amplifier having a gain of between 40 and 50 will get by, but for f-m and television servicing the gain should be approximately 2,000 to produce full screen patterns when the i-f stages are aligned individually. Most frequency-modulated signal generators, whether they are wobbulated by a rotating capacitor or by a reactance tube, complete the entire cycle from 446 to 466 and back to 446 kc at the same rate as the power-line frequency, usually 60 c. Thus, to observe this on the oscilloscope, the sweep frequency of the oscilloscope need only be 60 c. Also, since the oscilloscope is used to measure the varying rectified output of the detector, which is varying at only 60 c, the only requirement for the vertical amplifier of the oscilloscope is that it have a good response to a 60-c square wave.

To observe the i-f response curve of an AM receiver, the frequency-modulated signal is impressed upon the grid of the last i-f stage, and the oscilloscope is connected across the output of the detector, as shown in Fig. 14-7. As the frequency-modulated signal generator sweeps through this band of ± 10 kc, the detector responds to the varying d-c voltage which is directly proportional to the signal passing through the last i-f stage.

Step 1. Turn on the frequency-modulated signal generator (referred to hereafter as the "wobbulator") about 10 min. before it is to be used to permit the internal temperature to stabilize.

Step 2. Connect the wobbulator to the grid of the last i-f stage, as shown in Fig. 14-7.

Step 3. Connect the oscilloscope to the output of the detector (or the grid of the first audio amplifier), as shown in Fig. 14-7.

Step 4. Turn on the oscilloscope and set the VERTICAL POSITIONING and HORIZONTAL POSITIONING controls to place the trace near the center of the screen.

Step 5.   Set the INTENSITY and FOCUS controls to result in a trace of the desired intensity and optimum focus.

Step 6.   Set the HORIZONTAL GAIN control to result in a horizontal trace that ends about ¼ in. from each side of the screen.

Step 7.   Set the SYNC AMPLITUDE control to zero and the SYNC SIGNAL SELECTOR switch to LINE FREQUENCY or INTERNAL, whichever is available.

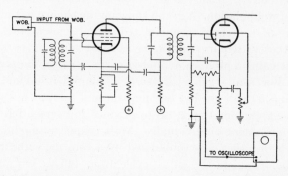

FIG. 14–7.   Circuit showing the connection for the wobbulator and the oscilloscope for the alignment of the last i-f stage of an a-m receiver.

Note

External synchronization may also be used; however, this requires that a synchronizing signal be applied to the EXTERNAL SYNC INPUT terminal. This voltage may be obtained from a special output terminal from the signal generator or from a low-voltage winding of a power transformer operating at line frequency.

Step 8.   Set the COARSE FREQUENCY and FINE FREQUENCY controls to result in a sweep frequency approximately equal to the power-line frequency.

Step 9.   Turn on the receiver.

Step 10.   After a sufficient warm-up time for the receiver, advance the VERTICAL GAIN control to obtain a usable amplitude of vertical deflection.

Step 11.   Synchronize the pattern on the screen.

Step 12.   Short-circuit the plates of the oscillator-tuning capacitor by connecting a wire between the rotor and stator plate terminals to prevent interference from the oscillator in making the following adjustments.

If the sweep frequency of the oscilloscope is set to the power-line frequency, two complete i-f response curves will appear on the screen of the oscilloscope, as shown in Fig. 14-8. These response curves appear to be quite narrow, and, as a matter of fact, they can hardly be regarded as curves as they appear here.

Note

The reason for the appearance of two response curves is shown in Fig. 14-9. The wobbulator completes a sweep of the frequencies from 446 to 466 kc in one sixtieth of a cycle (Fig. 14-9a). The frequency of the sweep of the oscilloscope is 60 c, or

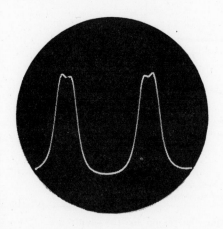

Fig. 14–8a. Oscillogram showing the double-frequency response curves obtained from the circuit of Fig. 14–7.

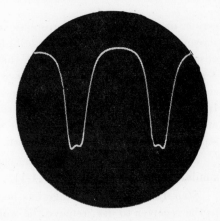

Fig. 14–8b. Same as Fig. 14–8a except that the amplifier of the oscillograph contains an extra stage which inverts the pattern.

one sweep in one sixtieth of a cycle (Fig. 14-9b). The i-f amplifiers transmit a signal to the detector as the wobbulator signal increases in frequency through the i-f range and decreases in signal through the i-f range (Fig.14-9c.)

Step 13. Advance the HORIZONTAL GAIN control of the oscilloscope excessively, in order to see the true shape of this curve.

This action may throw one or both of these patterns off the screen, but adjusting the HORIZONTAL POSITIONING control will probably bring back either one of the two patterns. A PHASING control on either the wobbulator or the oscilloscope will also return one of the patterns to the

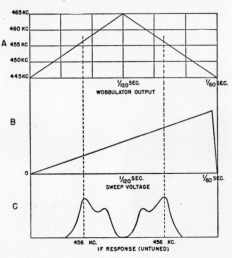

Fig. 14–9. Graphical representation showing the reason for the occurrence of two response curves.

center of the screen. The response curve expanded in this manner is shown in Fig. 14-10. The over-all shape of a single curve can now be observed, and it is quite evident that this stage is not properly tuned. A properly adjusted i-f response curve is one that is symmetrical on either side of an imaginary vertical line passing through the center of the curve. In this case, the properly tuned transformer has two peaks of equal amplitudes which are set to obtain the highest possible amplitude and still maintain a symmetrical pattern.

Step 14.   Adjust the i-f tuning capacitors to obtain a response curve similar to that shown in Fig. 14-11.

Step 15.   When this stage has been properly aligned, turn the power to the receiver to OFF, remove the wobbulator from the input of the last i-f stage, and connect it to the grid of the preceding i-f stage (in some receivers, this may be the grid of the converter stage).

Step 16.   Leave the oscilloscope connected to the output of the detector and turn on the power to the receiver.

When the signal is applied at this point, a distorted or untuned i-f response curve will again appear on the oscilloscope, despite the fact that the last stage has already been tuned. This, however, is due to mis-alignment in the i-f stage, which is now receiving the wobbulated signal, and the adjustments already made in the last i-f stage should *not* be changed. The two capacitors in the i-f transformer now to be adjusted should be tuned to obtain a symmetrical response curve similar to that shown in Fig. 14-11.

Step 17. If there are more than two i-f stages in the receiver being tested, the signal generator is then connected to the grid of the next pre-ceding stage, and the i-f tuning procedure is repeated.

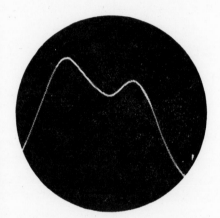

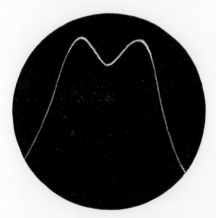

Fig. 14–10. Oscillogram of the re-sponse of a double-peaked i-f trans-former improperly tuned.

Fig. 14–11. Same as Fig. 14–10 except that this curve is properly tuned.

Another method for aligning the i-f stage of a receiver is also accept-able. This method requires the sweep frequency of the oscilloscope to be set to twice the wobbulating frequency, i.e., 120 c for a 60-c power-line frequency. Thus, as shown in Fig. 14-12a, one sweep of the oscilloscope occurs as the wobbulated signal increases, and the next sweep occurs as the wobbulated signal decreases (Fig. 14-12b). The two i-f curves, one showing the response to increasing frequency and the second showing the response to decreasing frequency, are superimposed on the screen of the oscilloscope. When the i-f stage is not tuned, two distinct curves can be seen (Fig. 14-12c), because they are not symmetrical on each side of the center frequency. Proper tuning of the i-f stage is obtained when the two curves are superimposed completely, one upon the other, as shown in Fig. 14-12d.

In following this procedure, the operator may find some difficulty in maintaining synchronization if the FINE FREQUENCY control is not carefully adjusted. It will then be found that the SYNC AMPLITUDE control will shift the two patterns so that they may be nearly superimposed horizontally. The adjustment of the i-f transformers themselves will then vary the vertical amplitude of the curves and they may be superimposed.

Checking the I-F Stages. To determine immediately whether there is trouble in the i-f stages of a receiver, the wobbulator can be connected to the grid of the converter stage. With the oscilloscope connected to the

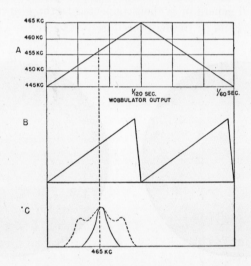

FIG. 14–12. Graphical representation showing how by increasing the sweep frequency two i-f response curves can be superimposed.

output of the detector, a good response curve will be observed on the oscilloscope if the i-f section of the receiver under test is in good condition. If, however, no response curve or a poor response curve is obtained, trouble is indicated in one of the i-f stages. By tracing the signal through the i-f section, stage by stage, using the oscilloscope connected across the detector as the indicator, the stage causing the trouble can quickly be found. The defective component can then be located by voltage or re-

FIG. 14–13. A drawing showing two i-f response curves superimposed. (They are slightly separated to show the presence of two curves).

sistance measurements. Whenever a component has been changed in one of the i-f stages, it is good practice to check the over-all response curve of the i-f stages to ascertain that the alignment has not been affected.

The Traveling Detector. The only disadvantage of the oscilloscope in aligning and checking i-f stages is that it must operate on the detected signal in order to present intelligible information to the serviceman. However, this limitation can be eliminated very easily by the construction of a device called a "traveling detector."

The traveling detector is essentially a crystal detector, which can be constructed in a short time by the radio serviceman. It can be assembled into a piece of Bakelite tubing mounted on the end of a length of coaxial

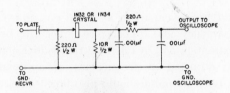

Fig. 14–14.   Circuit of a traveling detector.

cable to serve as connection to the oscilloscope. A circuit for the traveling detector, is shown in Fig. 14-14. This device will be useful in the larger a-m receivers and will be practically indispensible for f-m and television servicing. Its use is fully explained in the two chapters covering each of these subjects, Chaps. 15 and 16.

The Local Oscillator. The function of the oscillator is to furnish a signal to the converter, which is maintained at a fixed-frequency difference from the r-f signal. Maintaining this frequency difference throughout the tuning range is called "tracking." Two methods for maintaining tracking are in common use today. One method utilizes an oscillator-tuning capacitor, which is smaller than the tuning capacitor used in the r-f sections and which has specially shaped plates. The other method employs identical tuning capacitors for both the oscillator and the r-f sections, but requires that an additional capacitor be connected in series with the oscillator-tuning capicitor. Thus, in the circuit of Fig. 14-15, $C1$ is the tuning capacitor; $C2$ is the padding capacitor; and $C3$ is the trimmer capacitor in parallel with the tuning capacitor.

The tuning capacitor for the oscillator is on the same shaft as the tuning capacitors in the r-f section, and it is this capacitor which must track with the others throughout the tuning range. The padding capacitor adjusts the tracking at the low-frequency end of the band, and the trimmer capacitor adjusts the tracking at the higher end. Even with the compensating capacitors, it is not possible to obtain perfect tracking throughout the entire tuning range. However, the center of the range can be very close to perfect, most of the errors occurring at the two ends of the band. To accomplish this, it is advisable to adjust the padder capacitor at about one quarter of the distance from the low-frequency end of

Fig. 14–15. Circuit of the local oscillator of an a-m receiver.

the band, and the trimmer capacitor at about one quarter of the distance from the high-frequency end. Therefore, since the broadcast receiver tunes from approximately 550 to 1,550 kc, the padder and trimmer capacitors are usually adjusted at frequencies of approximately 800 and 1,300 kc, and the 1,000-kc point should also be checked to ascertain good tracking in the central portion of the range.

Aligning the Oscillator.

Step 1.   Connect the wobbulator to the grid of the converter tube.

Step 2.   Set the dial of the receiver to 800 kc.

Step 3.   Set the center frequency of the wobbulator to 800 kc.

Step 4.   Connect the VERTICAL INPUT terminals of the oscilloscope between the detector output and ground (the same as for i-f alignment).

Step 5.   Remove the wire short-circuiting the oscillator-tuning capacitor during i-f alignment.

Step 6.   Turn on the power to the receiver, the wobbulator, and the oscilloscope; and allow a 10 min. warm-up period for the oscillator frequency of the receiver to stabilize.

Step 7.   Adjust the oscillator-padding capacitor to obtain the maximum amplitude of the i-f response curve on the screen of the oscilloscope.

Step 8.   Set the wobbulator and the dial of the receiver to 1,300 kc.

Step 9.   Adjust the oscillator-trimmer capacitor to obtain the maximum amplitude of the i-f response curve.

Step 10.   Again, set the frequency of the wobbulator and the receiver dial to 800 kc, and readjust the padding capacitor.

Step 11.   Again, set the frequency of the wobbulator and the receiver to 1,300 kc, and readjust the trimmer capacitor.

Perhaps one more, final adjustment will be necessary on both of these capacitors before the optimum alignment is obtained. To check for good tracking, set the wobbulator and the receiver to 1,000 kc. The amplitude of the response curve should decrease only a slight amount as the oscillator is properly adjusted.

Tuning the R-F Stage. One adjustment must be made to tune each r-f stage. This adjustment is the trimmer capacitor on each of the r-f-tuning capacitors. The following procedure should be followed after the oscillator has been aligned:

Step 1. Connect the wobbulator between the antenna and ground terminals of the receiver.

Step 2. Connect the VERTICAL INPUT terminals of the oscilloscope between the output of the detector and ground.

Step 3. Set the wobbulator frequency and the receiver dial to 1,000 kc.

Step 4. Adjust the trimmer capacitors on each of the r-f tuning capacitors to obtain the maximum amplitude of the i-f response curve on the screen of the oscilloscope.

In receivers that have no r-f stage, it will be necessary to adjust only one trimmer capacitor.

Special Note in Aligning A-M Receivers. In the cheaper models of a-c–d-c receivers, it is extremely difficult to align the receiver by the visual method because 60-c pickup is prevalent throughout the chassis, and practically the entire receiver operates above ground potential. Although it is not impossible to follow the alignment procedure already described in this chapter, it is somewhat awkward. When such is the case, the oscilloscope cannot be connected into the detector circuit because the leads will pick up so much 60-c hum that the response curve will not be readily discernible. Instead, the oscilloscope should be connected between the two output terminals of the speaker transformer, and all signals from the wobbulator are connected to the antenna through a very small capacitor. Even the signal for aligning the i-f stages must be fed into the antenna with the local oscillator shorted out. This signal will pass through sufficiently strong when the r-f tuning capacitor is set to receive the lowest frequency, since there is usually no r-f stage in this type of set.

15 Servicing F-M Radio Receivers

The F-M Receiver. A block diagram of a typical f-m receiver is shown in Fig. 15-1. Essentially, it consists of an r-f stage, an oscillator stage, a converter stage, one or more i-f stages followed by one or more limiters, a discriminator, and an audio amplifier. From this, the strong similarity between the a-m and f-m receivers is quite apparent. However, two differences are immediately noticeable, namely, that the f-m receiver employs a limiter and a discriminator, both of which are not

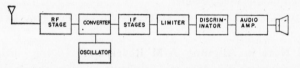

Fɪɢ. 15–1. Block diagram of an f-m receiver.

found in the a-m receiver. A third difference, which is not evident in the block diagram, is that the r-f and i-f sections of the f-m receiver have a much wider band pass and the tuning is therefore broader.

Frequency modulation employs much wider sidebands than standard amplitude modulation and therefore permits a wider range of audio signals to be transmitted. The sidebands of the f-m carrier may extend as high as 100 kc above and below the carrier frequency. This is the reason for the excellent quality of the sound transmitted by frequency modulation.

Another feature of frequency modulation is noise-free reception, which is a particularly welcome relief in areas where the atmospheric-noise interference level is high. The f-m signal reaching the receiver contains as much noise as any a-m signal, but it fails to pass through the receiver. Since noise affects the amplitude of the r-f carrier, it is difficult to eliminate in a-m receivers because the audio signal also affects the amplitude of the carrier. With frequency modulation, however, the audio signal merely varies the frequency of the r-f carrier and not the amplitude. Thus, the noise and audio signal are separate in an f-m signal, and the noise is eliminated by the limiter stage or stages. The action of the limiter is shown in Fig. 15-2.

The r-f carrier, frequency-modulated by the audio signal and amplitude-modulated by noise, is fed into the grid of the limiter. The limiter stage is essentially an amplifier that is designed to clip off any amplitude irregularities. Its output, then, is almost entirely void of amplitude modulation and thus devoid of noise.

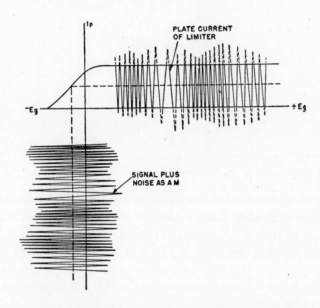

Fig. 15–2. The action of a limiter stage in an f-m receiver.

The discriminator of the f-m receiver serves the same function as the detector of the a-m receiver, that is, it separates the audio signal from its r-f component. This function is accomplished by a tuned circuit operating with a dual diode (Fig. 15-3). The discriminator circuit is tuned precisely to the intermediate frequency. When this frequency is fed into the discriminator transformer, the output of the stage is zero volts. Any deviation from this frequency, however, results in a positive or a negative voltage across the discriminator-load resistor. This output voltage is opposite in polarity for frequencies on opposite sides of the resonance frequency of the discriminator-transformer and increases in amplitude with an increase in the deviation from the resonant frequency. A characteristic discriminator curve, showing how the output varies with respect to deviation from the resonant frequency, is given in Fig. 15-4.

Alignment Procedure for F-M Receivers.   There are two procedures which can be followed for aligning the f-m receiver. One method is first to align the i-f transformer between the last i-f stage and the limiter, and then to proceed stage by stage toward the r-f section, aligning each stage in turn just as in the i-f alignment procedure for a-m receivers. The

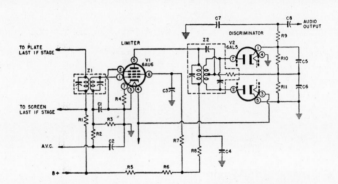

Fig. 15–3. Circuit showing the limiter and discriminator section of an f-m receiver.

vertical input terminals of the oscilloscope are connected across the grid-return resistor of the first limiter stage, as shown in Fig. 15-3.

The other method is to align each i-f stage separately with the aid of the traveling detector described in Chap. 11, and then to make final adjustments to achieve the best over-all response. This latter method is recognized as being the most accurate and is, therefore, presented here in the step-by-step procedure.

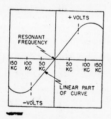

Fig. 15–4. Graph showing the ideal discriminator-response curve.

The discriminator transformer may be aligned either before or after the i-f stages. However, when a single limiter stage is employed, the i-f transformer in its grid circuit must be properly aligned first. Therefore, it is more convenient to complete the i-f alignment and leave the discriminator for attention later. Discriminator alignment will be discussed further along in the chapter. The alignment of the r-f section requires that the discriminator be properly aligned; hence, the procedure for r-f and oscillator alignment will follow the discriminator.

It should be noted that the procedures given in this chapter serve a double purpose. Since the sound that accompanies the television signal is transmitted by frequency modulation, the sound section of the television receiver is simply an f-m receiver which is tuned to the frequencies of the television channels. Therefore, the alignment procedure for the sound i-f, the limiter, and the discriminator stages of the television receiver is exactly the same as that for the f-m receiver. The only difference is that the intermediate frequency for the f-m receiver is 10.7 megacycles, * whereas the sound intermediate frequency for the television receiver is 21.9 megacycles.

Note

The intermediate frequency employed in prewar f-m receivers was 4.3 megacycles, and the sound intermediate frequency in prewar television receivers was 8.25 megacycles.

The alignment of the i-f stages of an f-m receiver requires a wobbulator (frequency-modulated signal generator) similar to that employed for a-m receivers. This wobbulator, however, must be capable of operating at the intermediate frequency of the receiver being aligned, and it should swing the center frequency a minimum of $\pm$ 200 kc and a maximum of $\pm$ 1 megacycle.

The schematic of a typical f-m receiver is shown in Fig. 15-5. The i-f amplifier consists of the tuned circuit in the plate of $V4$ (the converter stage), $V4$, and $V5$. The two limiter stages are $V6$ and $V7$, and the discriminator is $V8$. The r-f section consists of an r-f stage $V1$, the converter stage $V2$, and the local oscillator $V3$.

Aligning the First I-F Transformer.

Step 1. Connect the output of the wobbulator between the grid of $V2$ and ground.

Step 2. Remove $V1$, $V3$, and $V5$ from their sockets.

Step 3. Set the center frequency of the wobbulator to 10.7 megacycles.

Step 4. Connect the traveling-detector lead from the VERTICAL INPUT of the oscilloscope between the plate of $V4$ and ground.

Step 5. Turn on the oscilloscope and set the VERTICAL and HORIZONTAL POSITIONING controls to place the trace near the center of the screen.

Step 6. Set the INTENSITY and FOCUS controls to result in a trace of the desired intensity and optimum focus.

Step 7. Set the HORIZONTAL GAIN control to result in a horizontal trace that ends about ¼ in. from each side of the screen.

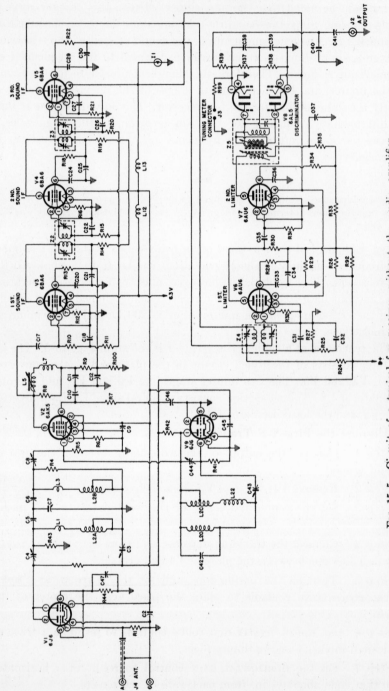

Fig. 15-5. Circuit of a typical f-m receiver without the audio amplifier.

Step 8. Set the SYNC AMPLITUDE control to zero and the SYNC SIGNAL SELECTOR switch to LINE FREQUENCY or INTERNAL, whichever is available.

Step 9. Set the COARSE FREQUENCY and FINE FREQUENCY controls to result in a sweep frequency approximately equal to the power-line frequency.

Step 10. Turn on the receiver.

Step 11. After a sufficient warm-up time for the receiver, advance the VERTICAL GAIN control to obtain a usable amplitude of vertical deflection.

Step 12. Synchronize the pattern on the screen.

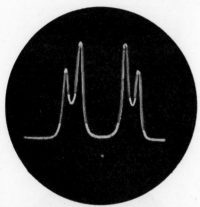 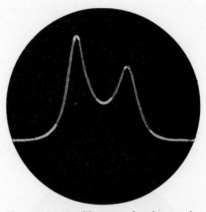

FIG. 15-6. Oscillogram showing dual i-f response curve improperly tuned.

FIG. 15-7. Oscillogram showing a single i-f response curve improperly tuned. This curve is obtained by expanding the sweep of Fig. 15-6 and adjusting the horizontal positioning control to obtain a single curve.

Two complete response curves should appear on the oscilloscope, as shown in Fig. 15-6.

Step 13. Increase the setting of the HORIZONTAL GAIN control and adjust the HORIZONTAL POSITIONING control to obtain a single i-f curve on the screen, as shown in Fig. 15-7.

In order to be absolutely certain that the i-f stages are tuned exactly to the intermediate frequency, it is necessary to add another signal to the receiver. This signal is obtained from a calibrated, single-frequency signal generator whose frequency can be set precisely to within 10 kc of the desired signal. This signal, called a "marker," or a "birdie," is superimposed upon the response curve to indicate the exact center frequency to which the intermediate frequency must be tuned. Hereafter, in the text, the calibrated, single-frequency signal generator will be referred to as the "marker generator," and the indication of the frequency of the marker generator on the response curve will be referred to as a "birdie."

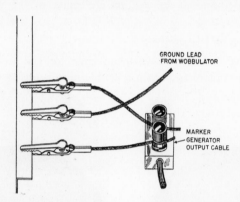

FIG. 15–8. Drawing to show the connection of both terminals of the marker generator to ground across the ground lead of the wobbulator.

It will be necessary for the serviceman to experiment with his own equipment to determine the most satisfactory method of connecting the marker generator. However, for the higher intermediate frequencies (`10

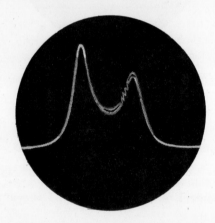

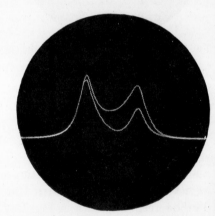

FIG. 15–9. Single untuned i-f response curve with the birdie signal superimposed.

FIG. 15–10. Same as Fig. 15–9 except too much birdie is applied.

megacycles or more), an ideal signal can be obtained rather simply. It is usually only necessary to attach wire-braid leads, about 3 in. long, to the ends of the termination cable from the marker generator. These leads are both connected to ground on either side of the ground lead of the wobbulator, as shown in Fig. 15-8. Although at first glance, this seems to short out the marker generator, there is enough coupling between the leads so that the birdie appears on the response curve.

The birdie may also be applied by connecting the marker generator in series with the ground lead of the wobbulator; or across a small resistor (10 ohms) in the ground lead of the wobbulator; or the marker generator may be coupled to the grid lead of the wobbulator by inductive coupling

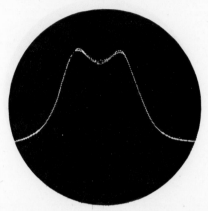

FIG. 15–11. Oscillogram showing i-f response curve properly tuned. Birdie is located midway between the two peaks.

(two or three turns of wire around the grid lead); or by coupling to the grid through a 10-$\mu\mu$f capacitor and a 10,000-ohm resistor in series. In any event, care must be taken that too much birdie is not added, for then it will be impossible to obtain proper tuning.

Step 14. Connect the leads from the marker generator to ground across the ground lead of the wobbulator and set the frequency of the marker generator to 10.7 megacycles (21.9 megacycles for television sound i-f stages).

The birdie appearing on the response curve can be seen in Fig. 15-9. This is the same response curve as that shown in Fig. 15-7 without the birdie. The effect of too much birdie on the same response curve is shown in Fig. 15-10.

Step 15. Adjust the tuning capacitors in the i-f transformer between $V2$ and $V4$ to obtain a nearly flat response curve which is symmetrical on both sides of the center frequency. The center frequency is, of course, indicated by the birdie. A typical, well-tuned i-f response curve is shown in Fig 15-11. In tuning the capacitors of the sound i-f transformers, it is necessary to use an r-f tuning wand, since these capacitors are in the plate circuit of the i-f stage and are, therefore, above ground. If a tuning wand is not used, hand capacitance will change the resonance of the circuit, and proper tuning will be impossible.

If too much signal is applied from the wobbulator, this stage may be overloaded and proper tuning will be impossible. An example of an overloaded response curve is shown in Fig. 15-12. To eliminate overloading, reduce the signal output of the wobbulator.

In performing this alignment procedure, it is worth noting that the automatic volume control need not be disconnected, since the low im-

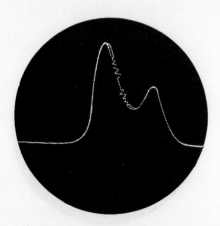

Fig. 15–12a. Oscillogram of i-f response curve slightly overloaded.

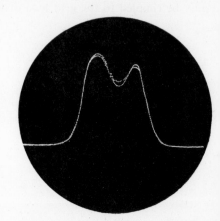

Fig. 15–12b. Oscillogram of i-f response curve excessively overloaded.

pedance of the wobbulator, which is connected directly across the grid resistor, automatically shunts the automatic volume control.

Step 16.   Switch off the power to the f-m receiver.

Note

The i-f transformers of f-m receivers may also be aligned by doubling the sweep frequency of the oscilloscope and superimposing the two response curves. This technique is explained in the alignment of the i-f stages of an a-m receiver. However, the alignment of the sound i-f stages of a television receiver should be done in accordance with the procedure outlined herein because it is more accurate. In television receivers, for tuning the sound and picture simultaneously, it is necessary that the sound channel be aligned to the precise intermediate frequency.

Aligning the Second I-F Transformer.

Step 1.   Replace $V1$ and $V5$ in their respective sockets and remove $V2$ and $V6$.

Step 2.   Remove the wobbulator from the grid of $V2$ and ground, and connect it between the grid of $V4$ and ground.

Step 3.   Connect the traveling detector between the plate of $V5$ and ground.

Step 4.   Connect the marker generator across the ground lead of the wobbulator, and tune the i-f transformer, which is located between **V4** and **V5**.

The tuned response curve will be similar to Fig. 15-11.

Aligning the Third I-F Transformer.

Step 1.   Replace *V2* and *V6* in their respective sockets and remove *V4* and *V7*.

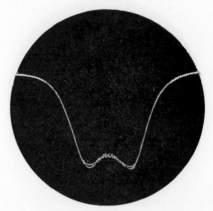

FIG. 15–13.   Oscillogram of the properly tuned i-f transformer which is located between *V5* and *V6*.

Step 2.   Remove the wobbulator from the grid of *V4*, and connect it between the grid of *V5* and ground.

Since *V6* is a limiter stage, a true response curve cannot be obtained from its plate. However, it is possible to obtain a true response curve from the grid-return lead of the i-f transformer being tuned. Since the combination of *R*1 and *C*1 effectively acts as a rectifier, it is not necessary to use the traveling detector for this stage.

Step 3.   Connect a coaxial lead from the VERTICAL INPUT terminals of the oscilloscope across the resistor *R*1 in the grid-return circuit of the first limiter stage. A 100,000-ohm ½-watt resistor should be inserted between the center conductor of the coaxial cable and *R*1 to prevent loading this circuit.

Step 4.   Connect the marker generator across the ground lead of the wobbulator, and tune the i-f transformer which is located between *V5* and *V6*.

The correctly tuned response curve for this stage is shown in Fig. 15-13. Notice that the polarity of this response curve is opposite that obtained in the two previous stages. It is important to note that the amplifiers of the oscilloscope or the polarity of the traveling detector may invert all of the response curves, depending upon the number of amplifiers in the oscilloscope and the polarity of the crystal in the traveling detector. In any event, to compare these curves, all that is necessary is to invert the book.

After all three sound i-f transformers have been aligned separately, it is necessary to make an over-all check. The reason for this is that the tuning of the i-f transformers may vary somewhat with fixed signal

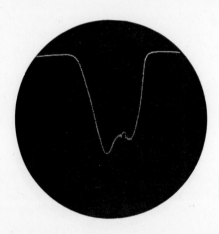

Fig. 15–14. Oscillogram showing the improper alignment that has occurred as a result of different signal amplitudes applied to the grids of the various stages.

amplitudes. Since the stages were aligned separately, each with an identical signal input, and since there is appreciable gain achieved in each stage, the second and third i-f transformers will probably be slightly out of alignment—the third transformer more than the second.

Procedure for Over-All I-F Alignment.

Step 1.   Replace $V4$ in its socket, and again remove $V1$ and $V3$.

Step 2.   Connect the wobbulator between the grid of $V2$ and ground.

Step 3.   Connect the marker generator across the ground lead of the wobbulator.

Step 4.   Leave the oscilloscope connected across the resistor $R2$ in the grid circuit of the first limiter tube.

Figure 15-14 shows the improper alignment that has occurred as a result of the different signal amplitude applied to the grids of the various stages. This, of course, is the over-all response curve. Note that the center frequency as indicated by the marker has shifted slightly.

Step 5.   Readjust the last i-f transformer to obtain a response curve as close as possible to that in Fig. 15-11 or 15-14.

Step 6.   Readjust the second i-f transformer to obtain an even better response curve.

Step 7. By making further minor adjustments of these two i-f transformers, obtain an over-all response curve that is equivalent in symmetry, amplitude, and accuracy of adjustment to the normal response curve for any single stage.

It is not necessary to determine the bandwidth of this response curve, because in nearly all instances the width will be maintained. However, it can be checked by shifting the birdie to each side, and, thus, it can be determined whether the over-all width is about 200 kc, i.e., 100 kc either side of the center frequency. The ideal curve is down not more than 6 db (50 per cent) at 150 kc on either side of the center frequency.

Aligning the Discriminator. The quickest method of aligning the discriminator transformer is by adjusting it as close as possible with a high-impedance d-c voltmeter. Then, the visual method (the use of the oscilloscope) is employed to set it exactly on frequency.

Step 1. Referring to Fig. 15-5, connect a high-impedance d-c voltmeter between the cathode pin 1 of the discriminator and ground.

Step 2. Using the marker generator, connect it between the grid and ground of the second limiter stage.

Step 3. Adjust the output of the marker generator to about 1/10 volt and set its frequency at the precise i-f frequency of 10.7 megacycles (4.3 megacycles for prewar frequency modulation, 8.25 megacycles for prewar television sound, and 21.9 megacycles for postwar television sound).

Step 4. Set the vacuum-tube voltmeter to the 3-volt range.

Step 5. Turn on the power to the receiver.

The polarity of the voltage that will be recorded by the output meter may be either positive or negative, depending upon the existing setting of the secondary of the discriminator coil.

Step 6. With an r-f tuning wand, adjust the secondary of the discriminator coil to obtain a reading of 0 volts on the voltmeter. (The secondary of this transformer is determined by the absence of B+ on its trimmer capacitor, whereas B+ is present on the primary trimmer capacitor.)

Some difficulty may be experienced at first in determining the correct setting of the secondary of the discriminator transformer, since three zero-voltage points may be obtained. One of these points exists when the secondary of the discriminator transformer is set quite far below the center frequency. The second exists when the secondary is set exactly on the center frequency, and the third occurs when the secondary is set far above the center frequency. The second of these three zero-voltage points is the correct setting. It may be easily determined, since a slight tuning of the secondary in one direction produces a positive voltage and a slight tuning in the other direction produces a negative voltage.

After the secondary of the discriminator transformer has been adjusted, it is then necessary to adjust the primary.

Step 6. Connect the voltmeter probe between the junction of the two cathode resistors $R2$ and $R3$ and ground.

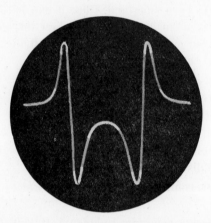 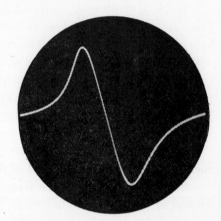

Fig. 15–15. Oscillogram showing a dual discriminator curve.

Fig. 15–16. Oscillogram showing a single discriminator curve obtained by expanding the sweep.

Step 7. Leaving the marker generator connected as previously, adjust the primary of the discriminator coil to obtain the maximum d-c output. The output will be a negative d-c voltage of approximately 1 volt.

Note

This voltage varies depending upon the amplification obtained in the second limiter stage and upon the value of the discriminator load resistors.

If the marker generator is quite accurate and the meter is dependable, this method of adjusting the discriminator transformer is also quite accurate. However, this procedure is not perfect, and the final tuning must be made with the wobbulator and the oscilloscope.

Adjusting the Discriminator Using the Wobbulator.

Step 1. Connect the wobbulator to the grid of the converter tube $V2$ of Fig. 15-5.

The wobbulator is connected to the converter stage to be certain that enough signal is used, so that the limiters are operating properly. The grid of the second limiter should draw current in order to load the discriminator transformer properly. In receivers employing only one limiter stage, the grid of this limiter should draw current when the discriminator transformer is adjusted finally.

Step 2. Remove the r-f amplifier *V*1 and the local oscillator *V*2 from their respective sockets.

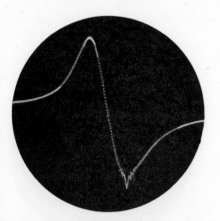 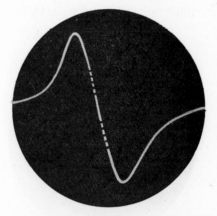

FIG. 15-17. Oscillogram of a single discriminator curve with the birdie slightly off the center frequency.

FIG. 15-18. Oscillogram of properly tuned discriminator curve.

Step 3. The VERTICAL INPUT terminals of the oscilloscope are connected directly between pin 1 of *V*8 and ground; that is, they are connected across the output of the discriminator tube.

The resulting pattern on a narrow sweep is shown in Fig. 15-15. This figure shows two discriminator-response curves for the same reason that two i-f-response curves appear.

Step 4. Increase the setting of the HORIZONTAL GAIN control of the oscilloscope and adjust the HORIZONTAL POSITIONING control to obtain a single discriminator curve, as shown in Fig. 15-16.

Step 5. Connect the marker generator across the ground lead of the wobbulator (as done in i-f alignment), and set its frequency to precisely 10.7 megacycles.

The birdie, as it appears on the response curve, is shown in Fig. 15-17. The error in aligning the discriminator transformer by the meter method is clearly shown here.

Step 6. Adjust the secondary of the discriminator transformer to move the response curve so that the birdie is exactly in the center of the straight portion of the curve, as shown in Fig. 15-18.

The correct adjustment of the secondary is manifested by the marker appearing as a slight oscillation on both sides of the zero-voltage base line while no oscillation is visible at this base line.

Step 7. Adjust the primary of the discriminator transformer to obtain the maximum amplitude of the positive and negative peaks.

The discriminator of the f-m receiver may also be aligned by doubling the sweep frequency of the oscilloscope and superimposing the two discriminator curves. Figure 15-19a shows the superimposed discriminator

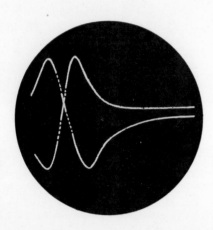 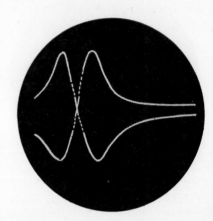

Fig. 15–19a. Two discriminator curves transposed but improperly tuned.

Fig. 15–19b. Two discriminator curves transposed and properly tuned.

curves slightly out of alignment, whereas Fig. 15-19b shows correct alignment. However, the step-by-step procedure outlined herein is more accurate and should always be followed in aligning the discriminator in the sound channel of a television receiver.

Checking the Limiting Action of the Limiters. The typical limiting action of a sound limiter is illustrated by the graph of Fig. 15-20. This curve is plotted with the input from the signal generator measured in microvolts along the horizontal axis and the d-c voltage output on the vertical axis. It can be seen here that the output voltage increases as the input voltage increases up to the value of about 150 μv input. At this point, the curve flattens sharply, and the output voltage remains constant, regardless of an increase in input voltage. The point at which the curve flattens sharply is known as the "knee" of the limiter. To check this, the limiting action of a limiter, the following procedure is in order:

Step 1. Connect the marker generator to the input of the converter stage, and set its frequency to 10.7 megacycles.

Step 2. Set the output attenuator of the marker generator to result in an output signal of approximately 1 μv.

Step 3. Connect the vacuum-tube voltmeter to the junction of resistors *R*2 and *R*3 in the cathode circuit of the discriminator (Fig. 15-5).

Step 4. Set the meter to read negative d-c volts. Use 0 to 10 volt scale.

Step 5. Gradually increase the voltage input to the grid of the converter stage, and observe the d-c voltage on the vacuum-tube voltmeter. At approximately 150 μv of input signal, the d-c voltage should stop increasing and remain constant regardless of the further increase in input signal. The reading on the d-c voltmeter at this point is approximately 6 volts. The limiter is operating correctly if this voltage is 6 volts ± 0.5 volt.

Note

The values of voltage given here are not necessarily accurate for all receivers, but they may be regarded as approximate.

Aligning the Local Oscillator. The local oscillator of the f-m receiver is aligned by exactly the same methods as are employed in aligning the a-m receiver. This procedure, as outlined in Chap. 14, can be followed precisely, except that the frequencies employed for frequency modulation are different. The frequency allocations for frequency modulation, as assigned by the Federal Communications Commission, are from 88 to 108 megacycles.

To summarize the procedure: the wobbulator is set to a center frequency of 93 megacycles and connected to the grid of the converter. The receiver dial is also set to 93 megacycles. The VERTICAL INPUT terminals of the oscilloscope are connected across the grid-return resistor of the first limiter stage. The oscillator padder is adjusted to produce the optimum i-f response curve on the screen of the oscilloscope. The frequency of the wobbulator and the receiver dial are both set to 103 megacycles, and the oscillator trimmer is tuned to result in the optimum response curve. The setting of the padding and trimmer capacitors is then balanced out to produce the optimum settings.

Aligning the R-F Section. The alignment of the r-f section of the f-m receiver is also similar to the alignment of the r-f section of the a-m receiver. The wobbulator is connected to the antenna and set to a center frequency of 98 megacycles. The receiver dial is also set to 98 megacycles. The trimmer capacitors on the variable tuning capacitors of each of the r-f stages is adjusted to produce the optimum i-f response curve on the oscilloscope.

Procedure for the Alignment of the Oscillator and R-F Stages. Leaving the oscilloscope connected as it is in the grid circuit of the first limiter stage, the oscillator tracking is adjusted as was done with a-m receivers, namely, the wobbulated signal generator was adjusted to the point that resulted in the largest amplitude of the i-f response curve. Similarly, the input signal was then injected into the antenna, and the r-f stage tuned also to result in the largest amplitude of the i-f response curve.

Aligning the I-F Amplifier Stage by Stage. To align the i-f amplifiers stage by stage, it is necessary to connect the oscilloscope into the grid circuit of the first limiter tube as shown above. The wobbulated signal generator set to a center frequency of 10.7 megacycles is then injected into the grid of the last i-f stage. The i-f response curve is obtained on the oscilloscope and is adjusted to be equivalent to that of Fig. 15-11. Then the wobbulated signal generator is connected to the grid of the preceding i-f stage, and this stage is adjusted to result in an over-all response which is also equivalent to that of Fig. 15-11. Because of the difference in signal amplitude, it is then necessary to readjust the transformer in the plate circuit of the last stage. After these three transformers have been adjusted to result in a properly tuned i-f response curve, the wobbulated signal generator is then connected to the grid of the mixer stage and again this transformer is tuned to result in a good curve. Again, compensation has to be made for the effect of different amplitude on the response curve, and the whole procedure becomes rather involved. Undoubtedly, the single-stage method of tuning is the better, that is, the more efficient.

16 Servicing Television Receivers

The Television Receiver. The television receiver is more complicated than the f-m or a-m receiver only to the extent that it contains two complete receivers in a single package. The circuits are all fundamentally the same as those in the f-m and a-m receivers, except for the addition of sweep circuits, the band width of the various r-f, i-f, and video amplifiers; and the operating frequencies of the r-f and i-f sections. The two receivers that make up the television receiver are a complete f-m receiver for the reproduction of the sound that accompanies the television program and a complete a-m receiver for the reproduction of the picture.

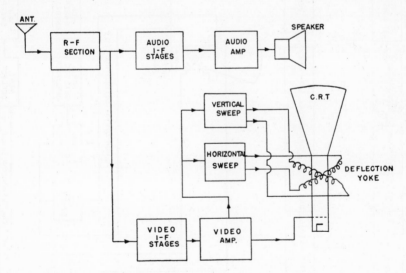

Fig. 16–1. Simplified block diagram of a television receiver.

A simplified block diagram of a television receiver is given in Fig. 16-1. This shows the television receiver divided into seven major sections, namely, the r-f section, the sound or audio channel, the picture or video channel, the vertical sweep generator, the horizontal sweep generator, the cathode-ray tube, and the power supply.

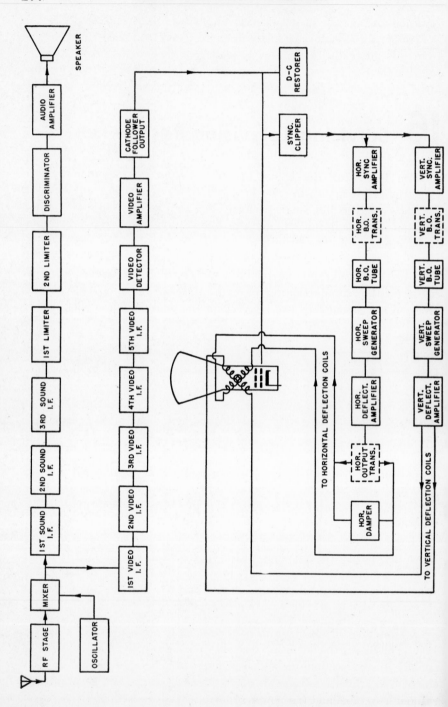

Functionally, the television receiver operates in this manner:

The r-f section tunes to the desired frequency and picks up the signal from the antenna. It contains a beat-frequency oscillator that is also tuned to the proper frequency to supply a beat frequency within the range of i-f frequencies necessary to the sound and video channels. This beat frequency is amplified and passed on to the sound and video channels where the two are separated.

The audio channel is tuned to accept only the sound i-f frequencies, which it amplifies, detects, amplifies again as an audio signal, and transfers to the loudspeaker.

The video channel is tuned to accept only the video i-f frequencies. which it amplifies and detects. It separates the video signal from the synchronizing signal and transmits it to the grid of the cathode-ray tube.

The synchronizing pulses passing to both the *vertical and horizontal sweep generators* synchronize them with the sweep generators of the iconoscope (or other type of pickup tube) in the television camera. The sweep generators provide suitable wave forms of the proper frequencies to the deflection plates or the deflection yoke of the cathode-ray tube to deflect the electron beam and form a rectangular-shaped pattern of light, called a "raster," on the screen of the cathode-ray tube. The intensity of this raster is varied by the video signal, which is applied to the grid of the *cathode-ray tube* so that the original image from the mosaic of the television camera is reproduced on the screen.

Deflection of the electron beam in the cathode-ray tube may be accomplished either by a deflection yoke for magnetic-type tubes or by deflection plates for electrostatic-type tubes. Both types of deflection are discussed in Chap. 4, but it should be stated here that the magnetic tubes are employed in the higher-priced television receivers, whereas the electrostatic tubes are found in the older or lower-priced receivers. In either case, a sweep generator is required, although the output wave forms differ, depending upon the type of deflection employed.

The next step in this discussion is to break these seven major blocks down into particular functions within these blocks. In making this step, the block diagram approaches that shown in Fig. 16-2. A working knowledge of this diagram will enable the repairman to localize trouble so that he may be able to attribute it even to a single tube.

The Power Supplies. The power supply consists of two, three, or four separate units, depending upon the size and type of cathode-ray tube. All receivers have at least two. One is a normal B+ supply consisting of

---

◀ Fig. 16–2. Detailed block diagram of a television receiver.

a full-wave rectifier with suitable filter and capable of supplying from +300 to +400 volts at sufficient current to operate all the tubes. The other is a high-voltage supply for the cathode-ray tube. For magnetic-type cathode-ray tubes, this consists of a positive supply of either the standard 60-c.p.s. type or a rectified r-f supply, which is capable of furnishing 8 to 15 kv at about 5 ma. This voltage is applied to the accelerating electrode. For electrostatic-type tubes it is usually necessary to furnish both a negative and a positive high voltage, frequently as high as −5

Fig. 16–3. Oscillogram showing the waveform of the horizontal sweep signal applied to the deflection yoke of the cathode-ray tube.

kv and +5 kv. The negative voltage is applied to the cathode and grid electrodes of the cathode-ray tube and the positive voltage to the intensifier with the accelerating electrode operated at ground.

Magnetic-Type Sweep Circuits. The next logical step is to break down the sweep generator into its constituent functions. In receivers employing magnetic deflection, the composite sync signal (containing both the horizontal and vertical sync pulses) is separated into its respective channels in the input circuits of the two sweep generators. The horizontal pulses then enter an amplifier stage whose plate load is a winding of a blocking-oscillator transformer. The secondary of this transformer is connected to a blocking-oscillator tube. This blocking-oscillator circuit triggers the sweep generator which generates the sweep waveform shown in Fig. 16-3. The horizontal sweep signal is then fed to the horizontal deflection amplifier. The plate load of the deflection amplifier is the primary of the horizontal output transformer. The secondary of this transformer is connected directly to the horizontal deflection yoke.

Usually a damping tube is connected across the output to the deflection yoke to prevent an overshoot from appearing at the top of the horizontal saw tooth.

The vertical sweep generator is essentially the same as the horizontal, except that a damping tube is not necessary in this circuit, because the overshoot is not normally present at the lower frequency.

Electrostatic-Type Sweep Circuits. In receivers employing electrostatic deflection the sweep generator consists of three tubes: a sync amplifier, a saw-toothed wave generator, and a phase inverter, as shown in Fig. 16-4. The vertical sync amplifier amplifies the vertical sync signal that is received from the video channel. This amplified sync signal synchronizes

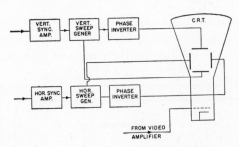

Fig. 16-4. Block diagram of electrostatic-type sweep circuits for a television receiver.

the vertical saw-toothed wave generator with that of the television camera. Part of the saw-toothed waveform thus generated by the saw-toothed wave generator is fed into the vertical-sweep phase inverter so that its phase is inverted 180 deg, and it is then applied to one of the vertical deflection plates of the cathode-ray tube. The other part of the saw-toothed wave signal is impressed on the other vertical deflection plate of the cathode-ray tube. The frequency of the saw-toothed wave generated by the vertical-sweep generator is 60 c.p.s. The horizontal-sweep generator in receivers employing electrostatic deflection is identical with the vertical-sweep generator, except that its frequency is 15,750 c.p.s.

The Television Transmitting Channel. Prior to a discussion of the signal circuits of the television receiver, it is necessary to analyze the distribution of signals in the television transmitting channel. The television channel is 6 megacycles wide. In order to reproduce high-definition pictures, the video signal contains frequency components as high as 4 megacycles. Most of the television channel is devoted to the transmission of the video signal. The video signal is transmitted as amplitude modulation by what is called "quasi single-sideband" or "vestigial single-sideband" transmission, which, essentially, makes use of only the upper sideband.

Thus, the video-signal carrier is located 1.25 megacycles above the low-frequency limit of the channel, and the sound-signal carrier is located 4.5 megacycles above the video-signal carrier. This arrangement allows 4 megacycles of the channel on which the picture signal may be transmitted without interference by the sound. Since the useful sideband components of the frequency-modulated sound carrier do not extend more than 100 kc above and below the carrier frequency, the sound signal occupies comparatively little room in the channel. Figure 16-5 shows how a typical television channel is divided to meet these standards, which were established by the RMA. The channel used in the illustration is television channel 5, which is allocated between the frequencies of 76 and 82 megacycles.

The R-F Section. Returning now to the actual signal circuits, the r-f block may consist of two or three tubes, depending upon the presence of an r-f amplifier. Assuming that there is an r-f amplifier, there are then

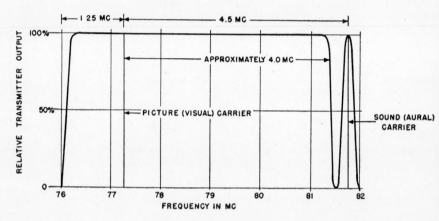

Fig. 16-5. Graph showing the division of a standard television channel into sound and picture signals.

three stages to this section: an r-f amplifier, a local oscillator, and a mixer. As in any superheterodyne receiver, each of these stages is tuned.

Because of the bandwidth of each channel and the wide range of tuning required to tune all of the 13 television channels, television tuning is frequently accomplished by pretuned *LC* circuits for each of the television channels. The desired channel is then tuned by switching in the proper *LC* circuits to receive that channel. Minor errors in the adjustment of each of these channels may be corrected with a small, variable, air-trimmer capacitor on the oscillator.

Another method of tuning is used in some of the present sets. This method incorporates three variable inductances and permits continuous tuning throughout the f-m and television spectrum. This is a patented tuning device called the Du Mont "Inputuner"* (developed by Paul Ware

*Trademark.

f the Allen B. Du Mont Laboratories), which incorporates the Mallory-Ware Inductuner. This device permits a television receiver to tune hroughout the wide range of frequencies required for frequency modulation and television (44 to 216 megacycles) as easily as a broadcast receiver tunes from 550 to 1,550 kc. The Inputuner accomplishes this by means of three variable inductors ganged together on a single shaft, just as three variable capacitors are ganged together in the broadcast receiver.

In the r-f section of the receiver, regardless of the tuning method employed, the tuned circuit of the r-f amplifier receives and amplifies the signal from the antenna. The local oscillator generates an r-f signal which is 21.9 megacycles* above the frequency of the audio signal carried being received. (In prewar television receivers, the oscillator is 8.25 megacycles above the audio carrier.) Both the output from the r-f stage and the output from the local oscillator are usually impressed on the grid of the mixer stage. The mixer stage then amplifies the intermediate frequencies, which vary from 21.65 to 27.65 megacycles.

As an example: To tune the television channel illustrated in Fig. 16-5, the r-f section must be tuned to receive the frequencies between 76 and 82 megacycles. The oscillator is then tuned to 103.65 megacycles (21.9 megacycles above the sound-signal carrier, which is 81.75 megacycles). The intermediate frequencies that will be amplified by the mixer stage are the differences between the upper limit of the channel (82 megacycles) and the oscillator frequency and the lower limit of the channel (76 megacycles) and the oscillator frequency.

$$
\begin{array}{ll}
103.65 \text{ mc} \qquad\qquad & 103.65 \text{ mc} \\
\underline{-82 \quad \text{mc}} & \underline{-76 \quad \text{mc}} \\
21.65 \text{ mc} & 27.65 \text{ mc}
\end{array}
$$

Thus, the intermediate frequency is a broad band of frequencies extending from 21.65 to 27.65 megacycles.

Table 16-1 shows the frequencies of each of the 13 television channels and the frequency of the local oscillator necessary to receive these channels. The last column of this table gives the same data for prewar sets, which utilize oscillators tuned to a frequency that is 8.25 megacycles above the audio-signal carrier frequency.

The signal output from the mixer stage of the r-f section is coupled to the grids of the first stages of both the sound and video i-f amplifiers. Since the stages of the sound i-f amplifier are tuned to 21.9 megacycles (8.25 mc prewar) with a relatively narrow bandwidth of ±100 kc, only

---

* All manufacturers do not use a local oscillator frequency of 21.9 megacycles. This figure may vary from 21.25 to 21.9 megacycles.

the sound signals pass through. On the other hand, the wide bandwidth employed in the video i-f stages does not normally have a sharp cutoff, so one or more sound traps must be employed to prevent the sound signal from passing through and thus getting into the picture. This arrangement will be discussed in greater detail under video i-f amplifiers.

The Sound Channel. After the sound signal enters the first sound i-f stage, it is handled exactly as in a normal f-m receiver. It passes through two or more i-f stages, one or more limiters, a discriminator, and two or more stages of audio amplifiers whose output drives the speaker. The technique of using the oscilloscope in troubleshooting, servicing, and

TABLE 16-1

Channel	Frequencies, Mc	Rec. Osc. Freq., Mc*	Sound Carrier, Mc	Video Carrier, Mc	Half-Wave Dipole, In.	Rec. Osc. Freq., Mc.†
1 ‡	44-50	71.65	49.75	45.25	125.7	58
2	54-60	81.65	59.75	55.25	103.6	68
3	60-66	87.65	65.75	61.25	93.6	74
4	66-72	93.65	71.75	67.25	85.6	80
5	76-82	103.65	81.75	77.25	74.6	90
6	82-88	109.65	87.75	83.25	69.5	96
7	174-180	201.65	179.75	175.25	33.4	188
8	180-186	207.65	185.75	181.25	32.2	194
9	186-192	213.65	191.75	187.25	31.3	200
10	192-198	219.65	197.75	193.25	30.3	206
11	198-204	225.65	203.75	199.25	29.4	212
12	204-210	231.65	209.75	205.25	28.5	218
13	210-216	237.65	215.75	211.25	27.7	224

* Using 21.9 mc sound intermediate frequency.
† Using 8.25 mc sound intermediate frequency.
‡ Discontinued.

aligning this portion of the television receiver is exactly the same as in the normal f-m receiver, except that the audio i-f stages are tuned to 21.9 megacycles (8.25 mc in prewar receivers).

The Video Channel. The video channel consists of several stages of i-f amplifiers, a video detector, and two or more stages of video amplification, as well as a sync separator and a d-c restorer. The output of the video amplifier is connected to the grid of the cathode-ray tube. The output of the sync separator is fed to the sweep generators to synchronize their action with the video signal. The d-c restorer maintains the average voltage applied to the grid of the cathode-ray tube at a constant level.

The video i-f amplifiers are tuned to pass frequencies from 22.4 to 26.4

megacycles (8.75 to 12.75 megacycles in prewar receivers). The ideal over-all response curve of the video i-f amplifiers should be practically flat from 22.4 to about 25.2 megacycles and then taper off to be down 6 db (50 per cent) at 26.4 megacycles. The low end of the curve should drop off sharply at 22.4 megacycles and be down to zero at 21.9 megacycles. This sharp drop in the curve is achieved by inserting wave traps tuned to the audio i-f frequency in the grid circuits of at least two of the video i-f stages. A graph of the ideal video i-f response curve is shown in Fig. 16-6.

It appears from this graph that the video response is not flat for 4 megacycles but, rather, for only about 2.8 megacycles. However, in Fig. 16-5, it can be seen that the low-frequency components of the video signal cause sidebands both above and below the video carrier. Those sidebands below the carrier are not affected by the single-sideband filter for about 1.2 megacycles. Thus, the voltage amplitudes at the frequencies between

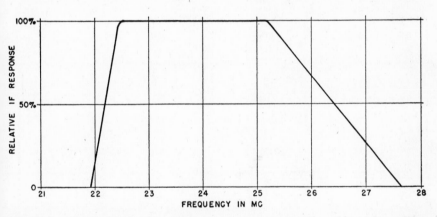

FIG. 16–6. Graph showing the ideal frequency response of a video i-f amplifier.

26.4 and 27.6 megacycles on the response curve of Fig. 16-6 are caused by the low frequency sidebands below the video carrier frequency of Fig. 16-5. Since the frequencies between 25.2 and 26.4 megacycles on the response curve represent the same video frequencies as those between 26.4 and 27.6 megacycles, the area under the curve between 26.4 and 27.6 megacycles adds to the area under the curve between 25.2 and 26.4 megacycles, resulting in a video i-f response curve that is effectively flat from 22.4 to 26.4 megacycles.

Aligning the Video I-F Stages. Since it is necessary that the points of 26.4, 22.4, and 21.9 megacycles on the response curve be set correctly,

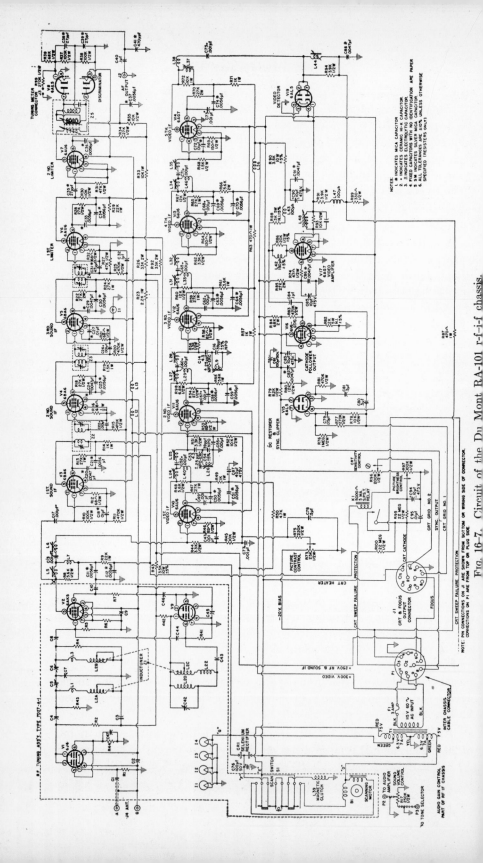

Fig. 16-7. Circuit of the Du Mont RA-101 r-f-i-f chassis.

an oscilloscope must be used as an indicator. Proper alignment of the video i-f stages of a television receiver requires that each stage be aligned separately. Since the over-all response curve calls for the 26.4 megacycle point to be down 6 db, and since all the i-f stages are connected in cascade, each individual stage should be tuned so that the 26.4 megacycle point is down 6 db divided by the number of stages. For example, if there are six i-f stages, including the first detector, each stage is tuned so that the 26.4 megacycle point is down 1 db. If there are only four i-f stages, including the first detector, each stage must be tuned so that the 26.4-megacycle point is down 1.5 db. The result of six stages in cascade with each stage 1 db down at 26.4 megacycles, or four stages in cascade with each stage 1.5 down at 26.4 megacycles, is an over-all response curve that is down 6 db at 26.4 megacycles.

The signal generator used to obtain the response curve should be capable of furnishing a frequency-modulated signal from 21 to 28 megacycles wobbulated at the power-line frequency (60 c). For convenience, this will be referred to as the "wobbulator." Also, a fixed-frequency signal generator is necessary to furnish a marker signal at 21.9, 22.4, and 26.4 megacycles. This will be called the "marker generator." The oscilloscope used as an indicator should have a good response to a 60-c wave.

The traveling detector must be used to detect the response curve in tuning all stages but the last. To ensure that each stage is separately aligned and that other stages do not affect this alignment, the tube preceding and the tube following the stage to be aligned should be removed from their respective sockets.

In order to give a step-by-step procedure for aligning the video i-f stages of a television receiver, the circuit of Fig. 16-7 is taken as a representative sample. This circuit was selected because it contains a total of six i-f stages, counting the mixer stage, which serves as an i-f amplifier for both the video and audio intermediate frequencies. The following procedure will serve for all receivers simply by connecting to comparable positions in the circuit to be tested.

Aligning the Fifth I-F Stage.

Step 1. Connect the coaxial lead from the vertical input terminal of the oscilloscope between the cathode of $V16$, pin 8, and ground.

Since the video signal has already been detected, the use of a coaxial lead for connection to the oscilloscope is sufficient. The metal braid of the lead should be connected to ground of the oscilloscope and the ground of the receiver while the inner conductor is used for the signal. This connection is made to the cathode follower stage of the video amplifier to avoid the possibility of excessive loading on the video detector.

Step 2.   Connect the wobbulator between the grid of *V*14, pin 4, and ground.

Step 3.   Set the wobbulator to furnish a frequency-modulated signal between 21 and 28 megacycles.

Step 4.   Remove *V*13 from its socket.

Step 5.   Switch on the power to the r-f–i-f chassis and also, of course, to the wobbulator and to the oscilloscope.

Step 6.   Adjust the VERTICAL GAIN control to obtain a satisfactory vertical deflection, and, using the linear time base in the oscilloscope, adjust the sweep frequency of the oscilloscope to stop the motion of the pattern as nearly as possible.

Step 7.   If the SYNC SELECTOR SWITCH of the oscilloscope has a LINE FREQUENCY position, set the switch to this position and then increase the SYNC SIGNAL AMPLITUDE control until the pattern remains stationary on the screen.

Step 7a.   (Alternate)   If the SYNC SELECTOR SWITCH of the oscilloscope has no LINE FREQUENCY position, set the switch to EXTERNAL and connect a low-voltage (2 to 6 volts) line-frequency signal to the EXTERNAL SYNC INPUT binding post, and increase the SYNC SIGNAL AMPLITUDE control until the pattern remains stationary on the screen. (The external sync signal may be obtained from the TEST SIGNAL output terminal on the front panel of the oscilloscope or from a filament transformer).

The pattern obtained on the oscilloscope will be similar to that shown in Fig. 16-8. This figure is a double response curve, owing to the fact that the signal generator sweeps from 28 to 21 megacycles and then from 21 back to 28 megacycles every 60 c (or the line frequency), which is the sweep frequency of the oscilloscope.

The polarity of the pattern on the oscilloscope, i.e., whether the deflection produced is above or below the base line, will depend upon the number of stages in the amplifier of the oscilloscope, the point in the receiver from which the signal was chosen, and the polarity of the crystal used in the traveling detector for detecting the response curves in the preceding stages. In Fig. 16-8, the deflection is in the negative direction, whereas Fig. 16-9 shows the same pattern when the deflection is in a positive direction.

Step 8.   Connect the output leads from the marker generator to ground but across the ground lead of the wobbulator. This is the same technique as that employed in aligning the discriminator of the f-m receiver.

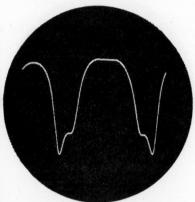

Fig. 16–8. Oscillogram of dual i-f response curve obtained from the fifth i-f stage.

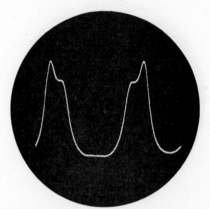

Fig. 16–9. Same as Fig. 16–8 except the curves are inverted.

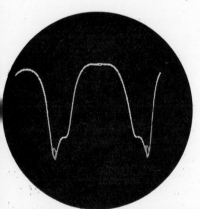

Fig. 16–10. Same as Fig. 16–8 except the birdie has been added.

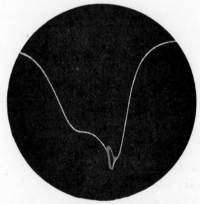

Fig. 16–11. Oscillogram of single video i-f response curve obtained by expanding the sweep of Fig. 16–8.

Step 9.   Set the frequency of the marker generator to 26.4 megacycles. This setting places a birdie, which appears on both of the i-f curves, as shown in Fig. 16-10.

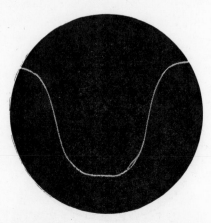

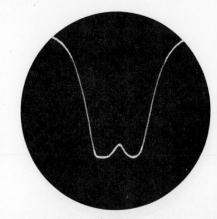

Fɪɢ. 16‡12*a*. Oscillogram of video i-f response curve excessively overloaded.

Fɪɢ. 16–12*b*. Oscillogram of video i-f response curve slightly overloaded.

Since these response curves are too narrow to permit accurate work, it is necessary to expand the horizontal sweep of the oscilloscope as was done in tuning the i-f stages of the f-m receiver.

Step 10.   Increase the setting of the ʜᴏʀɪᴢᴏɴᴛᴀʟ ᴀᴍᴘʟɪᴛᴜᴅᴇ control of the oscilloscope to obtain a wide sweep.

Step 11.   Position the trace with the ʜᴏʀɪᴢᴏɴᴛᴀʟ ᴘᴏsɪᴛɪᴏɴɪɴɢ control to obtain the single i-f response curve on which the birdie appears at the right.

The pattern that is obtained from steps 10 and 11 is shown in Fig. 16-11. Occasionally, an oscilloscope may be capable of positioning a trace further in one direction than in another. In such cases, the order of the two curves in Fig. 16-10 can usually be reversed by reversing the polarity of the power plug of the wobbulator. The response curves used in the text were selected so that the lower frequencies are to the left side of the screen and the higher frequencies to the right, which is the conventional method of plotting graphs.

The output of the wobbulator is set to approximately 1/10 volt. Be certain that too high an output is not used, otherwise the video amplifier will be overloaded. An overloaded i-f response curve is shown in Fig. 16-12.

Step 12.   Adjust the variable inductors *L*37 and *L*34, to obtain a response curve similar to that shown in Fig. 16-13. The response curve is adjusted so that the birdie indicating the frequency of 26.4 megacycles is down about 1 db (approximately 10 per cent) below the flat top (or adjacent peak) of the response curve. Proper tuning is obtained when a slight tuning of either inductor ($L34$ or $L37$) in either direction rocks the peaks of the response curve, and the birdie is at the point 1 db down.

The tuning of the variable inductors in these video i-f stages may be done with a screw driver if the tuning device is an iron slug that is maintained at ground potential. If tuning is accomplished by a ceramic capacitor, however, a tuning wand should be used.

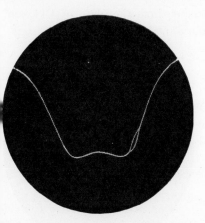
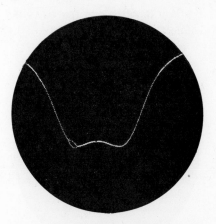

Fig. 16-13. Oscillogram of fifth video i-f response curve properly tuned, birdie at 26.4 megacycles.

Fig. 16-14. Oscillogram of fifth video i-f response curve properly tuned, birdie at 22.4 megacycles.

Step 13.   Figure 16-14 shows the position of the birdie when the marker generator is set to 22.4 megacycles. In most cases, it is not necessary to check this point, because the 22.4-megacycle point is determined in the over-all response by the sound traps.

Step 14.   Turn off the power to the receiver.

Aligning the Fourth I-F Stage.

Step 1.   Replace $V13$ in its socket, and remove $V12$ and $V19$.

Step 2.   Remove the connection of the wobbulator from the grid of $V14$ and connect it between the grid of $V13$, pin 1, and ground.

Step 3.   Remove the coaxial lead from the VERTICAL INPUT terminals of the oscilloscope and replace it with the traveling detector probe.

Step 4.   Connect the traveling detector between the plate of $V14$, pin 8, and ground.

Step 5. Set the marker generator to 26.4 megacycles.

Step 6. Tune the inductors *L*34 and *L*35, to obtain the response curve shown in Fig. 16-15.

Step 7. Adjust the inductors so that the 26.4-megacycle point is 1 db down on the curve.

Step 8. Turn off the power supplied to the receiver.

Aligning the Third I-F Stage.

Step 1. Replace *V*12 and *V*19 in their respective sockets and remove *V*11 and *V*14.

Step 2. Remove the wobbulator from the grid of *V*13, pin 1, and connect it between the grid of *V*12, pin 1, and ground.

Step 3. Remove the traveling detector from the plate of *V*14, and connect it between the plate of *V*13, pin 5, and ground.

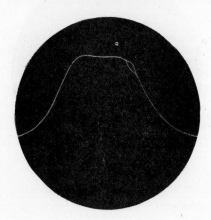 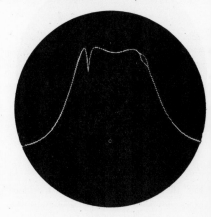

Fig. 16–15. Oscillogram of fourth video i-f stage properly tuned, birdie at 26.4 megacycles.

Fig. 16–16. Oscillogram of third video i-f stage properly tuned, birdie at 26.4 megacycles.

Step 4. Repeat the alignment procedure, this time tuning the inductances *L*31 and *L*32.

The frequency-response curve obtained by tuning these inductances is shown in Fig. 16-16. It will be noted that a slight nick or dip in the response curve is seen at the low end. This nick is at 21.9 megacycles and is due to the sound trap in the grid circuit of *V*12. This nick shows the sound trap absorbing the signal at 21.9 megacycles. The precise setting of this wave trap should be adjusted at this time.

Adjusting the Second Sound Trap. One of the easiest methods of adjusting a single sound trap is to use an excessively large marker signal. The five illustrations in Figs. 16-17 to 16-21, clearly indicate various stages in obtaining the correct adjustment.

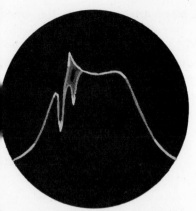

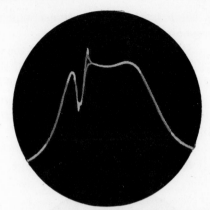

FIG. 16–17. Sound trap set much too low.

FIG. 16–18. Sound trap set a little too low

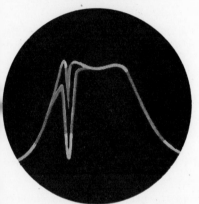

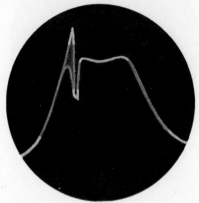

FIG. 16–19. Sound trap set exactly right.

FIG. 16–20. Sound trap set a little too high.

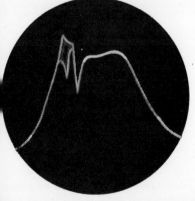

FIG. 16–21. Sound trap set much too high.

FIGS. 16-17 to 16-21. Adjusting the second sound trap by using excessive birdie signal.

Step 1. Leave all connections in place after adjusting the video response of the third i-f stage.

Step 2. Set the frequency of the marker generator to 21.9 megacycles.

Step 3. Increase the output of the marker generator until the birdie is relatively the same size as that shown in Fig. 16-17.

Step 4. Adjust the sound trap so that the birdie is exactly bisected by the dip that the trap causes in the response curve, as shown in Fig. 16-19.

Step 5. Turn off the power to the receiver.

Aligning the Second I-F Stage.

FIG. 16–22. Oscillogram showing the second video i-f stage properly tuned, birdie at 26.4 megacycles.

Step 1. Replace the tubes $V11$ and $V14$ in their sockets, and remove $V13$ and $V10$.

Step 2. Remove the wobbulator from the grid of $V12$, and connect it between the grid of $V11$, pin 1, and ground.

For this adjustment and all those remaining, the contrast control must be set to obtain maximum contrast.

Step 3. Remove the traveling detector from the plate of $V13$, and connect it between the plate of $V12$, pin 5, and ground.

Step 4. Repeat the alignment procedure for this stage by tuning the inductances $L27$ and $L28$, and obtain the response curve shown in Fig. 16-22.

The two sound traps, one in the grid circuit of the second video i-f stage and the other in the grid circuit of the third video i-f stage, are additive and produce a very pronounced dip in the response curve.

Note

Depending upon the effect of the sound traps, equal peak responses with 26.4 megacycle point 1 db down may be obtained with several different settings of $L27$ and $L28$. The only correct setting is the combination that gives a minimum dip or

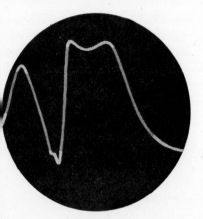

FIG. 16–23. Sound trap set a little too low.

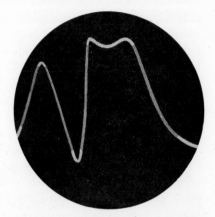

FIG. 16–24. Sound trap set exactly right.

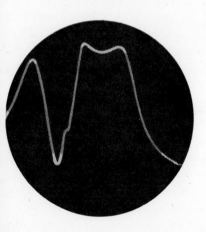

FIG. 16–25. Sound trap set a little too high.

FIGS. 16–23 to 16–25. Oscillograms showing the adjustment of the first sound trap.

a flat curve with the 26.4-megacycle point down 1 db. After the video response curve has been adjusted, the first sound trap should be set.

Adjusting the First Sound Trap. The first sound trap is adjusted with the equipment connected for aligning the second video i-f stage, and it is adjusted without the use of a birdie. Various settings of this trap are shown in the three illustrations in Figs. 16-23 to 16-25. Notice that a mistuning of the first trap tends to broaden the dip in the response curve by the irregularity that appears either to the right or to the left of the lowest point of the curve. Proper tuning is indicated when this irregularity coincides with the most negative peak.

Step 1. Leave all connections in place after tuning the second video i-f stage.

Step 2. Turn off or disconnect the marker generator.

Step 3. Adjust the first sound trap until the irregularity in the response curve (which is due to mistuning of the first sound trap) coincides with the large negative dip at the low end of the curve that is caused by the second sound trap.

Step 4. Turn off the power to the receiver.

Aligning the First I-F Stage.

Step 1. Replace $V10$ and $V13$ in their sockets, and remove $V2$ and $V12$.

Step 2. Remove the wobbulator from the grid of $V11$, and connect it between the grid of $V10$, pin 1, and ground.

Step 3. Remove the traveling detector from the plate of $V12$, and connect it between the plate of $V11$, pin 5, and ground.

Step 4. Repeat the alignment procedure, tuning the inductances $L2$ and $L25$, to obtain the response curve shown in Fig. 16-26.

Step 5. Turn off the power to the receiver.

Aligning the Video-Frequency Tuned Circuits in the Mixer Stage.

Step 1. Replace $V12$ in its socket, and remove $V11$.

In cases where the r-f section must always be completely shielded and it is impossible to connect the wobbulator to the tube base and still maintain the necessary shielding, an adapter tube must be made up in order to impress a signal on the grid of the mixer stage.

This adapter tube can be made by soldering phosphor bronze strips to pins 1 and 3 of a 6AK5 and running them up the outside of the tube. The strips, held in place by scotch tape, enable signals to be impressed on the grid of the mixer without removing the bottom plate.

Step 2. Insert the adapter tube into the socket of $V2$.

Step 3. Remove the wobbulator from the grid of $V10$, and connect it between the grid of the adapter tube, pin 1, and ground.

Step 4. Remove the traveling detector from the plate of $V11$, and connect it between the plate of $V10$, pin 5, and ground.

Step 5. Repeat the alignment procedure by varying the inductances $L5$ and $L6$, to obtain the response curve shown in Fig. 16-27.

Procedure for Checking the Gain of the Picture I-F, Stage by Stage.

Step 1. Connect the wobbulator and the traveling detector, as in the last step of the previous discussion, to the grid of $V2$ and the plate of $V10$, respectively, and set the contrast control for maximum contrast.

Step 2. Set the gain control of the oscilloscope to obtain a vertical deflection of the response curve that is precisely 0.5 in. (5 scale divisions).

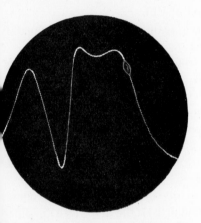

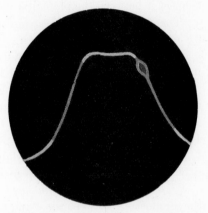

FIG. 16–26. Oscillogram showing the first video i-f stage properly aligned, birdie at 26.4 megacycles.

FIG. 16–27. Oscillogram showing the proper alignment of the video-frequency circuits in the mixer stage, birdie at 26.4 megacycles.

It is important that the gain control of the oscilloscope be set to this fixed figure (5 scale divisions) and not touched again during the succeeding measurements. In this way, the relative gain of each of the picture i-f stages can be observed.

Using the same voltage input signal and leaving the oscilloscope gain control set in the same position, the input signal and the oscilloscope are moved along stage by stage, checking the vertical deflection of the response curve as it appears on the oscilloscope. In checking each stage, the tubes of the preceding and the following stages are removed from their sockets.

Step 3. Remove the wobbulator from the grid of $V2$, and connect it between grid and ground of $V10$.

Step 4. Remove the traveling detector from the plate of $V10$, and connect it between the plate and ground of $V11$. The deflection of the

response curve at this stage should be approximately 0.8 in. (8 scal
divisions).*

Step 5.   Move the wobbulator from the grid of *V*10, and connect i
between the grid and ground of *V*11.

Step 6.   Remove the traveling detector from the plate of *V*11, an
connect it between grid and ground of *V*12.

The deflection produced by the response curve in this stage should b
approximately 0.8 in. (8 scale divisions).*

Step 7.   Remove the wobbulator from the grid of *V*11, and connec
it between the grid and ground of *V*12.

Step 8.   Remove the traveling detector from the plate of *V*12, an
connect it between the plate and ground of *V*13.

The deflection of the response curve again should be approximatel
0.8 in. (8 scale divisions).

Step 9.   Remove the wobbulator from the grid of *V*12, and connec
it between the grid and ground of *V*13.

Step 10.   Remove the traveling detector from the plate of *V*13, an
connect it between the plate and ground of *V*14.

The resulting deflection of the response curve should be about 1.5 in
(15 scale divisions).*

Step 11.   Remove the wobbulator from the grid of *V*13, and connec
it between the grid and ground of *V*14.

Step 12.   Use the coaxial lead (no traveling detector), and connec
the oscilloscope between pin 4 and ground of *V*17, the first video amplifier

The resulting deflection of the response curve should be about 3.5 in
(35 scale divisions).*

After aligning the picture i-f amplifier stage by stage, it is necessar
to make an over-all check of the video-i-f amplifier. In making a com
plete over-all check of the video-i-f amplifier, it is necessary that th
video amplifier be in good working condition.

Procedure for Over-All Check of the Video I-F Amplifier.   To de
termine whether the video i-f amplifier of a television receiver is operating
correctly, it is necessary to check the over-all video i-f response. Also
this response should be checked after every stage-by-stage alignment o
the i-f amplifiers as well as after any single stage has been serviced
Because regeneration in the video i-f amplifiers may exist if they are no
fully shielded, the bottom cover plate of the receiver should be in plac

* These values will vary with sets of different manufacturers.

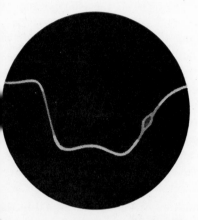

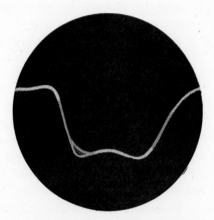

Fɪɢ. 16–28. Oscillogram showing the over-all video response curve of a properly tuned i-f amplifier, birdie at 26.4 megacycles.

Fɪɢ. 16–29a. Same as Fig. 16–28, except that birdie is at 22.4 megacycles.

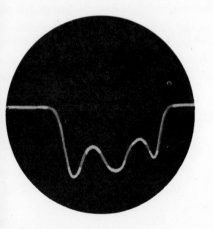

Fɪɢ. 16–29b. Same as Fig. 16–28, except that regeneration is present owing to lack of proper shielding in the video amplifier.

when this check is made. Regeneration is not evident when a single stage-by-stage examination is made, because the signal is isolated within a single stage. It is necessary that the video amplifier be in good working order before this test is made.

Step 1.   Be sure the bottom cover plate is on the chassis, and see that it is screwed down tight.

Step 2.   Replace *V*2 with the adapter tube (refer to Fig. 16-7).

Step 3.   Connect the wobbulator to the grid of the adapter tube, pin 1

Step 4.   Connect the oscilloscope, using the coaxial lead, to pin 7 of *J*1. (This is the video output to the grid of the cathode-ray tube.)

Step 5.   Turn on the power and note the video i-f response curve as it appears on the screen of the oscilloscope.

Figure 16-28 shows a typical over-all response curve. The 26.4-mega cycle point is indicated by the birdie and is 6 db down on the high end of the curve. Figure 16-29 shows the same response curve with the birdie set at 22.4 megacycles.

Procedure for Checking the Attenuation of the Sound Signal in the Video I-F Channel.   The effect of these two traps, one in the grid circuit of the second video i-f stage *V*11, and the other in the grid circuit of the third video i-f stage *V*12, is additive. The total over-all attenuation to the sound signal should be 40 db* down. Therefore, each trap is responsible for 20 db* attenuation. The expression "40 db down" means that the voltage of the sound signal in the video channel bears a ratio to the video signal of 1:100; i.e., for every volt of sound signal there are 100 volts of video signal. The expression "20 db down," attributed to each of the sound traps, means that the voltage of the sound signal in the video channel bears a ratio to the video signal of 1:10; i.e., for every volt of sound signal there are 10 volts of video signal. To measure the total attenuation of the sound traps, the following procedure should be followed:

Step 1.   Connect the marker generator between the grid of *V*2 and ground.

Step 2.   Set the frequency of this signal generator to the sound i-frequency, viz., 21.9 megacycles.

Step 3.   Modulate this frequency of 21.9 megacycles with a 400-c.p.s. sine wave.

Step 4.   Connect the VERTICAL INPUT terminals of the oscilloscope between the grid of the cathode-ray tube and ground.

With sufficient input signal and the gain control of the oscilloscope

* These figures may vary somewhat with sets made by different manufacturers

et to a rather high level, a 400-c wave will appear on the screen of the cathode-ray tube.

Step 5. Set the VERTICAL GAIN control of the oscilloscope so that this 400-c wave produces a deflection of 2 in. on the screen of the oscilloscope (20 scale divisions).

Step 6. Make the final minor adjustments of the wave traps to give minimum deflection of this 400-c wave.

Step 7. Again adjust the gain control of the oscilloscope to produce 2-in. deflection.

Step 8. Change the frequency setting of the marker generator so that it falls within the band pass of the video i-f signal, for example, 25 megacycles.

The pattern appearing on the oscilloscope will be greatly increased and much overloaded.

Step 9. Utilizing the attenuator in the output circuit of the signal generator, step down the signal output of the marker generator until the amplitude of the 400-c wave is again 2 in.

Step 10. Note the attenuation introduced into the signal output of the marker generator. This is the attenuation produced by the sound traps in the video i-f channel.

The total over-all attenuation should be equal to a ratio of 100:1 or more which is the equivalent of 40 db down. It is not uncommon to attain a ratio of 200:1 with the proper setting of the two traps.

If the total over-all attenuation is less than 100:1, each trap should be checked in turn.

Procedure for Checking Attenuation of Sound Traps Separately.

Step 1. Leaving the signal generator connected as it is, remove the bottom cover plate, and connect the oscilloscope by means of the traveling detector between the plate of *V*11, pin 5, and ground.

Step 2. Repeat the procedure for checking attenuation.

This trap should attain an attenuation of 10:1. If it measures correctly, this trap is set correctly, and no trouble is indicated.

The trouble, then, is probably in the second trap, which is located in the grid circuit of the third video i-f amplifier.

Step 3. Connect the traveling detector between the plate of *V*12, pin 5, and ground.

Step 4. Repeat the attenuation procedure.

Once the trouble has been localized to the proper trap, it will probably be found that the series or parallel capacitor in the sound-trap circuit is out of tolerance. The tolerance of these capacitors must be held **very** close.

Final Sound-trap Adjustment. The tuning of a television receiver is determined by tuning for clearest sound and, therefore, by the exact setting of the discriminator. To obtain a clear picture, free from interference, it is also equally important that the sound channel fall precisely on a frequency to which sound traps are adjusted. In order to assure that the sound traps and the discriminator transformer are in exact agreement, a final adjustment must be made after the set has been properly aligned, checked, and the bottom chassis plate set in place with all screws tight. To make this adjustment, proceed as follows:

Step 1. Connect the marker-signal generator to the antenna terminals of the receiver with enough resistance to match the 75-ohm input impedance of the receiver to the output impedance of the signal generator.

Step 2. Connect the oscilloscope to the video of the receiver.

Step 3. Adjust the receiver to a free channel in the lower television bands.

Step 4. Set the marker-signal generator to the same frequency as the receiver, and adjust carefully until a null is obtained on the tuning indicator.

If the receiver has no tuning indicator, a milliammeter, preferably zero-centered milliammeter, will serve this function. The milliammeter should be connected to the output of the discriminator in the audio channel through a series resistance of about 100,000 ohms. The other end of the meter should be connected to ground. Adjust the tuning of the receiver for the null point between two peaks.

Step 5. Reduce the setting of the contrast control until no overload is observed on the oscilloscope when the signal generator is modulated 30 percent with 400 c.

Step 6. Adjust the two sound trap coils $L9$ and $L26$ until a minimum of 400-c output is obtained.

Types of R-F Sections. As explained earlier in this chapter, there are two distinctly different types of tuning employed in television receivers, viz., the switching to pretuned circuits for each television channel and the Inputuner, which permits continuous tuning throughout the range of the television channels. These circuits constitute the r-f section of the television receiver.

The Inputuner Type of R-F Section. The manufacturers of the Inputuner, the Allen B. Du Mont Laboratories, recommend that the serviceman should not attempt to service this device, but rather return it to the factory. However, some checks must be made to determine whether the trouble is really in this section of the receiver.

To determine if this type of r-f section is operating correctly, it will e necessary to check the following: dial calibration, r-f and converter ain, and band pass. These checks may be made with the equipment previously used in the video i-f adjustments. The video and sound i-f amlifiers must be operating properly, having the proper gain and band pass. ^he bottom plate should be in place on the chassis and all screws tight

Procedure for Checking the Dial Calibration of the R-F Section.

Step 1. Connect the marker-signal generator to the antenna terninals of the receiver with enough resistance in series to match the 5-ohm input impedance of the receiver to the output impedance of the ignal generator.

Step 2. Set the signal generator to 71.75 megacycles.

Step 3. Adjust the receiver to the same frequency and then carefully djust for a null or no-deflection point on the tuning indicator of the reeiver.

Step 4. The dial pointer should lie within the limits of the red dot n the dial which represents channel 4.

Step 5. Set the receiver to the extreme high-frequency end of the dial.

Step 6. Adjust the signal generator to approximately 218 megaycles, and then carefully adjust for a null on the tuning indicator.

Step 7. The signal-generator frequency should fall between 217.5 nd 218 megacycles.

If both points, channel 4 and the high-frequency end, lie within the alibration limits, the tuner is correctly calibrated.

Procedure for Checking the Sensitivity of the Inputuner Section.

Step 1. Connect the marker-signal generator to the antenna terninals of the receiver with enough series resistance to match the 75-ohm nput impedance of the receiver to the output impedance of the signal ;enerator.

Step 2. By means of the coaxial lead, connect the VERTICAL INPUT ;erminals of the oscilloscope to the video output of the receiver.

Step 3. Calibrate the oscilloscope so as to be able to read 25 volts oeak to peak.

Step 4. Tune the receiver to a free television channel (one on which no signal is being transmitted) in the lower television bands.

Step 5. Adjust the marker-signal generator to the center of the television channel.

Step 6. Amplitude-modulate the signal generator 30 per cent with a 400-c sine-wave signal.

Step 7. Set the receiver contrast control to maximum, and adjust the output of the calibrated signal generator until 25 volts peak to peak of the 400-c signal is obtained on the oscilloscope.

The output of the signal generator required to obtain this level should not be greater than 150 μv.

If a percentage modulation is other than 30 per cent, then a 25-volt peak-to-peak output should be obtained with a signal S in microvolts as given by

$$S = \frac{90}{2M}$$

where M is the modulation factor.

Procedure for Checking the Band Pass of the Inputuner Section

Step 1. Connect the wobbulated signal generator to the antenna terminals of the receiver with enough resistance to match the 75-ohm input impedance of the receiver to the output impedance of the wobbulator.

Step 2. View the output on an oscilloscope connected to the video output of the receiver.

Step 3. Tune the receiver to a clear channel in one of the low television bands.

Step 4. Set the wobbulated signal-generator center frequency to the frequency to which the receiver is tuned. If the center frequency of the wobbulator is not sufficiently high, adjust the wobbulator center frequency to one half or one third of the receiver frequency and operate on a harmonic of the wobbulator output.

Step 5. Adjust the width of the sweep of the wobbulator until it is at least ±5 megacycles.

Step 6. Adjust the wobbulator output voltage until a readable pattern is obtained on the oscilloscope. Care should be taken to ensure that the amplifier is not overloaded.

Step 7. Comparing this over-all pass characteristic to that obtained with the video i-f amplifier alone, the Inputuner should not contribute more than 3 db dip and/or 3 db difference between the peaks of the pass characteristic. It should not cause the video carrier to vary by more than ±3 db. If any of these limitations are exceeded, the tuner is not operating properly.

It is to be emphasized that these limitations apply only to what the Inputuner contributes to the over-all pass characteristic and not to the over-all pass characteristic itself.

Step 8. This procedure should be repeated if possible on one of the high television channels.

The Switch-Type R-F Section. The adjustment of the switch-type r-f section of a television receiver is similar to the adjustment of the r-f section of the f-m receiver. The problem of tracking is not present in this ype of television receiver, because the oscillator has a separately tuned ank circuit for each of the television channels.

Generally, the principle is to set the wobbulator center frequency to he sound-carrier frequency of the channel to be tuned and to apply this ignal to the grid of the mixer stage. The oscillator-tank capacitor is hen tuned to obtain the optimum setting of the discriminator curve of he audio channel. The wobbulator is then connected in turn to the grid of the r-f stage and the antenna-input terminals, and the r-f–tank and antenna-tank capacitors, respectively, are adjusted to obtain the greatest amplitude of the discriminator curve. Final adjustment of the three capacitors is obtained after the output of the wobbulator has been matched to the input of the receiver.

In order to allow for some tolerance in this adjustment, the Vernier tuning capacitor is set to one half of its maximum capacitance, i.e., the plates should be only one half meshed. To determine whether the oscillator is set to the proper frequency, the marker generator should be connected and set to produce a birdie at the sound-carrier frequency. This birdie should fall in its proper position on the discriminator curve.

Procedure for Adjusting the Switch-Type R-F Section.

Step 1. Connect the wobbulator between the grid and ground of the mixer stage.

Step 2. Connect both output leads of the marker generator to ground but across the ground lead of the wobbulator.

Step 3. Set the mid-frequency of the wobbulator to the sound-carrier frequency of the channel being tuned.

Step 4. Set the marker generator to the frequency of the channel being tuned.

Step 5. Connect the coaxial lead from the VERTICAL INPUT terminals of the oscilloscope between the discriminator output and ground.

Step 6. Turn on the power to the receiver.

Step 7. Set the vernier-tuning capacitor of the oscillator to one half its maximum capacitance.

Step 8. After adjusting the wobbulator output so that the sound i-f section is not overloaded, adjust the oscillator-trimmer capacitor until a discriminator curve appears on the oscilloscope. Correct adjustment of the oscillator is indicated when the birdie appears on the straight-portion discriminator curve with an equal number of oscillations above and below the zero voltage point.

Step 9. Turn off the power to the receiver.

Step 10. Connect the wobbulator between grid and ground of the r-f stage.

Step 11. Turn on the power to the receiver.

Step 12. With the mid-frequency of the wobbulator set to the sound carrier frequency, adjust the r-f tank capacitor to obtain the maximum amplitude of the discriminator curve as it appears on the oscilloscope.

Step 13. Turn off the power to the receiver.

Step 14. Connect the wobbulator to the antenna input terminals of the receiver with enough series resistance to match the output impedance of the wobbulator to the input impedance of the receiver.

Step 15. Connect the marker generator to ground but across the ground lead of the wobbulator.

Step 16. With the mid-frequency of the wobbulator and the marker generator both set to the sound-carrier frequency, adjust the antenna tank capacitor to obtain the maximum amplitude of the discriminator curve.

Step 17. Readjust the r-f tank capacitor to compensate for any previous impedance mismatch.

Step 18. Readjust the oscillator-tank capacitor; it will probably be misadjusted now that the impedances are properly matched.

Step 19. Readjust all three tank capacitors until the optimum setting for each is obtained.

Step 20. Turn off the power to the receiver.

It is extremely important that the marker generator be used to adjust the oscillator frequency of the television receiver, because, if the oscillator is even slightly off frequency, it will detract from the quality of the picture.

Troubleshooting the Sweep Circuits. The only method for locating trouble in the sweep circuits of a television receiver is inspection of the circuits with an oscilloscope for the presence of the proper waveform at the key points in the circuit. Photographs of the various waveforms and the points in the circuit where they occur are included in the servicing information furnished by the manufacturers of the receiver.

When trouble has been traced to the sweep circuits, the circuits should be examined until one of the test points indicates no output or a badly distorted output. That stage is then checked by means of voltage and resistance measurements to locate the defective component.

The sweep circuit and the waveforms at the various test points of the Du Mont Model RA-101 Teleset are reproduced in Fig. 16-30 to serve as a guide in servicing sweep circuits. The circuits from which these patterns were obtained are shown in Figs. 16-31 and 16-32.

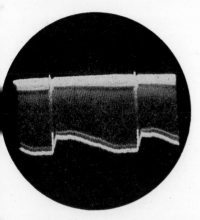

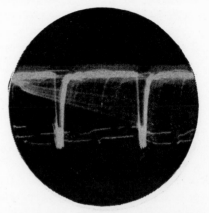

FIG. 16–30a. Waveform at pin 1 of *V*2 on a 30-c sweep frequency (Fig. 16–31).

FIG. 16–30b. Waveform at pin 1 of *V*2 on a 7.5-kc sweep frequency (Fig. 16–31).

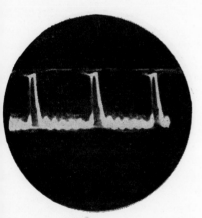

FIG. 16–30c. Waveform at pin 2 of *V*2 on a 7.5-kc sweep frequency (Fig. 16–31).

FIG. 16–30d. Waveform at pin 8 of *V*1 on a 7.5-kc sweep frequency (Fig. 16–32).

FIG. 16–30. Oscillograms of waveforms that are found in the circuits of FIGS. 16–31 and 16–32.

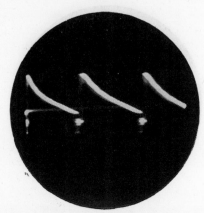

Fig. 16–30e. Waveform at white lead of discriminator-transformer on a 7.5kc sweep frequency (Fig. 16–32).

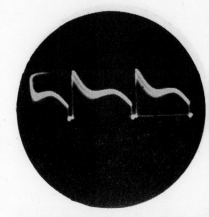

Fig. 16–30f. Waveform at red lead of discriminator-transformer on a 7.5kc sweep frequency (Fig. 16–32).

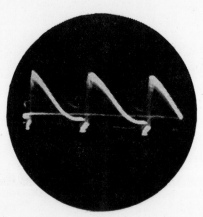

Fig. 16–30g. Waveform at blue lead of discriminator-transformer on a 7.5kc sweep frequency (Fig. 16–32).

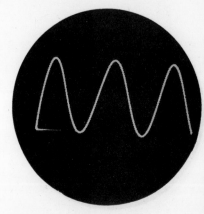

Fig. 16–30h. Waveform at pin 8 of V4 on 7.5-kc sweep frequency (Fig. 16–32).

Fig. 16–30. (Continued).

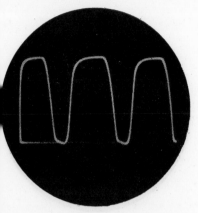

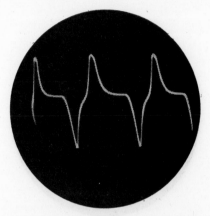

Fig. 16–30*i*. Waveform at pin 3 of *V3* on 7.5-kc sweep frequency (Fig. 16–32).

Fig. 16–30*j*. Waveform at pin 4 of *V2* on 7.5-kc sweep frequency (Fig. 16–31).

Fig. 16–30*k*. Waveform at pin 5 of *V2* on 7.5-kc sweep frequency (Fig. 16–31).

Fig. 16–30*l*. Waveform at pin 7 of output to yoke on 7.5-kc sweep frequency (Fig. 16–31).

Fig. 16–30. (*Continued*).

Fig. 16-30m. Waveform at pin 4 of V6 on 7.5-kc sweep frequency (Fig. 16–31).

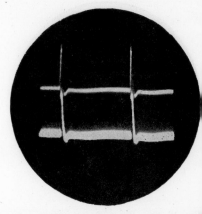

Fig. 16-30n. Waveform at pin 8 of V6 on 30-c sweep frequency (Fig. 16–31).

Fig. 16-30o. Waveform at pin 8 of V6 on 7.5-kc sweep frequency (Fig. 16–31).

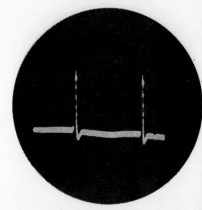

Fig. 16-30p. Waveform at junction of R25 and R26 on 30-c sweep frequency (Fig. 16–31).

Fig. 16–30. (Continued).

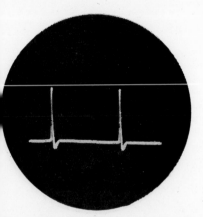

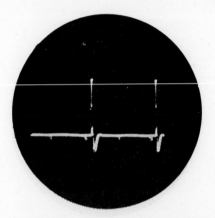

FIG. 16–30*q*. Waveform at junction of R26 and R24 on 30-c sweep frequency (Fig. 16–31).

FIG. 16–30*r*. Waveform at red lead of vertical blocking-oscillator transformer on 7.5kc sweep frequency (Fig. 16–31).

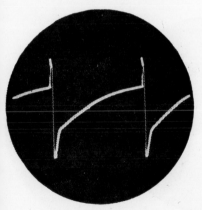

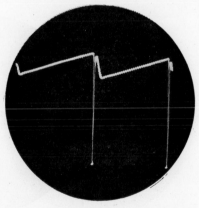

FIG. 16–30*s*. Waveform at pin 4 of *V7* on 30-c sweep frequency (Fig. 16–31).

on 30-c sweep frequency (Fig. 16–31). FIG. 16–30*t*. Waveform at pin 5 of *V7*

FIG. 16–30. (*Continued*).

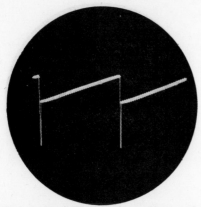

Fig. 16–30u. Waveform at pins 1 and 4 of V8 on 30-c sweep frequency (Fig. 16–31).

Fig. 16–30v. Waveform at pins 2 and 5 of V8 on 30-c sweep frequency (Fig. 16–31).

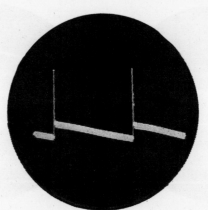

Fig. 16–30w. Waveform at pin 2 of output to yoke on 30-c sweep frequency (Fig. 16–31).

Fig. 16–30. (Continued).

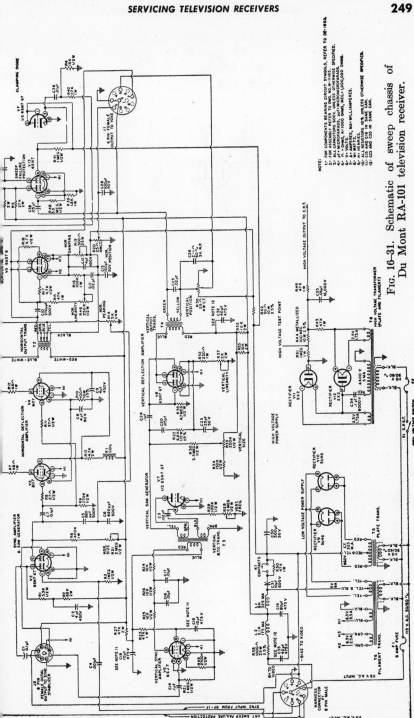

Fig. 16-31. Schematic of sweep chassis of Du Mont RA-101 television receiver.

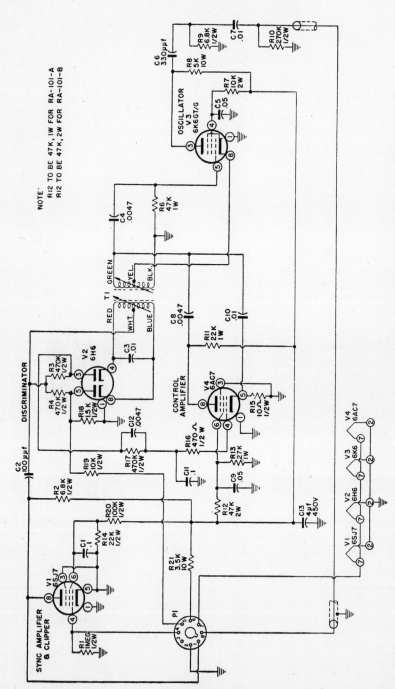

FIG. 16-32. Schematic of phase-discriminator chassis of Du Mont RA-101 television receiver.

17 Use at the Radio Transmitter

Introduction. The most publicized use of an oscilloscope at a radio transmitter is as a modulation monitor. Without a doubt, the oscilloscope is the most reliable device for continuous monitoring of instantaneous percentage modulation. The features of the oscilloscope that make it so reliable are (1) the fact that indication is obtained by the deflection of the *inertia-free* electron beam of the cathode-ray tube, and (2) the fact that the oscilloscope is coupled directly to the r-f output of the transmitter with no intervening circuits.

In addition to its use as a modulation monitor, the oscilloscope is a valuable aid in adjusting the tuned circuits of the transmitter to resonance, neutralizing the r-f amplifiers, and troubleshooting the complete trans-

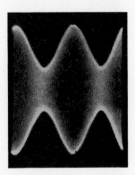

Fig. 17–1. Oscillogram showing the wave-envelope pattern.

Fig. 17–2. Oscillogram showing the trapezoid pattern.

mitter. Each of these uses will be explained, and step-by-step procedures for performing each function will be given in the succeeding pages of this chapter.

The Oscilloscope as a Modulation Monitor. Two different types of patterns may be obtained on the screen of the oscilloscope for the measurement of percentage modulation. These two types are called the "wave-envelope" and the "trapezoid" and are illustrated in Figs. 17-1 and 17-2, respectively.

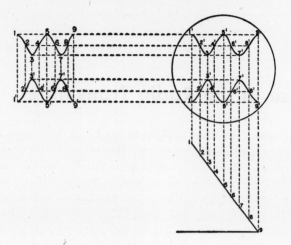

FIG. 17-3. Projection drawing showing how the wave-envelope pattern is displayed on the screen.

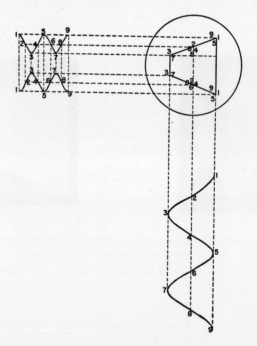

FIG. 17-4. Projection drawing showing how the trapezoid pattern is displayed on the screen.

The wave-envelope pattern is the result of applying the modulated r-f output of the transmatter to the vertical plates of the cathode-ray tube and a linear time base to the horizontal plates. A projection-type drawing (Fig. 17-3) shows how this pattern is obtained on the screen.

The trapezoid pattern may be obtained with the simplest of oscilloscopes, since all that is required is a cathode-ray tube and its power supply, and a means for connecting signals to the deflection plates. This

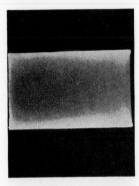

FIG. 17–5. Oscillogram showing an unmodulated r-f carrier.

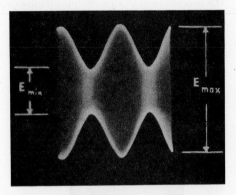

FIG. 17–6. Oscillogram showing the wave-envelope pattern with maximum and minimum values labeled.

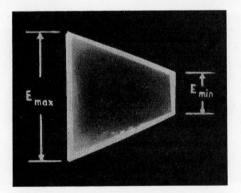

FIG. 17–7. Oscillogram showing the trapezoid pattern with maximum and minimum values labeled.

pattern is obtained by applying the modulated r-f output of the transmitter to the vertical plates of the cathode-ray tube and applying the modulating signal to the horizontal plates. Figure 17-4 is a projection drawing which shows rather clearly how the trapezoid appears on the screen as a result of these two signals.

Calculating Percentage Modulation. The application of a modulating signal to the r-f carrier wave causes the amplitude of the carrier to increase when the modulating signal is positive and to decrease when the modulating signal is negative. Figure 17-5 shows an unmodulated r-f carrier, and Fig. 17-6 shows the wave-envelope pattern of the same carrier modulated with a 400-c a-f signal. Figure 17-7 shows the trapezoid pattern resulting from the same conditions as those in Fig. 17-6. Notice how the modulation varies the amplitude of the r-f carrier.

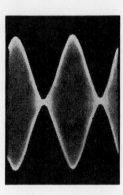

Fig. 17–8. Wave-envelope pattern showing 100 per cent modulation.

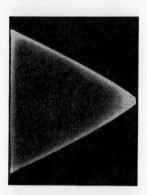

Fig. 17–9. Trapezoid pattern showing 100 per cent modulation.

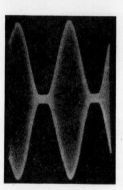

Fig. 17–10. Wave-envelope showing overmodulation.

Fig. 17–11. Trapezoid showing overmodulation.

Percentage modulation may be calculated from either of two formulas:

$$\frac{E_{max} - E_c}{E_c} \times 100 = \text{percentage modulation} \tag{1}$$

or

$$\frac{E_{max} - E_{min}}{E_{max} + E_{min}} \times 100 = \text{percentage modulation} \tag{2}$$

where E_c = the amplitude of the carrier;

E_{max} = the maximum amplitude of the carrier with modulation;

E_{min} = the minimum amplitude of the carrier with modulation.

Obviously, Eq. (2) is the more convenient, since the modulator does not have to be turned off to measure the amplitude of the r-f carrier.

Assuming the values E_c = 0.8 in.

E_{max} = 1.2 in.

E_{min} = 0.4 in.

and substituting in Eq. (1),

$$\frac{1.2 - 0.8}{0.8} \times 100 = \frac{0.4}{0.8} \times 100 = 50 \text{ per cent}$$

Substituting in Eq. (2),

$$\frac{1.2 - 0.4}{1.2 + 0.4} \times 100 = \frac{0.8}{1.6} \times 100 = 50 \text{ per cent}$$

Since the maximum efficiency of a transmitter is reached at 100 per cent modulation, it would be ideal to operate at this point continuously.

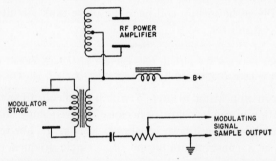

Fig. 17–12. Circuit of a sampling network to obtain the modulating signals.

However, the transmitter should never be overmodulated, since this results in harmonic distortion which increases the channel width and thus interferes with other stations. The oscilloscope indicates 100 per cent modulation and overmodulation more efficiently than any other method and thus permits the use of an average percentage modulation which is higher than is permissible with other existing monitoring techniques. Figures 17-8 through 17-11 show 100 per cent modulation and overmodulation as indicated with both the wave-envelope and trapezoid patterns.

Coupling the Oscilloscope to the Transmitter. Since very few oscilloscopes contain amplifiers that have a linear frequency response at radio frequencies, the r-f signal should be connected directly to the vertical deflection plates of the cathode-ray tube. The r-f signal from the transmitter is picked up by a coil of a few turns of wire. The connection from the pickup coil to the oscilloscope should be made with coaxial cable to prevent the leads from picking up stray signals. When the oscilloscope is used in conjunction with low-power transmitters, however, connection to the pickup coil can be made with a twisted-pair line.

Obtaining the Wave-Envelope Pattern.

Step 1.　Connect the leads from the pick up coil to the vertical deflection plates of the cathode-ray tube in the oscilloscope.

Note

If the oscilloscope employs single-ended deflection, connect the shield of the coaxial cable to ground and the center conductor to the free vertical deflection plate.

Step 2.　Ground the cabinet of the oscilloscope to ground of the transmitter so that the metal cabinet shields the cathode-ray tube from the effects of stray oscillations.

Step 3.　Set the COARSE FREQUENCY and FINE FREQUENCY controls of the oscilloscope to result in a sweep frequency of about 100 cps.

Step 4.　Adjust the HORIZONTAL GAIN control to result in a trace covering about three fourths of the width of the screen.

Step 5.　Place the pickup coil near the plate-tank circuit of the final stage of the transmitter.

Note

The coupling between the pickup coil and the plate-tank circuit should not be any closer than is necessary to result in a conveniently sized pattern on the screen.

The pattern appearing in step 5 will be difficult to synchronize in normal operation of the transmitter because the frequency and the amplitude of the modulation are both constantly changing. For test purposes, however, when a constant amplitude of a single frequency is used to modulate the carrier, synchronization can be accomplished by switching the SYNC SIGNAL SELECTOR to EXTERNAL and connecting a low-voltage sample of the modulating signal to the EXTERNAL SYNC INPUT terminal.

Obtaining the Trapezoid Pattern.

Step 1.　Repeat steps 1, 2, and 5 of the preceding discussion.

Step 2.　Connect a signal-sampling network from the output of the modulation transformer, as shown in Fig. 17-12.

Step 3.　Connect the modulation signal to the HORIZONTAL INPUT terminals of the oscilloscope.

Step 4.　Set the HORIZONTAL INPUT switch to permit the signal applied to the HORIZONTAL INPUT terminals to be amplified by the horizontal amplifier.

Step 5.　Set the HORIZONTAL GAIN control to obtain a deflection of about three fourths the width of the screen.

Note

The pattern that appears on the screen is a trapezoid as long as the carrier is modulated. When the carrier is not modulated, there is no modulating voltage and, thus, no horizontal deflection. The resulting pattern, when there is no modulating voltage, is a straight vertical line, which represents the amplitude of the unmodulated r-f carrier.

Adjusting the Tank Circuits to Resonance. The oscilloscope provides a highly satisfactory method for adjusting the various tank circuits of the transmitter to resonance. The pickup coil connected to the vertical deflection plates of the cathode-ray tube produces the maximum deflection of the electron beam when the tank circuit is adjusted to resonance. The horizontal sweep circuit of the oscilloscope is used for horizontal deflection, and no attempt is made to synchronize the sweep, since the amplitude of the vertical deflection is the only measurement to be made.

Fɪɢ. 17–13. Auxiliary tank circuit.

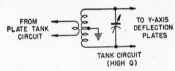

FROM PLATE TANK CIRCUIT

TO Y-AXIS DEFLECTION PLATES

TANK CIRCUIT (HIGH Q)

It is advisable to incorporate an additional tank circuit in the line between the pickup coil and the vertical deflection plates to increase the signal when the low-level stages of the transmitter are being adjusted. This circuit is advised for two reasons: (1) It may be impossible in some of the smaller transmitters to obtain sufficient signal on the vertical deflection plates; and (2) even in the larger transmitters, the coupling necessary to obtain sufficient vertical deflection may be so close that the pickup coil loads the tank circuit being tuned to such a point that mistuning of that stage results.

This tank circuit, consisting of an inductance and a capacitance coupled to a link coil at the end of the line from the pickup coil, is shown in Fig. 17-13. It must be designed to tune to the frequency of the transmitter, and the Q of the circuit must be kept high. This circuit will increase the voltage of the signal from the pickup loop by resonance and furnish a sufficient signal to the deflection plates with a minimum of coupling between the circuits of the transmitter and the pickup coil. In the construction of this auxiliary tank circuit, it must be well shielded either by being in a case of its own or by being built into the case of the oscilloscope. If it is constructed as a separate unit, its case must also be connected to ground of the transmitter.

Tuning Procedure.

Step 1. Connect the line from the pickup coil to the link of the auxiliary tank circuit, and connect the output of the tank circuit to the vertical deflection plates.

Step 2.   Couple the pickup coil to the oscillator tank circuit of the transmitter.

Step 3.   Adjust the variable capacitor of the auxiliary tank circuit to obtain the maximum deflection on the screen of the oscilloscope.

Step 4.   Loosen the coupling between the pickup coil and the oscillator tank circuit if the deflection on the oscilloscope is too large.

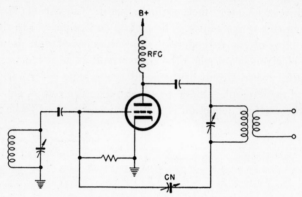

Fig. 17–14.   Circuit showing inductive coupling to the oscilloscope to use the instrument for neutralization.

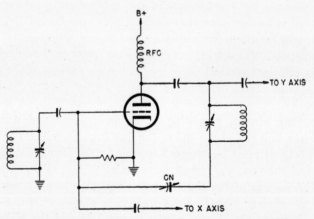

Fig. 17–15.   Circuit showing capacitive coupling to the oscilloscope to use the instrument for neutralization.

Step 5.   Adjust the variable capacitor in the oscillator tank circuit to obtain the maximum amplitude of the signal on the screen of the oscilloscope.

Note

Oscillator circuits having tank circuits in both the grid and the plate circuits will require that the grid circuit be tuned first.   The plate circuit is then tuned and the grid circuit returned to compensate for the change in load.

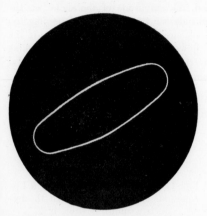

Fig. 17-16. Plate circuit not tuned, stage not neutralized.

Fig. 17-17. Plate circuit not tuned, stage not neutralized.

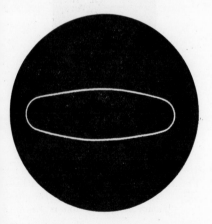

Fig. 17-18. Plate circuit tuned but stage not neutralized.

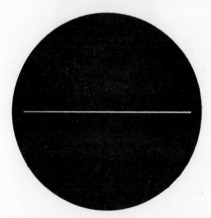

Fig. 17-19. Plate circuit tuned and stage neutralized.

Figs. 17-16 to 17-19. Oscillograms showing the various patterns encountered in neutralizing a transmitter.

Step 6.   Adjust each of the following tank circuits to obtain maximum deflection on the screen of the oscilloscope.

Note

With each successive stage that is tuned, the amplitude of the signal on the oscilloscope increases. Excessive signal amplitude can be reduced by loosening the coupling between the pickup coil and the tank circuit that is being tuned. If the distance between the two becomes too large, however, there is the chance of picking up a signal from another circuit. If such is the case, the amplitude of the signal on the oscilloscope can be reduced by detuning the auxiliary tank circuit.

Neutralizing R-F Amplifiers.   Neutralization is required in triode r-f amplifiers to compensate for feedback which occurs through the grid-

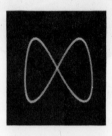

Fig. 17–20. Oscillogram showing a Lis-Lissajous figure indicating that the frequency multiplication is 2.

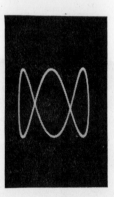

Fig. 17–21. Oscillogram showing a Lissajous figure indicating that the frequency multiplication is 3.

Fig. 17–22. Oscillogram showing a Lissajous figure indicating that the frequency multiplication is 4.

plate capacitance of the tube. It consists of coupling some of the radio frequency from the output circuit and introducing it into the input circuit (or vice versa) in such a way as to cancel the current flowing through the grid-plate capacitance. Neutralization is most commonly accomplished by capacitors, although inductances can also be employed.

The neutralization procedure is essentially the same for all circuits. All circuits up to and including the grid circuit of the stage to be neutralized must be properly tuned and neutralized. The stage being neutralized must be in operating condition except that no plate voltage is applied to this stage. The grid circuit must be excited from the preceding stage.

The oscilloscope is coupled to the stage being neutralized by two pickup coils, as shown in Fig. 17-14. If it is desired, small capacitors may be substituted for the pickup coils and connected as shown in Fig. 17-15.

Step 1.   Connect the pickup loop (or capacitor) from the grid circuit of the stage to be neutralized to the horizontal deflection plates of the oscilloscope and the pickup loop (or capacitor) from the plate circuit of the same stage to the vertical deflection plates.

Step 2.   Turn on the power to all the stages prior to and including the stage being neutralized, with the exception of the plate voltage on this latter stage.

The pattern on the screen of the oscilloscope will probably be similar to that in Fig. 17-16 or to that in Fig. 17-17 if the plate tank circuit is not properly tuned and the stage is not neutralized.

Step 3.   Adjust the tuning of the plate tank circuit to obtain a pattern similar to that shown in Fig. 17-18.

Step 4.   Adjust the neutralizing capacitor with a tuning wand to approach the pattern shown in Fig. 17-19.

Note

The adjustment of neutralization may affect the tuning of the grid tank circuit or the driving tank circuit (the plate tank circuit of the preceding stage). Therefore, both of these circuits should be readjusted as neutralization is approached. The proper tuning of these two tank circuits at this time is indicated by the maximum horizontal deflection.

Step 5.   When neutralizing push-pull amplifiers, both stages should be neutralized together.

Frequency-Multiplier Stages. A frequency-multiplier stage is essentially an r-f amplifier whose plate tank circuit is tuned to a multiple of the frequency of the grid tank circuit. Since the plate efficiency of a frequency-multiplier stage decreases rapidly with an increase in the frequency multiplication, the frequency-doubler circuit is most common. It is interesting to note that when triodes are employed as frequency multipliers, neutralization is no longer required.

The technique employed for tuning a frequency multiplier is similar to that employed for neutralizing to the extent that a Lissajous figure indicates proper tuning.

Step 1.   Connect one pickup loop to the vertical deflection plates of the oscilloscope and couple it loosely to the plate tank circuit of the multiplier stage.

Step 2. Connect a second pickup loop to the horizontal deflection plates of the oscilloscope and couple it loosely to the grid tank circuit of the same stage.

Step 3. Adjust the plate tank circuit to obtain the Lissajous figure which indicates the proper multiplication.

Figure 17-20 indicates a frequency multiplication of two; Fig. 17-21 indicates a multiplication of three; and Fig. 17-22, a multiplication of

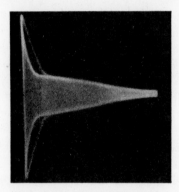   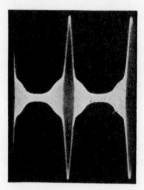

Fɪɢ. 17–23. Trapezoid pattern.   Fɪɢ. 17–24. Wave envelope pattern.

Taken from output stage of transmitter and show: overmodulation, excessive grid bias, incorrect neutralization; and trapezoid shows phase distortion.

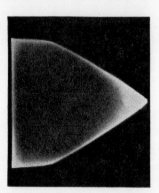   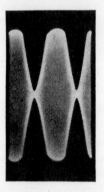

Fɪɢ. 17–25. Trapezoid pattern.   Fɪɢ. 17–26. Wave envelope pattern.

Taken from output stage of the transmitter and show: 100 per cent modulation, and insufficient excitation of output stage.

four. These illustrations indicate, respectively, the first, second, and third harmonics of the fundamental frequency. Note that in each of these illustrations, the plate tank circuit, and thus the higher frequency, has been coupled to the vertical deflection plates.

Troubleshooting the Transmitter. Troubleshooting the transmitter can best be achieved by a quick stage-to-stage check for tuning, measurement of gain, and neutralization. Trouble can be quickly localized as being in the r-f or the a-f sections of the transmitter, and the respective section should then be checked carefully. Trouble in the audio section of the transmitter is located in the same way as in the audio section of a

Fɪɢ. 17–27. Trapezoid pattern.   Fɪɢ. 17–28. Wave envelope pattern.

Taken from the output stage of the transmitter and show: overmodulation, parasitic oscillations, and trapezoid shows phase distortion.

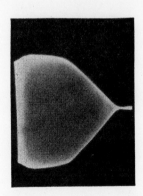
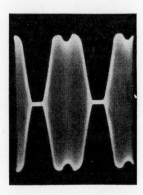

Fɪɢ. 17–29. Trapezoid pattern.   Fɪɢ. 17–30. Wave envelope pattern.

Taken from the output stage of the transmitter and show: overmodulation, and insufficient excitation of output stage.

receiver. See Chaps. 13 and 14 for complete details of the use of the oscilloscope in audio amplifiers.

The illustrations in Figs. 17-23 through 17-30 show some of the effects of improper transmitter adjustment or trouble as they are seen in

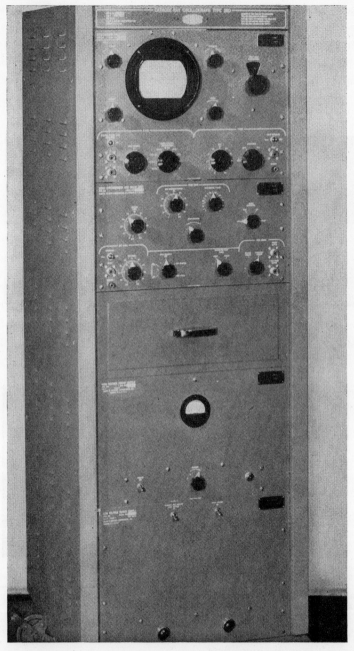

FIG. 17–31. The Du Mont Type 280 cathode-ray oscillograph designed for making precision measurements on a television picture signal.

the wave-envelope and trapezoid patterns taken from the plate tank circuit of the final stage.

Television Transmitters. The television transmitter is of course much more complicated than any a-m or f-m transmitter, since it not only employs both types of transmitters, but it must transmit an accurate video signal. Into this video signal must be mixed the very precise synchronizing pulses to synchronize the sweep generators of the receiver to the sweep generators in the television cameras. In view of the accuracy of the measurements which must be made in conjunction with television transmitting, it is interesting to note that the Allen B. Du Mont Laboratories have developed a precision instrument called the "Type 280 Cathode-Ray Oscillograph." The instrument is designed specifically for measuring all the characteristics of the television signal which are required by the Federal Communications Commission. At this writing this is the only commercial instrument designed for this purpose. The unit is shown in Fig. 17-31.

18 Using the Oscillosope in Teaching

Introduction. The value of the oscilloscope as a visual aid in the teaching of such subjects as sound, electricity, and electronics is practically immeasurable. In addition, certain phenomena in the study of light and magnetism can also be illustrated dynamically with the oscilloscope. This chapter merely gives a succession of demonstrations that are made more vivid by using the oscilloscope.

The instructor should consider this chapter as being merely introductory to the use of the oscilloscope as a visual aid. Many more demonstra-

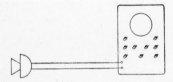

Fig. 18–1. Connecting a microphone to an oscilloscope.

tions than are included here can be, and have been, performed to give the student a better understanding of these subjects. Undoubtedly, some of the subjects discussed in this, as well as the other chapters of this book will suggest many more demonstrations that fit a particular course of study.

Study of Various Types of Sounds. One of the most simple, entertaining, and, at the same time, instructive demonstrations with the oscilloscope is obtained by merely viewing various sounds converted into electrical impulses by means of a microphone.

As shown in Fig. 18-1, simply connect either a crystal or a dynamic microphone to the VERTICAL INPUT terminals of the oscilloscope. Connect the outside shield of the microphone cable to ground and the inner conductor to the other input terminal. A carbon microphone will also serve the purpose, but it is necessary to use a battery in the primary circuit and a microphone transformer connected as in the circuit of Fig. 18-2.

Incidentally, some oscilloscopes may not have enough gain in the vertical amplifiers to give suitable deflection on the screen of the cathode-ray tube. If such is the case, it will be necessary to amplify the signal from the microphone before connecting it to the input of the oscilloscope. A simple, single-stage, class A amplifier can readily be constructed for this purpose. The complete circuit for such a case is given in Fig. 18-3.

The controls of the oscilloscope should be set as follows:

Step 1. Set the INTENSITY and FOCUS to obtain desired brightness and optimum focus.

Step 2. Set the VERTICAL and HORIZONTAL POSITIONING controls to center the trace.

FIG. 18-2. Connecting a carbon microphone to an oscilloscope.

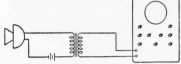

Step 3. Set the COARSE FREQUENCY and FINE FREQUENCY controls to obtain a sweep of about 30 c—just fast enough so that the flicker is not objectionable.

Step 4. Leave the SYNC SELECTOR switch in any position.

Step 5. Set the SYNC AMPLITUDE control at zero.

Step 6. Set the HORIZONTAL GAIN control to result in a trace that is ¼ in. from the edges of each side of the screen.

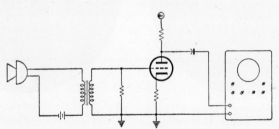

FIG. 18-3. Connecting a carbon microphone through a single-stage amplifier to an oscilloscope.

Step 7. Set the VERTICAL GAIN control to result in the desired vertical deflection.

Step 8. Speak or whistle into the microphone and observe the complex waveform that appears on the screen.

Step 9. Strike a tuning fork, and hold it close to the microphone. Observe the sine wave that appears on the screen. This is the waveform of a pure tone.

If possible, use tuning forks that are mounted on a resonant box. This type will result in sound that is loud enough for the microphone to pick up from a reasonable distance.

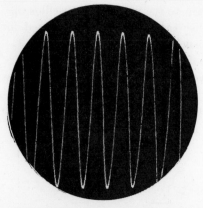

Fig. 18–4. Oscillogram obtained when C-256 c.p.s. is struck hard.

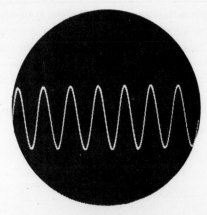

Fig. 18–5. Oscillogram obtained when C-256 c.p.s. is struck moderately.

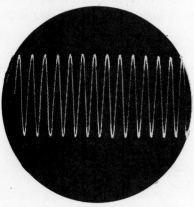

Fig. 18–6. Oscillogram obtained when C-512 c.p.s. is struck moderately.

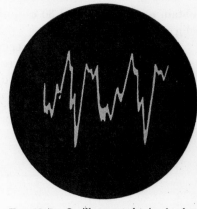

Fig. 18–7. Oscillogram obtained when G-392 c.p.s. is produced by a single reed of an accordion.

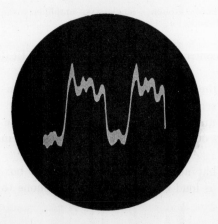

Fig. 18–8. Oscillogram obtained when E-329.6 c.p.s. is produced by the D string of a violin.

Step 10. Strike the tuning fork hard, and observe the amplitude of the signal.

Step 11. Strike the tuning fork gently, and observe the amplitude of the signal.

These signals give the student a visual interpretation of amplitude.

Step 12. Strike a tuning fork of 256 vibrations per second, and count the number of cycles appearing on the screen of the cathode-ray tube.

Step 13. Strike a tuning fork of 512 vibrations per second and count the number of cycles appearing on the screen of the cathode-ray tube.

These views give the student a visual interpretation of frequency.

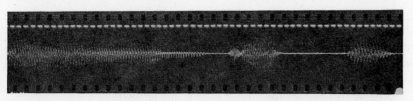

FIG. 18–9. A moving-film recording of the word "scientific." The evenly spaced dots across the top of the film are timing markers at intervals of 1/50 sec.

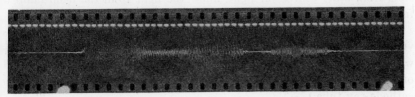

FIG. 18–10. A moving-film recording of the word "physics."

Step 14. Compare the waveforms resulting from sounds produced by various musical instruments such as a violin, a trumpet, an accordian, and others.

Some typical examples of sounds that have been photographed from the screen of a cathode-ray tube are shown in Figs. 18-4 to 18-13.

Demonstration of Beats. Keep the oscilloscope connected as it was for the study of various sounds, and place two tuning forks of nearly the same frequency near the microphone. As a suggestion, tune the forks previously to produce approximately one beat per second; e.g., use a standard fork at 256 vibrations per second and place a rider on one of the prongs of another similar fork to change its frequency to 255 vibrations per second.

Step 1. Strike one fork and observe the pattern on the screen of the cathode-ray tube.

Step 2. Strike the other fork, and observe that, as the sounds from the two forks interfere with each other, a minimum sound is heard and a minimum deflection is simultaneously observed on the screen of the cathode-ray tube. Correspondingly, as a maximum sound is heard, a maximum deflection is observed on the screen. A photographic recording of this phenomenon on a moving photographic film is shown in Fig. 18-14.

Step 3. Change the frequency of the second fork from 255 to about 248 vibrations per second. The beats are now so rapid that it is difficult to hear them, but they show clearly on the oscilloscope.

In addition to this experiment, the instructor will probably find the oscilloscope, used in this manner, quite helpful in tuning a vibrating string or another instrument to a specifically desired pitch.

Demonstrations with the Photocell.   The use of the oscilloscope in the study of light is rather limited, since light is not regarded as a varying quantity in most of the standard courses. However, one interesting observation that may be made is the instantaneous light ouput from a neon lamp.

Step 1. Construct the circuit shown in Fig. 18-16.

Step 2. Shielding the neon lamp and the photocell as much as possible from other sources of light, allow the light from the neon lamp to fall on the photocell.

Step 3. The voltage from the photocell is then connected to the VERTICAL INPUT terminals of the oscilloscope. (With most oscilloscopes, it will probably be necessary to pass the voltage from the photocell through one or two amplifying stages first to obtain sufficient deflection on the cathode-ray tube.)

Step 4. When the COARSE FREQUENCY and FINE FREQUENCY controls are adjusted to the power-line frequency or a submultiple thereof, a pattern similar to that of Fig. 18-17 will be seen on the cathode-ray tube.

Note

The deflection produced by the signal may be in the opposite direction from that shown in Fig. 18-17. This will depend upon the number of amplifiers through which the signal from the photocell has been amplified and is not particularly significant.

The light received by the photocell is obtained first from one plate of the neon lamp and then from the other as the alternating voltage changes polarity. Therefore, the frequency of the impulses transmitted by the photocell is twice the power-line frequency. The fact that there is not a continuous emission from the photocell is indicated by the spaces between the impulses. These spaces are due to the fact that the neon lamp is not lighted from the time that the instantaneous voltage of $\frac{1}{2}$ cycle falls below the extinction potential of the lamp until the time that the instantaneous voltage of the next cycle reaches the firing potential of the lamp.

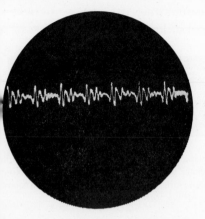

FIG. 18–11. Oscillogram of the letter *A* pronounced as in star.

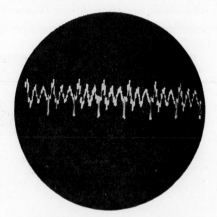

FIG. 18–12. Oscillogram of the letter *A* pronounced as in later.

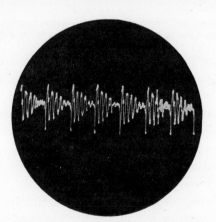

FIG. 18–13. Oscillogram of the letter *A* pronounced as in fast.

It is also interesting to note that the photocell can be oriented so that it picks up the light from only one plate of the neon lamp. The wave-form of the photocell output under these conditions is shown in Fig. 18-18a. The waveform of the photocell output when it is oriented to receive light only from the other plate is shown in Fig. 18-18b.

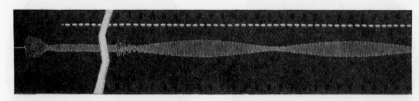

Fig. 18–14. A moving-film recording showing approximately 2 beats per second. The dots on the upper edge of the film indicate time intervals of 1/50 second. Note the large amplitude at the extreme left as the first fork is struck and the transient that also occurs as the second fork is struck.

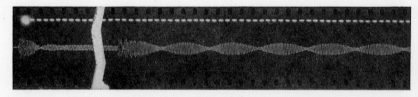

Fig. 18–15. A moving-film recording under the same conditions as in Fig. 18–14 except that the beat frequency is about 8 beats per second.

Demonstrations in Alternating Current.   The most logical and first demonstration in the field of a-c phenomena is to display a sine wave showing how the voltage starts from zero, builds up to a maximum in one direction, decreases to zero, builds up to a maximum in the other direction, and again decreases to zero, only to repeat the cycle. Amplitude and frequency can also be readily demonstrated from the discussion in Chap. 11. Alternating-current measurements can be made and demon-strated from the discussion in Chap. 12.

Another interesting demonstration in a-c circuits can be conducted with the circuit given in the demonstration with the photocell (Fig. 18-16).

Step 1.   Connect the VERTICAL INPUT terminals of the oscilloscope to the lead from the switch in the circuit of Fig. 18-16.

Step 2.   Turn the switch in Fig. 18-16 to the current position. Although the oscilloscope is essentially a voltmeter, it can be used to show current when it is connected across a resistance whose value is small

ompared with the impedance of the entire circuit. Thus, the waveform
btained in step 2 and illustrated in Fig. 18-19a shows the waveform of the
urrent passing through the neon lamp. Notice that the current increases
apidly and passes through a peak. As the current begins to decrease in
he same manner as it increased, the extinction potential of the lamp is
eached, and the current is immediately reduced to zero. No current flows
n the opposite direction until the voltage increases to the firing potential
f the lamp. At this time, the current again begins to flow.

The Oscilloscope as an Alternating Voltage Indicator. Probably
one of the chief uses of the oscilloscope in the demonstration of a-c cir-
uits is its use as a voltage indicator. It may be connected to nearly any
a-c source, within the frequency limits of the amplifier and the voltage
rating of the input capacitor and give a reliable indication. Furthermore,
an oscilloscope with a 5-in. diameter screen is probably larger than the
face of any a-c meter which is readily available. For experiments on in-

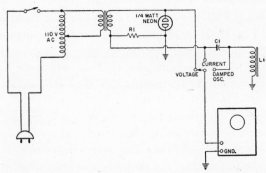

Fig. 18–16.   Circuit for an interesting experiment with a photocell.

duction, magnetic coupling between transformer windings, effect of the
turns ratio of a transformer on voltage, and resonance, the oscilloscope
gives a reliable and easily read indication of voltage.

As an example of the use of an oscilloscope to indicate voltage, construct the simple transformer shown in Fig. 18-20.

Step 1.   Connect an a-f signal generator to the primary of the transformer.*

Step 2.   Connect the two leads from the secondary of the transformer
to the VERTICAL INPUT terminals of the oscilloscope.

Step 3.   Set the a-f signal generator to a frequency of 1,000 c.

Step 4.   Adjust the COARSE FREQUENCY and FINE FREQUENCY controls
of the oscilloscope to result in a sweep frequency of about 100 c.

Step 5.   Set the VERTICAL GAIN control to obtain the desired vertical
deflection, and observe the pattern on the screen of the oscilloscope.

Step 6. Increase the number of turns on the secondary by 10 per cent and note the increase in amplitude on the screen of the oscilloscope.

Note

If the amplitude of the vertical deflection were set to 2 in. (20 scale divisions in step 5, the amplitude, as a result of step 6, will be 22 scale divisions. Increasing the number of turns by 50 percent will result in an increase in amplitude of 50 percent of step 5. Other increases or decreases in the number of turns of the secondary can be made to further illustrate the turns ratio of a transformer.

Step 7. Interchange the connections to the primary and secondary of the transformer and observe the large increase in the amplitude of the signal on the screen of the oscilloscope. The transformer is now a step-up transformer.

Step 8. Close the core of the transformer by adding three more bars to form a rectangle.

Step 9. Note the large increase in the amplitude of the output voltage due to the concentration of the magnetic flux.

Demonstrating Full-Wave and Half-Wave Rectification. The circuit shown in Fig. 18-21 is recommended for use in demonstrating the principles of rectification and filtering as used in a typical low-voltage power supply. It is also recommended that the schematic be drawn on a board and the components be mounted as close as possible to their respective symbols. The completed unit is then mounted upright and makes an excellent piece of equipment for classroom demonstration. The author has made a hobby of constructing such units and recommends that they be made as versatile as possible. The power transformer, the rectifier tube, the fuse, the pilot lights, the switches, and the line cord are the only components that are permanently wired. The leads of all the other components are soldered into phone tips so that they may be quickly removed and replaced with other components of different values. The output of voltages of this power supply are each connected to separate pins of an octal-tube socket so that they are available for the operation of other demonstration units.

Half-Wave Rectification.

Step 1. Set the switches in the following positions: $S1$, $S2$, $S4$, and $S6$ open; $S3$ and $S5$ closed.

Step 2. Connect the VERTICAL INPUT terminals of the oscilloscope to $J1$ and $J6$.

Step 3. Close the switch $S1$.

---

* This experiment can be performed with 110-volt 60-c alternating current, but much larger coils must be employed and caution must be used in handling the higher voltages. The use of a signal generator is much safer and more convenient

Step 4.   Set the COARSE FREQUENCY and FINE FREQUENCY controls to a sweep frequency equal to one half of the power-line frequency, and synchronize the pattern appearing on the screen of the cathode-ray tube. This waveform is shown in Fig. 18-22. This is the voltage output of the power transformer, approximately 300 volts (rms).

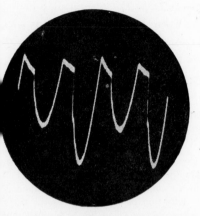

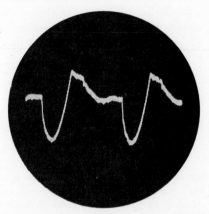

FIG. 18–17. Oscillogram of the light output of both plates of a simple neon bulb.

FIG. 18–18*a*. Oscillogram of the light output of one of the plates of a simple neon bulb.

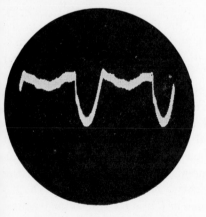

FIG. 18–18*b*. Oscillogram of the light output of the other plate of a simple neon bulb.

Step 5.   Throw the switch *S*3 to the off position, and remove the VERTICAL INPUT lead from *J*1 and connect it to *J*3.

Step 6.   Throw on the switch *S*3.

The pattern in Fig. 18-23 shows that electrons flow from the cathode of *V*1 to *P*1 during the half cycle when *P*1 is charged positively, and that they do not flow when the voltage swings *P*1 negative for a half cycle.

Step 7.   Close the switch *S*2. The pattern of Fig. 18-24 now appears on the oscilloscope.

This pattern shows that the electrons flow from the cathode of $V1$ to $P1$ when $P1$ is charged positively and from the cathode to $P2$ when $P2$ is charged positively. Furthermore, the voltage on the cathode changes in direct proportion to the voltage applied to the plate.

Step 8. It is interesting to compare the peak voltage obtained at $J3$ with the peak positive voltage appearing at $J1$ or $J2$. Also, it may be desirable to prove the phase difference between $J1$ and $J2$ by means of a Lissajous figure (explained in Chap. 11).

Step 9. Turn off $S3$ and connect the VERTICAL INPUT lead to $J4$.

Step 10. Close $S6$ so that the capacitor $C2$ is connected across the output of the power supply.

Step 11. Turn on $S3$ and observe the filtering action of this capacitor (Fig. 18-25).

Note

The d-c component of the output of the power supply is prevented from appearing on the screen by the capacitors in the amplifier. However, if it is desirable to show the d-c component of the signal with the a-c component superimposed upon it, $J4$ must be connected directly to one of the deflection plates, and $J6$ to the other deflection plate. This type of connection is illustrated in Chap. 10. The output of the power supply connected directly to the vertical deflection plates of an oscilloscope is illustrated in Figs. 18-26, 18-27, and 18-28. These figures correspond to Figs. 18-23, 18-24, and 18-25, respectively.

Step 12. Open the switch $S5$ so that the inductance $L1$ is now in the circuit. The output waveform as seen through the vertical amplifier is shown in Fig. 18-29 and as the result of direct connection to the vertical deflection plates in Fig. 18-30.

Step 13. Close the switch $S4$ so that the capacitor $C1$ is now connected in the circuit. The output waveform as seen through the vertical amplifier is shown in Fig. 18-31, and Fig. 18-32 shows the same waveform connected directly to the vertical deflection plates.

Many more waveforms can be shown with this demonstration unit such as the effect of changing the value of any of the components of the filter, the filtering effect of $C3$ on the negative bias voltage, and the change in the d-c output voltage with the change in $R1$ or $R2$. A voltmeter may be connected in any of the test jacks to measure voltage output or voltage drop across various components. Also, the jumper between $J13$ and $J14$ in the primary circuit may be removed for the connection of a 0- to 1,000-ma. milliammeter to measure the primary current as a function of the load in the secondary.

Audio-Amplifier Demonstrations. The schematic of Fig. 18-33 is recommended for demonstrating the characteristics of triodes, pentodes, and beam-power tubes and for demonstrating resistance coupling, a

ypical cathode follower, a typical phase inverter, and single-ended or
ush-pull output stages as well as input attenuators. As suggested for the
emonstration unit on the power supply, this schematic can be painted
n a board with quickly interchangeable components mounted as close as
ossible to their respective symbols.

The tube $V1$ is a 6J5 which can be connected as a triode amplifier or
s a cathode follower. The gain control can be in the grid circuit or in the

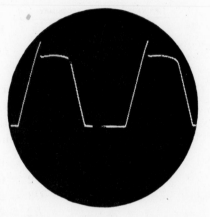

Fig. 18–19a. Oscillogram showing the waveform of the current passing through a neon bulb when 60-c alternating current is applied.

Fig. 18–19b. Oscillogram showing the waveform of the voltage across a neon bulb.

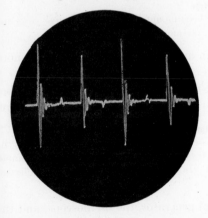

Fig. 18–19c. Oscillogram showing the output waveform of the series resonant circuit $C1$ $L1$ as it is shock-excited.

cathode circuit, depending upon the use to which this tube is put. The
second stage is a conventional pentode amplifier using a 6SJ7 tube. Provision is made in the plate circuit of this tube for connecting an RC network for tone control.

The third stage can consist of either a single-ended power-output stage utilizing a 6V6 or the components selected to make this stage a phase inverter stage using a 6J5. $V4$ and $V5$ are laid out as push-pull stage utilizing 6V6 tubes. The loudspeaker should be a 5-in., or smaller, p-p loudspeaker, which is driven by an output transformer using only one ha of the primary winding for the single-ended stage. The power suppl demonstrator can be used to furnish power to this unit, provided that is made to furnish enough current.

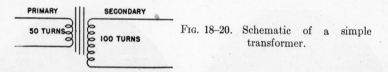

Fig. 18–20.   Schematic   of   a   simple transformer.

Single-Stage Triode Amplifier.

Step 1.   Select the components necessary, and connect $V1$ as a triod amplifier, removing $R1$ and using the potentiometer $R2$ for a volume con trol. Approximate values are given below:

$$C1 = 0.1 \ \mu f$$
$$C2 = 0.1 \ \mu f$$
$$C3 = 25 \ \mu f$$
$$R2 = 500,000 \ \text{ohms}$$
$$R3 = 7,500 \ \text{ohms}$$
$$R4 = 1,000 \ \text{ohms}$$

Note

When all the above components have been mounted in their respective jacks an a jumper is connected between $J1$ and $J2$, the amplifier is complete.

Step 2.   Connect the ouput of an audio-signal generator to the inpu terminals of the amplifier.

Step 3.   Connect the VERTICAL INPUT terminals of the oscilloscope be tween $J8$ and one of the ground terminals on the demonstration board

Note

The leads from the oscilloscope may be plugged into pin jacks, or they may b terminated with alligator clips and clipped to the phone tips of one of the compo nents in an equivalent part of the circuit. It will probably be found that alligato clips are the most convenient.

Step 4.   Turn on the audio-signal generator, the oscilloscope, and the power to the amplifier.

Step 5.   Set the audio-signal generator to a frequency of 1,000 c.

Step 6.   Adjust the COARSE FREQUENCY and FINE FREQUENCY control of the oscilloscope and synchronize four or five cycles of the wave on the screen.

Step 7.   Set *R2* to utilize the full signal from the signal generator.

Step 8.   Set the VERTICAL GAIN control of the oscilloscope to obtain precisely 2.5 in. or precisely 4.5 in. peak to peak of vertical deflection whichever is most convenient on the particular oscilloscope being used).

Step 9.   Without changing the setting of the VERTICAL GAIN control of the oscilloscope, remove the connection of the VERTICAL INPUT lead from J8 and connect it to *J4*.

Step 10.   By means of the calibrated scale, measure the peak-to-peak vertical deflection now appearing on the screen.

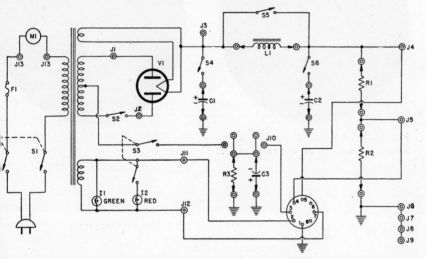

Fig. 18–21.   Circuit of a demonstration board for illustrating the theory of a power supply.

Step 11.   Assuming that the deflection in step 8 was 4.5 in., or 45 scale divisions, and that the deflection in step 10 was 0.3 in., or 3 scale divisions, the gain of this stage is 15.

$$\text{Gain} = \frac{\text{output voltage}}{\text{input voltage}}$$

The deflection produced on an oscilloscope is directly proportional to the voltage; therefore,

$$\text{Gain} = \frac{\text{output measured in inches or scale divisions}}{\text{input measured in inches or scale divisions}}$$

Step 12.   Connect a jumper from *J8* to *J10* and insert *R7* (1 megohm) into its pin jacks. *R7* is the grid-return resistor of the next stage.

Step 13.   Remove the oscilloscope lead from *J4* and again connect it to *J8*.

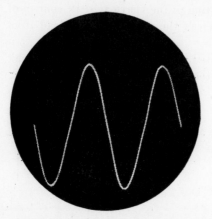

Fig. 18–22. Oscillogram showing wave-form at the plate of the rectifier V1.

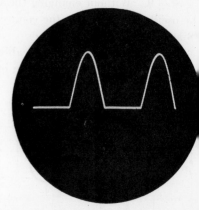

Fig. 18–23. Oscillogram showing wave-form at J3 with S2, S4, and S6 open and S3 and S5 closed.

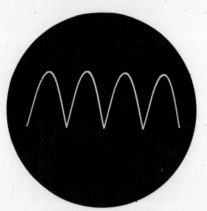

Fig. 18–24. Oscillogram showing wave-form at J4 with S4 and S6 open and S2, S3, and S5 closed.

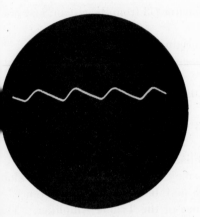

FIG. 18–25. Oscillogram showing waveform at $J4$ with $S4$ open and $S2$, $S3$, $S5$ and $S6$ closed.

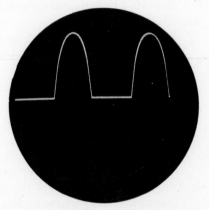

FIG. 18–26. Same as Fig. 18–23 but connections were made directly to the deflection plates.

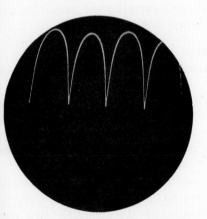

FIG. 18–27. Same as Fig. 18–24, but connections were made directly to the deflection plates.

FIG. 18–28. Same as Fig. 18–25, but connections were made directly to the deflection plates.

Step 14. Note the effect of the addition of this resistor on the gain of the stage.

Step 15. Change the value of R3, the plate-load resistor, to 15,000 ohms and measure the gain.

Step 16. Remove the cathode capacitor C3 from the circuit, and note the effect on the gain.

Step 17. Change R3 back to its original value of 7,500 ohms.

Step 18. Remove the cathode capacitor C3 from the circuit, and note the effect on the gain.

Step 19. Substitute a value of 0.01 μf for C3 and note the effect on the gain.

Step 20. Change the value of C3 to 1 μf and note the effect on the gain.

Step 21. Change the value of C3 back to the original 25 μf.

Each of the remaining components may, in turn, be changed in value and the effect on the gain of the stage may be noted in each instance.

Measuring the Frequency Response of the Triode Amplifier. The frequency response of the triode amplifier used in the foregoing procedure may be checked rather simply with an oscilloscope:

Step 1. Connect the VERTICAL INPUT leads of the oscilloscope to J7 and one of the ground connections.

Step 2. With the signal generator connected to the input terminals and set to a frequency of 1,000 c, set the VERTICAL GAIN control of the oscilloscope to obtain a convenient vertical deflection.

Note

The output of the signal generator should be constant throughout the range of frequencies covered.

Step 3. Gradually decrease the frequency of the signal generator.

Step 4. Plot the amplitude of the pattern on the oscilloscope at every 100 c below 1,000 c and at every 10 c below 100 c as shown in the graph in Fig. 13-1. (Refer to amplifier discussion in Chap. 8.)

Step 5. Increase the frequency above 1,000 c and plot the amplitude at every 1,000 c up to 10 kc and at every 10 kc up to 100 kc.

The range of frequencies throughout which the amplitude does not vary more than 10 per cent is usually regarded as the linear frequency response of the amplifier.

Each of the components of the amplifier may again be changed noting the effect of each on the frequency response of the amplifier.

Further Uses of the Amplifier Demonstration Board. The phase of the voltage appearing at the plate of an amplifier can readily be com-

FIG. 18–29. Oscillogram showing waveform at J4 with S4 and S5 open and
S2, S3, and S6 closed.

FIG. 18–30. Same as Fig. 18–29 but
connections were made directly to the
deflection plates.

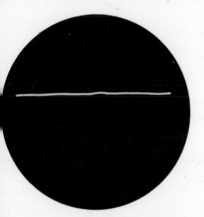

FIG. 18–31. Oscillogram showing waveform at J4 with S5 open and S2, S3,
S4 and S6 closed.

FIG. 18–32. Same as Fig. 18–31, but
connections were made directly to the
deflection plates.

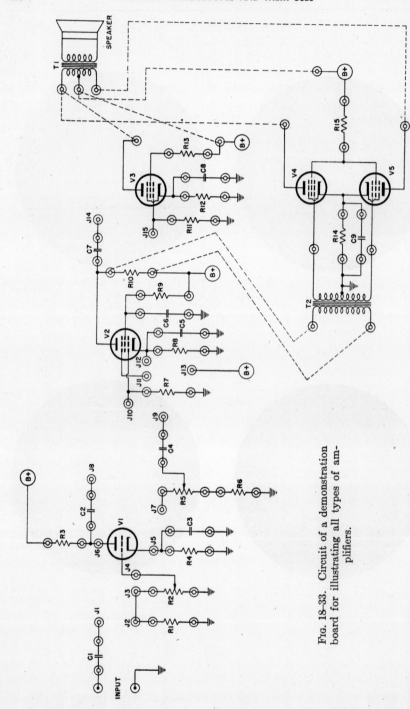

Fig. 18-33. Circuit of a demonstration board for illustrating all types of amplifiers.

pared with the phase of the voltage on the grid or the cathode. Similar experiments on gain and frequency response can be conducted on each of the other amplifiers, and a complete amplifier of two, three, or more stages can be developed and tested. Instructors in more advanced classes can assign problems in the design of audio amplifiers to specifications of gain and frequency response, and the designs can be checked in a very short time.

Other Demonstration Boards. There is probably no limit to the number of different demonstration boards that can be constructed. Figure 18–34 shows a demonstration board of a tuned r-f receiver that was

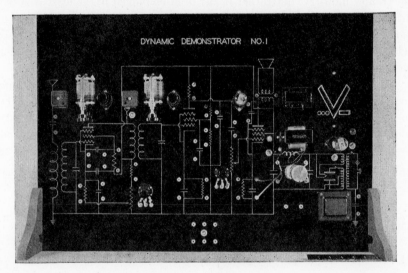

Fig. 18–34. A demonstration board on the TRF receiver. (*Courtesy, Signal Corps Laboratories*).

made for use in the Signal Corps Civilian Training School at Fort Monmouth, New Jersey. The idea for this board was conceived from the Dynamic Demonstrator of the Superheterodyne receiver, which was marketed by RCA. The RCA Demonstrator is designed specifically for the teaching of radio servicing and is, therefore, not as versatile as is sometimes desirable for classroom work.

This basic idea, however, may be expanded to demonstrate nearly all of the various circuits covered in radio-repair courses as well as in radio-engineering courses. The author has seen similar demonstration units on multivibrators, clipper circuits, differentiation and integration networks, frequency-divider circuits, and many others. The schools conducted by the Armed Forces for the training of radio and radar technicians are very strong advocates of this method of teaching.

19 Additional Industrial Applications of the Oscilloscope

Introduction. The use of the oscilloscope is not confined only to the electronics industry, but rather it has been employed by at least a dozen different industries for dozens of different purposes. The oscilloscope is particularly valuable in many fields since a knowledge of instantaneous relationships of related phenomena cannot be obtained by any other method.

Electronic Control Equipment for Resistance Welding. Electronic control of welding equipment is required to perform four functions: (1) to make and break the primary circuit of the welding transformer; (2) to control the current that flows through the material being welded and

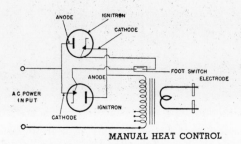

MANUAL HEAT CONTROL

Fig. 19–1. Circuit showing the use of two ignitrons to make and break the primary circuit of an arc welder.

thus the welding heat; (3) to control the time that this current is allowed to flow; (4) to start and stop the current at the right point on the current wave.

The ignitron tube is employed to make and break the primary circuit of resistance-welding equipment. This tube is simply a mercury-vapor rectifier which is capable of handling currents as high as 10,000 amp. Usually, two ignitrons are incorporated in welding-control equipment. They are connected to achieve full-wave rectification of the a-c power, as shown in Fig. 19-1.

Heat-control units utilize two thyratrons, one for each ignitron, to control the conduction through the ignitrons. When all of the current

286

available for the ignitrons passes through the primary of the transformer, the heat transmitted to produce the weld is referred to as "100 percent heat." The thyratrons in the heat-control unit are capable of controlling the ignitrons to result in 100 percent heat or any lower heat depending upon the thickness or types of metals being welded. This unit permits finer control of the heat than adjusting taps on the transformer winding

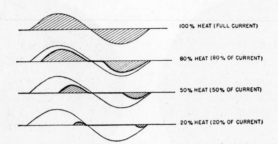

Fig. 19–2.   Various degrees of heat may be used for welding. The heat used is a function of the percentage of the current that is used.

by operating in the ignitor circuit of the ignitron. It permits the ignitron to operate only on a portion of full current, as shown in Fig. 19-2.

The synchronous timer measures the time in number of cycles that heat is applied to the weld. The timer is set before the weld is made. This device is responsible for seeing that the ignitrons start conducting at the proper point on the voltage wave; that they conduct only for the previously set number of cycles; and that they stop conducting at the proper point on the voltage wave. If the points on the voltage wave for starting and stopping conduction are not carefully controlled, large transient currents may be developed in the weld which, in short-time welds of a few cycles, produce a large variation in the quality of the weld.

Typical patterns obtained in servicing and adjusting electronic-control equipment for resistance welding are shown in Figs. 19-3 to 19-5. Figure 19-3 shows the current waveform in the primary of the power transformer with the heat control set for 100 percent heat. Figure 19-4 shows the waveform of the current, also in the primary of the welding transformer with the heat control set to about 50 percent heat. Figure 19-5 shows the pattern obtained at the same point in the circuit when one ignitron intermittently conducts late.

Use with Other Electronic Control Equipment. The use of electronic control equipment is not confined to resistance welding. Electronic control equipment for the speed of rotating machinery and other operations in the mechanical engineering field are also quite popular. The oscilloscope is an invaluable aid in adjusting and servicing electronic control equipment, regardless of the equipment to which it is applied. Phase measurements and current and voltage relationships are the chief factors in the operation of this equipment. The oscilloscope is far superior to any other instrument in indicating this type of measurement.

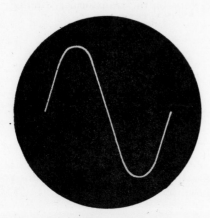

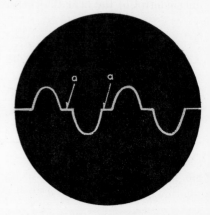

FIG. 19-3. Oscillogram showing the current in the primary of a welding transformer using 100 per cent heat.

FIG. 19-4. Same as Fig. 19-3 except that only 50 per cent of the available heat is used.

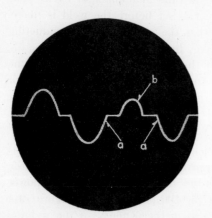

FIG. 19-5. Same as Fig. 19-4 except that one ignitron is intermittent. Note the difference in amplitudes of the two positive peaks.

Armature Testing. Another interesting application of the oscilloscope is its use in the testing of armatures of small d-c or universally wound motors. The hand testing of the armature is very slow, inaccurate, and tiring, whereas the oscilloscope method is much faster and more accurate because it is less tedious. The operator merely places the armature in a field coil and turns it by hand while he observes the pattern on the screen of the oscilloscope.

In Fig. 19-6, F represents the field coil into which the armature A is inserted. A pair of brushes is adjusted to make contact with the proper commutator bars. The field coil is fed by a convenient a-f voltage which also feeds a phase-shifting and amplitude-control circuit. The output of

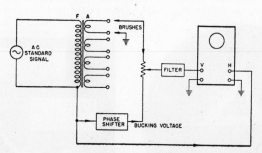

Fig. 19–6. Circuit for the production testing of armatures.

this latter circuit is adjusted to a voltage that is equal in amplitude and opposite in phase to the output of the armature winding being tested. The balance point of these two circuits is coupled to the vertical amplifier of the oscilloscope through a low-pass filter.

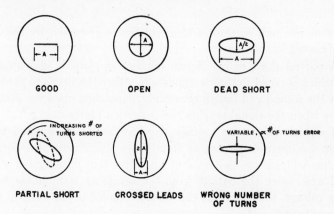

Fig. 19–7. Various patterns obtained in armature testing.

Another signal is taken from standard a-f supply, which is equal in voltage but 90 deg out of phase with the output from the armature. This voltage is connected to the horizontal amplifier of the oscilloscope.

The various patterns obtained with this method of testing armatures are shown in Fig. 19-7. The following is an analysis of each pattern:

1. A good armature winding is indicated by a horizontal line, since the output of the armature is exactly canceled by the bucking voltage.

2. An open armature winding is indicated by a circle. Since the output of the armature is zero, the complete bucking voltage is applied to the vertical channel, which is equal in amplitude but 90 deg out of phase with the voltage applied to the horizontal channel.

3. A dead short in an armature winding results in an ellipse that is elongated along the horizontal axis. This would be the same as Fig. 19-7b,

Fig. 19–8. Oscillogram showing modulated envelope of a complete pressure cycle in a gasoline engine.

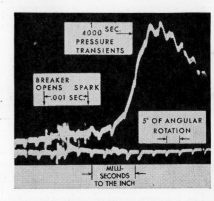

Fig. 19–9. Oscillogram showing a demodulated explosion curve. (*Courtesy, Electro Products Labs.*)

except that one half of the bucking voltage is grounded by the shorted armature.

4. A partial short or insufficient number of turns is indicated by an ellipse which is tilted so that it appears in either the first and third quadrants or the second and fourth quadrants, depending upon the phase relationships when the signal reaches the deflection plates.

5. Too high an output voltage from an armature winding tilts the ellipse in the opposite quadrants from those of the preceding paragraph.

6. Crossed leads are indicated by an ellipse that is elongated along the vertical axis, since the output from the armature is in phase with the bucking voltage, thus doubling the voltage applied to the vertical channel of the oscilloscope.

Measurements of Pressure. The oscilloscope may be used to record the dynamic pressures occurring within closed cylinders, whether they be in tanks, hydraulic systems, gasoline engines, or Diesel engines. One device for converting pressure to electrical energy is known commercially as the "electropressuregraph." *

The pickup unit is inserted into a tapped hole in the engine, pump, or other device being tested. This pickup contains a pressure-actuated dia-

* Manufactured by Electro Products Laboratories, Chicago, Ill.

phragm which controls an electronic circuit. The output of the diaphragm is coupled to a unit containing an amplfier, an oscillator, and a demodulator. The output of this unit is connected to the oscilloscope to produce a modulation envelope that shows a complete pressure cycle in the cylinder of a gasoline engine (Fig. 19-8). The output may also be demodulated for viewing transient pressures, such as those which occur as a result of explosions within the cylinder of an engine (Fig. 19-9).

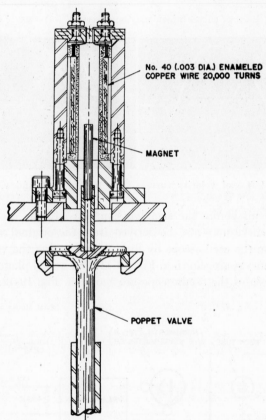

Fig. 19-10. A transducer for converting reciprocal motion into electrical energy.

Investigations of Valve-Gear Problems. The oscilloscope was used by M. C. Turkish to collect data relative to the manufacture, construction, and performance of Poppet valves and their associated parts.† His device for converting valve motion into electrical energy is shown in Fig. 19-10. The output of this magnetic-type pickup device may be con-

† Michael C. Turkish, *Valve Gear Design*, Detroit, Mich.: Eaton Manufacturing Co., Wilcox-Rich Division, 1946, pp. 121-130.

nected directly to the input of the oscilloscope to obtain a trace on the screen for showing the velocity of the valve. For observing the lift of the valve, however, it is necessary to integrate the velocity curve by an

VALVE VELOCITY CURVE—OBTAINED DIRECTLY / FROM VALVE MOTION PICKUP   VALVE LIFT CURVE—OBTAINED BY INTEGRATING THE VELOCITY CURVE   VALVE ACCELERATION CURVE—OBTAINED BY DIFFERENTIATING THE VELOCITY CURVE

Fig. 19–11.   Various curves which may be observed in the study of valve gear.

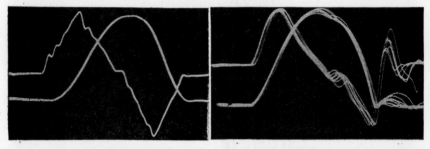

Fig. 19–12*a*. Lift and velocity curves   Fig. 19–12*b*. Lift and velocity curves
at low speed.   at high speed.

electronic circuit before the signal is connected to the oscilloscope. An acceleration curve may also be derived from the original velocity curve and viewed on the oscilloscope by first differentiating the velocity curve. These three curves are shown in Fig. 19-11, and actual photographs taken from the screen of the oscilloscope are shown in Fig. 19-12.

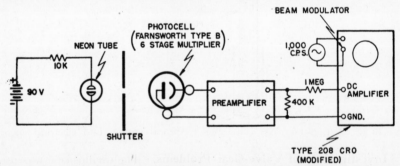

Fig. 19–13.   Circuit which may be used to test the action of camera shutters.

Testing Photographic Shutters.   The simplest method for testing a photographic shutter is to apply a sine wave of known frequency to the vertical channel of the oscilloscope. This wave should be synchronized on a sweep frequency the period of which is longer than the operating time of the shutter. Then, if the shutter is used to photograph the pattern on the screen, the number of the cycles on the recording can be counted. The time that the shutter was open is equal to the time required by the number of cycles recorded. For example, if a sine-wave frequency of 1,000 c is used, and only 10 c are recorded, the shutter was open for 1/100 sec. A cathode-ray tube with a P11 screen should be employed so that the persistence of preceding traces will not give sufficient light to

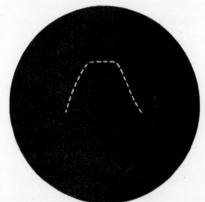

Fig. 19–14. Oscillogram showing the action of a camera shutter. The blanking markers occur at intervals of 1 msec.

permit them to be recorded. For recording shutter speeds of longer than ½ sec a special low-frequency time-base generator will probably be needed with a general-purpose oscilloscope.

Shutters can also be tested by means of the arrangement shown in

Fig. 19–15. The Du Mont Type 275-A Polar Coordinate Indicator and its two-phase generator.

Fig. 19-13. This method requires that the oscilloscope contain a direct-coupled amplifier, and best results are obtained when a single-sweep type of sweep circuit is used. Light from a neon tube, operated from a d-c source passes through the shutter as it is opened. This light activates the photoelectric cell which generates a voltage that is directly proportional to the intensity of the light striking its plate. This voltage is amplified by the preamplifier and the direct-coupled amplifier of the oscilloscope

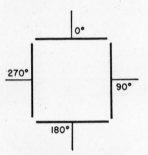

Fɪɢ. 19–16. Drawing of the plates of the cathode-ray tube to show the phase differences applied to each plate to obtain a circular trace.

and is displayed as a pulse on the screen. Beam modulation is then employed to measure the time that the shutter is open. A typical example of the pattern obtained by this method is shown in Fig. 19-14. The characteristics of flash bulbs can also be observed with a circuit similar to that shown in Figure 19-13.

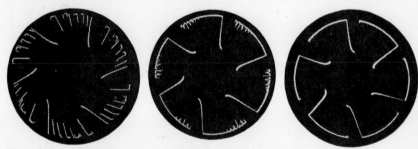

Fɪɢ. 19–17. Oscillograms showing difference in contact bounce in the breaker points of a distributor as the tension of the spring is varied. Figure 19–17a shows excessive bouncing; 19–17b shows moderate contact bounce; while 19–17c shows freedom from bounce.

Rotary-Motion Studies. For studying problems relative to rotating machinery it is convenient to use a circular time base. The Allen B. Du Mont Laboratories have developed an instrument known as the "Cathode-Ray Polar-Coordinate Indicator." This device employs a small two-phase generator that is connected mechanically to the rotating machine under test to produce the circular trace.

The two sine-wave outputs of the generator are 90 deg out of phase and furnish the input signals to two circle amplifiers. The outputs of these amplifiers are applied to the deflection plates of the cathode-ray tube so that a sine wave is applied to each deflection plate at such a phase relationship as to produce a circular trace. This phase relationship is shown in Fig. 19–16. The signal to be observed is amplified and used to modulate each of the circle amplifiers, so that signals appear as radial displacements of the trace.

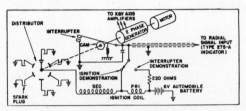

Fig. 19–18. Circuit for checking ignition in an automobile engine.

This instrument may be used with any transducer, such as a pressure pickup, a vibration pickup, a displacement pickup, a photocell, and so on. One of its interesting applications is its use to determine the proper tension on the spring of the contact points in an automobile distributor. Figure 19-17 shows the patterns obtained when different spring tensions are used.

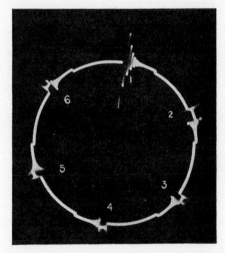

Fig. 19–19. Oscillogram showing the spark applied to each cylinder of a gasoline engine. Cylinder 1 did not fire because of an open circuit.

The use of the polar-coordinate oscillograph in combustion and ignition studies is exemplified in the circuit of Fig. 19-18. With this circuit the ignition system of an automobile engine may be studied. A typical oscillogram which was observed from this set-up is shown in Fig. 19-19. This illustration shows the spark applied to each cylinder of the engine. This oscillogram shows an open circuit to cylinder 1.

20 Photographing Cathode-Ray Patterns

Purpose of Photography. Photography of patterns from the screen of a cathode-ray tube may be desirable for any of several reasons: (1) for the detailed study of single unrepetitive transients; (2) to furnish a permanent record of investigations for the illustration of reports; (3) to record patterns that are either too rapid or too slow for visual observation; (4) to furnish a means for comparing the performance of two identical systems at widely separated times, places, or operating conditions, or of different systems under identical conditions; (5) to facilitate the measurement of amplitude and time.

Photography with a Still Camera. The recording of single continuous or repetitive images or of transients is most frequently accomplished with the use of a still camera. To photograph from the face of a cathode-ray tube, it is necessary that all external light be removed from the face of the tube lest the film become fogged. Elimination of light may be accomplished either by darkening the room completely or by using a lighttight shield between the camera and the face of the cathode-ray tube. Nearly all the oscillograms appearing in this book were taken with a still camera using a lighttight shield between the camera and the face of the tube.

There are three types of recordings that can be made with a still camera: (1) photography of stationary patterns using a continuously running sweep (the signal and sweep must be synchronized of course); (2) photography of single transients using a single sweep; (3) photography of repetitive transients using repetitive sweeps.

Usually, no difficulty is experienced in obtaining sufficient exposure when photographing a stationary pattern on a continuously running sweep, since the camera shutter may be left open for as long as is necessary. On the other hand, some experience will prove necessary in order to obtain negatives of the desired density in all instances. As a guide for exposure times, Table 20-1 is included. This will give the reader a standard from which he can vary to suit his own needs. The data in this table, incidentally, were obtained on the basis that the pattern consists of 10

TABLE 20-1

AVERAGE EXPOSURE GUIDE FOR SINGLE-EXPOSURE RECORDING

With a Stationary Pattern of Ten Sine-Wave Cycles on the Screen or When the Sweep Speed Is Much Less than the Signal Writing Speed

Medium Intensity Settings—Lens Speed=f/2.8; E.K. Panatomic-X Film*; D-76 Developer, 14 Min[4]

Du Mont Cathode-ray Oscilloscope Type No.	Tube[1] Type No.	Accelerating Voltage	Exposure		
			Diaphragm Setting	Seconds Time or Bulb	Sweep Frequency, Cycles
208-B	5LP11A	1,400	5.6	1	15–30,000[2]
241	5JP11A	1,500	5.6	1	15–30,000[2]
247	5CP11A	3,000	8	1/2	60–30,000[2]
247-A + 263-A	5RP11A	11,550	16	1/2	60–30,000[2]
256-D	5CP11A	4,000	11	1/2	80–2,000[3]
248	5JP11A	4,000	11	1/2	60–100,000[2]
248-A + 263-A	5RP11A	12,000	16	1/2	60–100,000[2]
274	5BP11A	1,000	4	1	60–30,000[2]
275-A	5CP11A	3,000	8	1	1–60
279	5SP11A	4,500	16	1	2–30,000[2]
280	5RP11A	11,900	16	1/2	30[3]
288	5RP11A	19,000	16	1/2	30[3]
281	5RP11A	8,000	16	1/2	60[2]
281 + 263-A	5RP11A	14.000	16	1/4	60[2]
281 + 286	5RP11A	29,000	16	1/4	60[2]

* RELATIVE EXPOSURE GUIDE FOR OTHER EMULSIONS

Type of Film	Developer	Time-Minutes[4]	Multiply Exposure By
E.K. Panatomic-X	EK D-76	14	1
E.K. Plus-x	EK D-76	16	1/3
E.K. Super XX	EK D-76	20	1/4
E.K. Linagraph Pan (5244)	SD 19a	17	1/8
E.K. Linagraph Ortho (5211)	SD 19a	17	1/8
Agfa Ultra Speed Pan	Agfa 47	8	1/4
Agfa Superpan Supreme	Agfa 47	7	1/3
E.K. Super XX	SD 19a	17	1/6
E.K. 1115 Recording Paper	D72 1/1	1	4
E.K. 697 Recording Paper	D72 1/1	1	2
E.K. 1127 Recording Paper	D72 1/1	1	2
E.K. 1057 Recording Paper	D72 1/1	1	4

NOTES

1. To obtain approximate exposures for other screen types, multiply by the **following** factors: P1-3x, P2-5x, P5-2x, P7-2x.

2. For lower sweep frequencies than those given, increase the exposure **proportionately.**

3. For shorter sweeps, increase the exposure proportionately.

4. For tank development of 5-ft lengths. When using processing units for 100-ft lengths, multiply these developing times by 2. For further instructions, see the **instruction** booklet included with the processing unit. (*Courtesy, Allen B. Du Mont Laboratories, Inc.*)

sine waves spread across the width of the screen with a vertical amplitude of 2 in. peak to peak. Allowances must be made for any differences from these conditions. Furthermore, different diaphragm settings than those given in Table 20-1 may be used with corresponding differences in exposure time. The relationship betwen these two factors is discussed later under the heading, *Lens Speed*. Also, a P11 type screen is used in all

Fig. 20–1. Oscillogram of a transient caused by the starting current characteristic of a synchronous motor.

instances since this phosphor has the highest photographic efficiency of the present RMA screen types. Different screens can be used, but they will require somewhat longer exposure times to obtain the same negative density.

The photography of single transients requires that the writing speed of the spot be known in order to determine the correct exposure. The determination of writing speed of the spot is discussed quite fully in a later paragraph of this chapter. The photography of repetitive transients

Fig. 20–2. Moving-film recording of the transient of Fig. 20–1.

on repetitive sweeps is very similar to the technique of photographing stationary patterns for repetition rates above 15 per second. If the repetition rate is below this figure, the same considerations apply to this type of photography as apply to single transient photography.

Photography with Continuous Motion Camera. For photography with a continuous-motion camera, the signal to be studied is frequently applied to one axis of the oscilloscope, and no sweep signal is applied to the other axis. The continuous motion of the film (perpendicular to the deflection of the electron beam) serves the function of the time base. This type of photography is used chiefly to detect slight variations occurring over long periods of time, to observe very low frequency signals, and also to record the entire transient in cases where the recurrence of the transient s not controllable, and where the initiation time of the sweep does not permit the display of the complete transient. Figure 20-1 presents a still recording of a transient showing the starting current characteristic of a synchronous motor. Figure 20-2, however, shows a moving-film recording of the same transient. It is obvious that the moving film recording is much more readable.

As a general rule, photography with a continuous motion film camera uses a large amount of film so that it is usually most economical to use a still camera whenever possible. However, a limited amount of film may

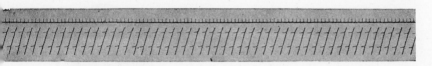

FIG. 20-3. Moving-film recording using a double exposure. The top trace shows a series of pulses recorded with the motion of the film acting as the time base. The lower recording utilizes the driven sweep circuit of the oscilloscope, and the motion of the film is merely to separate the individual traces. Note how much more readable the lower recording is.

be used with a continuously moving film camera by employing a different technique. This method utilizes both the oscilloscope sweep and the motion of the film to record each successive sweep across the width of the film. Using this technique the speed of the film need only be sufficient to

FIG. 20-4. The General Radio Type 651-AE oscillograph recorder.

separate the sweeps. An example of this type of recording on the same film with a normal continuous recording is shown in Fig. 20-3.

Types of Cameras. Practically any camera can be used to photograph stationary patterns appearing on the face of the cathode-ray tube. However, it is most practical to use a camera that mounts directly on the oscilloscope and has a lighttight shield that extends between the camera and the cathode-ray tube. Without this type of camera the entire room must be darkened, and a tripod must be used to support the camera. Both of these factors cause inconvenience to the individual taking the pictures and his associates. The only still camera on the market at this writing which mounts on the oscilloscope and has a lighttight shield is the *Du Mont Type 271-A*. This camera has been described in Chap. 12. On the other hand, there are three cameras which are available for obtaining continuous moving-film records. One of these cameras is the *West-*

Fig. 20–5. The Du Mont Type 314 oscillograph record camera mounted on an oscilloscope.

ern Electric Fastax, another is the *General Radio Type 651-AE Oscillo-graph Recorder,* (Fig. 20-4), and the other is the *Du Mont Type 314 Oscillograph-record Camera* (Fig. 20-5). These three cameras are not competitive since they operate over different ranges of film speeds. The Du Mont Type 314 operates with film speeds between 1 in. per min and 5 ft per sec. The General Radio Type 651-AE operates at film speeds between 5 and 35 ft per sec, and the Western Electric Fastax operates at speeds above 35 ft per sec.

The construction of the two available moving-film cameras is such that the film moves in a vertical direction. Thus, for continuous recording it is necessary for the spot to be deflected horizontally, i.e., perpendicular to the motion of the film. In order to deflect the spot horizontally, it is necessary to connect the signal to the horizontal amplifier, using no sweep signal. However, since the vertical amplifier is usually better from the standpoint of gain and frequency response, it is possible to use the vertical amplifier, and then either reverse the connections to the deflection plates or rotate the cathode-ray tube through 90 deg.

Speed of the Film. The correct film speed for continuous recording, i.e., when the motion of the film is used as the time base, is very simple to calculate. First, determine the most desirable distance between peaks and substitute in the following equation:

$$s = d \times f$$

where s = the film speed in inches per second;

d = distance between peaks in inches;

f = signal frequency in cycles per second.

When the time base of the oscilloscope is used (a driven sweep) and the signal is applied to the vertical axis, speed of the film s is equal to the spacing between successive sweeps d_s times the repetition rate of the driven sweep r.

$$s = d_s \times r$$

However, d_s must be greater than the vertical amplitude of the signal h times the image reduction ratio m (the magnification ratio).

Type of Film. The film used in the photography of cathode-ray patterns should be of the highest sensitivity. Panchromatic film is usually recommended because it is sensitive to a wide range of color. The typical films recommended for this type of work are Eastman Kodak Super XX, Linagraph Ortho (#5211), Linagraph Pan (#5244), Panatomic X, Type 1115 Recording Paper, Type 697 Recording Paper, Type 1127 Recording Paper, or Agfa Ultra Speed Pan, or Superpan Supreme.

Lens Speed. The faster the lens, the higher the photographic writing rates that may be recorded. An $f/1$ lens is the basis for most of the data for calculating exposure time. It is generally known that lenses of slower speeds than $f/1$ vary in efficiency inversely as the square of their f value. For example, an $f/2$ lens can record writing speeds which are only one fourth as fast as an $f/1$ lens, and an $f/3$ lens will record speeds of only one ninth the value of an $f/1$ lens.

Image-Reduction Ratio. Another factor having an effect on the exposure time used in taking the picture is the image-reduction ratio of the camera. In cameras using a fixed focus lens this ratio is always constant. However, cameras mounted on tripods will vary with each setup unless the distance between the camera and the cathode-ray tube is kept constant. As the camera is moved away from the tube, the image-reduction ratio becomes greater.

Orthochromatic film is recommended where the maximum sensitivity is not the prime factor. Ortho film is easier to handle than panchromatic because ortho film may be developed under a safelite.

The effect of an increased reduction on the film is to concentrate all the available light from the pattern on a smaller area of film thus reducing the exposure time. Likewise, an increase in the image reduction ratio will permit higher writing speeds to be recorded with the same exposure time. The maximum increase in writing speed that can be obtained by increasing the image reduction ratio is by a factor of four.

Writing Speed of the Spot.   The writing speed of the spot is another factor that must be considered in the photography of cathode-ray patterns. In a signal such as the square wave, the writing speed varies widely and results in large variations in brightness over different parts of the pattern. For example, at the horizontal tops and bottoms of the square waves, the beam moves rather slowly. However, where the beam writes between

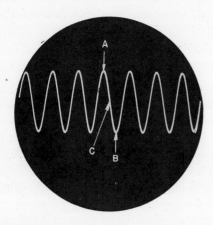

Fig. 20–6.   Oscillogram   of   a   50-kc sine wave.

the positive and negative voltage values, the beam is required to move very rapidly. As a result, the light emitted while the beam travels horizontally is very bright compared to the light emitted while the beam travels vertically. The writing rate of the luminescent spot is defined as the total distance of travel of the spot, both vertically and horizontally, in a given unit of time. For example, Fig. 20-6 shows a sine wave whose peak-to-peak amplitude is 2 in. and whose frequency is 50 kc per sec. The writing speed of the spot as it passes points A and B is relatively slow, but the speed as it crosses the X axis, point C, is extremely rapid. The spot travels the distance from A to B in 1/100,000 sec, or in 10 μsec, so that its average speed is 2 in. per 10 μsec, or 0.2 in. per μsec. However, the maximum speed of the spot occurs as it passes point C, and the speed, at this point, is equal to 0.75 in. per μsec.

NOMOGRAPH RELATING AMPLITUDE, FREQUENCY, AND MAXIMUM WRITING SPEEDS FOR SINUSOIDAL TRACES

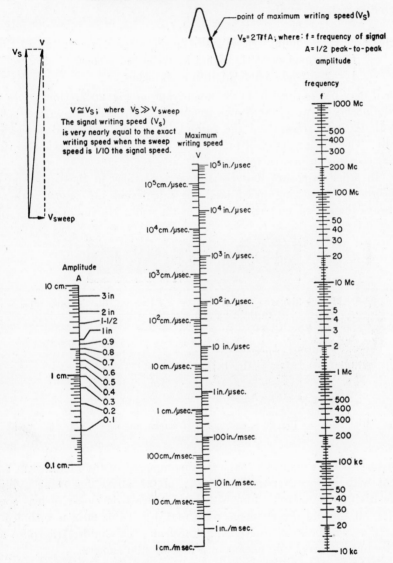

point of maximum writing speed (V_S)

$V_S = 2\pi f A$; where: f = frequency of signal
$A = 1/2$ peak-to-peak amplitude

$V \cong V_S$; where $V_S \gg V_{sweep}$
The signal writing speed (V_S)
is very nearly equal to the exact
writing speed when the sweep
speed is 1/10 the signal speed.

1 μsec. = 1 microsecond = 1/1,000,000 second.
1 msec. = 1 millisecond = 1/1000 second.

1 Mc = 1 megacycle per second = 1,000,000 cps.
1 kc = 1 kilocycle per second = 1000 cps.

Frequency range may be extended below 10 kc or above 1000 Mc by applying a suitable factor.

Fɪɢ. 20-7. Nomograph relating amplitude, frequency, and maximum writing speeds for sinusoidal frequencies.

This value is approximate since it ignores the sweep speed which is relatively slow in comparison. Maximum writing speeds may be calculated from the formula

$$V = 2\pi f A$$

where V = maximum writing speed in inches per second;

f = frequency of the signal in cycles per second;

A = the peak signal amplitude in inches;

Or it may be obtained from the nomograph of Fig. 20-7, which gives the relationship between amplitude, frequency, and maximum writing speed. Both the nomograph and the formula apply to sinusoidal waveforms only. The writing speed of pulses is usually the same as their rise time, viz., so many inches per microsecond.

In order to ensure that the dimmest portions of the trace may be recorded, the writing speed used for calculations of exposure time is always the maximum writing speed of the spot. Maximum photographic

FIG. 20-8.   Moving-film recording made from a P1 screen. The blurring effect is due to the persistence of the screen.

FIG. 20-9.   Same as Fig. 20-8, except a P11 screen was used. Note the absence of blurring.

writing speed is defined as "the maximum speed of the luminescent spot that will produce a negative density of 0.1 above fog using a high-sensitivity photographic film with high-contrast developer, a lens speed of $f/1.0$, and an object-image ratio of 1:1." Table 20-2 is included to serve as a guide in photographing transients. This information also applies to photography by means of a moving film camera.

Photographing Transients.   For the recording of transients, the common practice is to open the shutter of the camera prior to the occurrence of the transient, leave it open for the duration of the transient, and close the shutter after the transient has occurred. With this method, any light emitted from the screen of the cathode-ray tube, such as from a spot caused by the electron beam at rest, from extraneous signals, or from

TABLE 20-2

AVERAGE SINGLE-TRANSIENT RECORDING SPEEDS OF DU MONT
CATHODE-RAY OSCILLOSCOPES WITH THE DU MONT
TYPE 314 OSCILLOGRAPH-RECORD CAMERA
USING AN F/2.8 OR F/1.5 LENS

For E.K. Linagraph Ortho (5211), Linagraph Pan (5244), and SD-19a—Developer,
17 Min.* For E.K. Super XX Developed in SD-19a, Maximum Photographic
Writing Speeds Will Be About One-half the Given Values

Du Mont Cathode-ray Oscilloscope Type No.	Tube Type	Maximum Accelerating Potential, Volts		Maximum Photographic Writing Speed[1] with P11 Screen			
				In. μsec		Cm per μsec	
		E_{b2}	E_{b3}	F/2.8	F/1.5	F/2.8	F/1.5
208-B	5LP11A	1,120	1,400	0.08	0.32	0.2	0.8
213-A	5LP11A	1,000	2,000	0.314	1.25	0.8	3.2
241	5JP11A	1,100	1,500	0.08	0.32	0.2	0.8
247	5CP11A	1,550	3,000	0.8	3.2	2.0	8
247-A + 263-A	5RP11A	1,550	11,550	10	40	25	100
248	5JP11A	2,000	4,000	1.26	5	3.2	12.8
248-A + 263-A	5RP11A	2,000	12,000	17.3	69	44	176
256-D	5CP11A	2,000	4,000	1.26	5	3.2	12.8
274	5BP11A	1,000	1,000	0.04	0.16	0.1	0.4
275-A	5CP11A	1,500	3,000	0.08	3.2	2	8
279	5SP11A	1,700	4,500	1.6	6.4	4.07	16.28
280	5RP11A	1,900	11,900	15.7	63	40	160
288	5RP11A	1,900	19,000	23.6	95	60	240
281	5RP11A	4,000	8,000	14.2	57	36	144
281 + 263-A	5RP11A	4,000	14,000	35.4	142	90	360
281 + 286	5RP11A	4,000	29,000	70	270	176	685

* For tank development of 5-ft lengths in a tank such as the Eastman Kodak Daylight Tank. When using the Du Mont Type 2512 Processing Unit for processing *100-ft lengths,* multiply the developing time by 2. For further instructions, see the instruction booklet included with the processing unit.

NOTES ON TABLE 20-2

1. These maximum photographic writing speeds are referred to the face of the cathode-ray tube and are defined as the highest writing speeds of the fluorescent spot which can be photographed under the given conditions of accelerating potential, type of cathode-ray tube screen, film material, and processing procedure with the Type 314 Oscillograph-Record Camera.

The figures are based on a minimum usable photographic density of 0.1 above film fog. These recording speeds may be obtained with an average cathode-ray tube of the type given in the table, when fresh film stock is used and processed in a high emulsion speed developer as indicated above. There are various techniques for increasing film speeds and a deviation of as much as ± 100 percent from the figures given, may be obtained, depending upon the age of the cathode-ray tube and the actual processing procedure.

2. *Determination of Exposure for Slow Speed Transients or Continuous Motion Recording.* As mentioned above, the writing speeds listed would yield photographic recording densities of about 0.1 above fog. At slower writing speeds, proportionately higher densities will be obtained. However, because of the film latitude and wide range of usable recording densities, overexposure will usually not be obtained until the writing speeds are less than one tenth that of listed values. For recording writing speeds less than one tenth the maximum, the effective exposure may be decreased by one of the following methods:

a. Stopping down the lens aperture.

b. Turning down the brightness control of the cathode-ray oscilloscope.

c. Or, *preferably*, using a slower-speed, fine-grain film, such as E.K. Panatomic X, developed in a standard developer such as D-76.

3. *Repetitive Transients.* Decrease the exposure proportionately to the repetition rate increase above 1 per second.

4. The maximum photographic writing rates specified above represent the limitations of the particular cathode-ray tube used at the operating voltages available in the oscillograph. These figures do not pertain to any frequency limitations of the oscillograph amplifiers since such specifications are included in the regular oscillograph instruction manual.

(*Courtesy, Allen B. Du Mont Laboratories, Inc.*)

---

stray electron emission from the cathode, will fog the film as long as the shutter is open. As a result, most oscilloscopes that are used for this purpose are provided with a connection to the *Z* axis, so that the grid of the cathode-ray tube may be cut off when no signal is displayed, and pulsed to normal intensity just prior to the initiation of the transient. Also, automatic beam-control circuits are employed in more expensive oscilloscopes. These control circuits keep the beam of the cathode-ray tube extinguished until the sweep is initiated. At this time, a pulse is automatically impressed upon the grid of the cathode-ray tube to return the beam to its initial brightness for the duration of the sweep.

Type of Screen Material. Although stationary patterns can be recorded from any screen type because it is possible merely to use a longer exposure, the best type of cathode-ray tube screen for photographic purposes is a P11 screen. This material emits a blue light and has the highest photographic efficiency of any presently known phosphor. Futhermore, its persistence characteristic is very low, so that it can conveniently be used with continuously moving film cameras. Figure 20-8 shows the blurring effect that is the result of the persistence of the screen material of a P1 screen when a continuous-motion recording is made of a 60-c sine-wave signal. On the other hand, Fig. 20-9 shows a continuous-motion recording of a 1,000-c sine wave from a P11 screen. Even at this higher frequency, no blurring is noticed.

A P5 screen is similar to the P11 screen, but its efficiency is not nearly so high. However, the persistence of this screen is less than that of the

P11 screen, so that the P5 screen should be used for continuously moving film photography when frequencies higher than approximately 200 kc are to be recorded. The P11 screen will produce a blurred image at approximately this frequency, whereas the P5 screen will record even higher without blurring.

Photographing Both Equipment and a Pattern on the Screen of the Cathode-Ray Tube. The problem of obtaining a photograph of the complete apparatus and the oscillogram on the screen of the cathode-ray tube is rather tricky. If a photographer attempts to take this complete

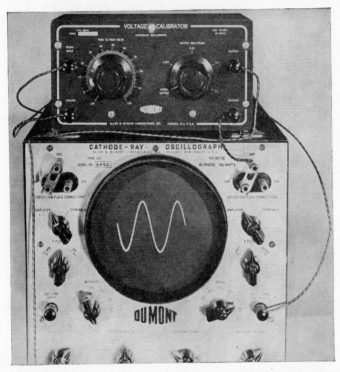

FIG. 20–10. Photograph of both the equipment and an oscillogram on a single film. This is a double exposure—once as a normal picture with the tube covered by black paper, and a second exposure in total darkness except for the light from the trace on the cathode-ray tube.

setup, he will find that when he uses enough light to obtain a good picture of the equipment, there will be too much light reflected from the screen of the cathode-ray tube to permit the oscillogram to record on his negative. If the light on the apparatus is reduced, the rest of the equipment becomes too dark to be considered a desirable photograph. However, both can be obtained on a single negative by means of the following procedure. This procedure may also be applied to photographing a picture on the screen of a television tube, whether it be a television receiver or a station monitor in a large control desk.

Step 1.   Set up lights and camera in order to obtain a good picture of the complete quipment.

Step 2.   Cut a piece of dull-finished black paper so that it fits precisely the exposed face of the cathode-ray tube.

Step 3.   Photograph the complete setup.

Step 4.   Leaving the camera and all apparatus in exactly the same position, cut off all lights and darken the room completely.

Step 5.   Remove the black paper from the face of the cathode-ray tube.

Step 6.   Obtain the desired pattern on the screen and re-expose the same negative for the length of time needed to obtain a good reproduction of the oscillogram.

The picture will appear as shown in Fig. 20-10. The only thing really wrong with the photograph is the fact that the face of the cathode-ray tube appears black, owing, of course, to the black paper.

Glossary

GLOSSARY

A

a-c The abbreviation for alternating current.

accelerating electrode The last electrode of the electron gun of an electrostatic-type cathode-ray tube. Its purpose is to accelerate the beam before it is deflected.

A-F, a-f Abbreviations for audio frequency.

aligning Adjusting or tuning two or more circuits to pass a definite frequency.

amplifier A circuit designed to increase the voltage or power of a signal.

amplitude The extent or swing of an oscillation on either side of the mean position. The amplitude of an a-c signal is synonymous with voltage.

AM, a-m Abbreviations for amplitude modulation.

amplitude modulation The system of radio broadcasting in which the amplitude of the transmitting signal varies with the instantaneous amplitude of the intelligence being transmitted. Also, amplitude modulation adds sideband frequencies above and below the assigned carrier frequency which are equal to the frequency of the sound wave being transmitted.

anode The electrode that is charged positively either in a vacuum tube or in an electrolytic solution, such as in electroplating or in batteries. It is the electrode that receives electrons.

attenuator A device for reducing the amplitude of an electrical impulse or signal.

audio Pertaining to frequencies or phenomena of sound waves audible to the normal human ear between 20 and 20,000 cycles per second.

audio amplifier A vacuum-tube device that increases either the voltage or the power of a-f signals.

audio frequency A vibration that occurs within the range of the human ear. The nominal values for audio frequencies are from about 20 to 20,000 cycles per second.

axis A fixed line along which distances, time, or other values may be plotted as in a graph.

B

bandpass The bandpass of an amplifier is defined as the range of frequency which will be amplified by that amplifier.

bandwidth Synonymous with bandpass.

beat frequency The resulting frequency obtained when two different frequencies are combined and rectified. The beat frequency is equal to the difference between the two original frequencies.

bias The fixed voltage applied between the control grid and the cathode of electron tubes.

biased-off The condition where the voltage that is applied between the grid and cathode electrodes of an electron tube is sufficient to prevent electrons from passing from the cathode to the anode.

binding post A device for connecting two or more wires together.

birdie A slang expression describing the appearance of a marker signal on the response curve as observed on an oscilloscope.

blank [the beam] To decrease momentarily the intensity of the trace to the point where it is no longer visible.

bleeder A series of resistors that serves as a voltage divider as well as a means for discharging the filter capacitors of a power supply.

311

C

calibrate To determine the standards of any scientific apparatus or to determine the quantitative graduations of a device.

capacitance The ratio of an electrostatic charge stored in a body to the electrostatic potential of that body.

capacitor A device for storing electrical energy. This device consists of two conducting surfaces separated from each other by a dielectric or insulating material, such as air, oil, paper, glass or mica, or other nonconducting substance.

carrier A radio wave upon which is superimposed the intelligence which is being transmitted. In radio reception the radio is tuned to receive the carrier frequency, and the radio circuits detect and make audible or visible the intelligence that is transmitted on this carrier.

cathode The electrode that is charged negatively either in a vacuum tube or in an electrolytic solution. The cathode is the electron-emitting electrode.

center-tap A connection to the center of the winding of a transformer.

circuit A complete path through which an electric current may flow.

clipper stage A circuit designed to clip either the positive or negative peaks of a wave or to level the peaks off at any desired voltage.

coaxial cable A cable consisting of two conductors, one of which is in the center of the cable and separated by some dielectric material from the other conductor, which is around the outside.

compensate To devise a circuit that will counterbalance certain characteristics in another portion of the circuit.

converter stage That stage in a superheterodyne radio receiver which changes the modulated r-f signals to a lower frequency, known as the "intermediate frequency."

cycle One complete oscillation. In describing a waveform, one cycle has been completed when the voltage starts at zero, increases to a maximum in one direction, returns to zero, increases to a maximum in the other direction and again returns to zero. When the word cycle is used to mean cycles per second, it is then a measure of frequency.

D

damping tube An electron tube connected in a circuit to reduce the oscillation that usually occurs in a waveform that increases in amplitude very rapidly.

db The abbreviation for decibel, a unit of sound intensity.

d-c The abbreviation for direct current.

deflection A deviation from the mean position. In cathode-ray tubes the mean or normal position of the fluorescent spot is in the exact center of the cathode-ray tube screen. A deflection of the beam will cause the spot to deviate from this position.

deflection plate A metallic plate connected to the electron gun of the cathode-ray tube to produce electrostatic deflection.

detector The stage in the receiver that separates the intelligence being transmitted from the carrier frequency.

differentiation circuit An electronic circuit that converts a square-wave into a series of positive and negative pulses. This circuit performs electronically the same function as that which is performed mathematically by differentiating an equation.

diode An electron tube containing only two elements, a cathode and an anode.

dielectric The insulating material which is used between the plates of a capacitor.

direct current An electric current which flows only in one direction.

discriminator An electronic circuit used in an FM receiver to separate the intelligence being transmitted from the frequency modulated carrier.

distortion The result obtained from electronic circuits which, because of design, do not faithfully reproduce the original signal.

E

electrode An element that performs a specific function within a vacuum tube or one of the plates in an electrolytic solution.

electron beam A beam of electrons.

electronics The branch of science that relates to the conduction of electricity through gases or in a vacuum and the applications of this phenomenon to radio, industry, diathermy, etc.

electrostatics That branch of electrical science which treats the phenomena of electricity at rest; frictional electricity; the response to fixed electrical charges.

exponentially Producing a variation in accordance with a continuously increasing or decreasing exponent.

F

farad A unit of capacitance. One farad, however, is too large for practical use. The microfarad is used as the unit of capacitance for practical purposes. One microfarad equals one millionth of a farad.

FCC The abbreviation for Federal Communications Commission.

feedback A transfer of electrical energy from one point in a circuit back to a preceding point to control the energy of the output.

fidelity The faithfulness with which a signal is reproduced by an electrical system.

filament A resistance wire used to generate the heat required for electron emission in an electron tube.

filter An electronic circuit composed of one or more resistors, inductors, or capacitors, or any combination of these parts, which accepts or rejects the frequencies for which it is designed.

fires A slang expression used as a synonym for ignites. A gas-filled vacuum tube is ignited, or fired, when the difference in potential between the cathode and the anode is sufficient to cause the gas to ionize.

flat frequency response In an electrical system a flat frequency response is said to exist when between certain frequencies the curve of frequency plotted against relative output voltage is flat throughout that range of frequencies.

FM, f-m Abbreviations for frequency modulation.

frequency The number of complete cycles, usually per second, that are made by any oscillation. The frequency of a radio wave is equal to the velocity at which the wave travels divided by the wave length.

frequency response A graph of the output of a circuit (usually an amplifier) plotted against the different frequencies within its operating range.

G

gain The ratio of the output voltage to the input voltage of an amplifier system.

galvanometer A device for quantitatively measuring voltage or current.

grid The electrode mounted between the cathode and the anode of electron tubes to control the flow of electrons from the cathode to the anode.

ground The electrical potential of the earth or, more commonly, a common reference point from which to measure voltage.

H

helical The shape of coils in a spiral.

high frequency A frequency of thousands of cycles per second. High frequency is only relative and may range anywhere from 10,000 c to 10,000 megacycles, depending upon a given reference.

horizontal amplifier The amplifier that is associated with the horizontal channel of an oscilloscope.

horizontal channel Those circuits of an oscilloscope which are connected to the horizontal deflection plates, thus deflecting the beam of the cathode-ray tube in a horizontal direction.

I

I-F, i-f Abbreviations for intermediate frequency.

ignitron A mercury-vapor tube which is used as a switch for large currents.

impedance The total opposition in an electrical or electronic circuit to the flow of an alternating or pulsating current at a given frequency.

inductance The property, usually of a coil, that tends to prevent any change in current flow. Inductance is effective only on alternating or pulsating currents. Inductance is measured in henrys.

inductor A component that possesses the property of inductance, usually a coil.

inertia The property of a body that enables it, if in motion, to remain in motion in a straight line or, if at rest, to remain at rest unless acted upon by an outside force.

in phase Two a-c waves are said to be in phase if they are of the same frequency and pass through the maximum and minimum voltage values at the same instance.

input The signal applied to a given circuit is the input signal. The circuit that receives a signal from an outside source is known as the "input circuit."

intensifier electrode The electrode of an electrostatic-type cathode-ray tube, which consists of a band of graphite material coated on the sides of the glass bulb. Its purpose is to accelerate the electron beam after the beam has been deflected.

intensity Brightness.

ionize The process by which molecules break up to form ions. In gas-filled electron tubes the application of a difference in potential between the cathode and the anode will cause the gas in the tube to ionize when the potential difference becomes sufficiently high.

J

jack A plug-in type of terminal widely used in radio apparatus.

K

kc The abbreviation for kilocycles per second.

kilocycle 1,000 cycles. Kilocycle, or the abbreviation kc, usually means thousands of cycles per second.

kilovolt 1,000 volts.

L

LC circuit A circuit consisting of an inductor and a capacitor.

limiter A stage commonly found in an f-m receiver that removes amplitude modulation from the frequency-modulated signal, thereby limiting interference.

linearity Uniformity.

logarithmic variation Variation in accordance with the logarithm of a function.

low frequency A relative value of frequency. (See also high frequency.)

M

ma The abbreviation for milliampere.

magnetic Possessing magnetic properties.

marker generator A signal generator used as a standard to provide a marker signal for indicating specific frequencies.

mc An abbreviation for megacycles per second.

meg An abbreviation for megohm.

megacycle 1,000,000 cycles. This word is usually used to indicate millions of cycles per second.

megohm 1,000,000 ohms.

μf The abbreviation for microfarad.

microfarad One millionth of a farad.

$\mu\mu$f The abbreviation for micromicrofarad.

micromicrofarad One millionth of a microfarad.

μsec The abbreviation for microsecond.

microsecond One millionth of a second.

μv The abbreviation for microvolt.

microvolt One millionth of a volt.

milliammeter A meter for measuring electric current. The meter is calibrated in milliamperes.

milliampere One thousandth of an ampere.

millimeter One thousandth of a meter, or one tenth of a centimeter.

millisecond One thousandth of a second.

mixer stage Synonymous with converter stage. (See converter.)

modulation The process of varying either the amplitude, frequency, or phase of the r-f carrier in accordance with the intelligence being transmitted.

monitor A receiver, or sometimes merely a speaker, to check a radio broadcast.

mm The abbreviation for millimeter.

msec The abbreviation for millisecond.

μsec The abbreviation for microsecond.

multivibrator A specialized oscillatory circuit whose output is a nearly perfect square wave.

N

neutralization A compensation circuit usually used to prevent undesirable characteristics, such as oscillation.

nuclear Pertaining to the nucleus of atoms.

null detector A detector of the point of minimum signal or the point of no signal.

O

ohm The unit of electrical resistance. The resistance of a device is said to be one ohm when a d-c potential of one volt will cause a current of one ampere to flow through the device.

oscillation A vibration, or the swinging back and forth through a normal rest position.

oscillator A vacuum-tube circuit that produces electrical oscillations.

oscillogram A photograph of a pattern appearing on the screen of an oscilloscope.

oscillograph A device for plotting oscillations.

oscilloscope A device that employs a cathode-ray tube for plotting oscillations.

output The signal obtained from a given circuit.

out of phase When two similar waveforms of the same frequency do not reach their maximum and minimum peak voltages at the same instant they are said to be out of phase.

overloaded When a signal applied to an amplifier is so large that the amplifier cannot amplify that signal without distortion, the amplifier is said to be overloaded.

P

peak The maximum instantaneous value of an a-c voltage or current.

peak to peak A measure of an a-c voltage or current from the maximum instantaneous value in one direction to the maximum instantaneous value in the other direction.

pentode An electron tube having five electrodes. Normally these electrodes are cathode, control grid, screen grid, supressor grid, and plate.

phase Any particular stage in the cycle of an a-c voltage or current.

phenomenon Any physically observable fact.

pips Pulses that represent targets on a radar screen.

p-m The abbreviation for permanent magnet.

polarity The quality of having two opposite poles, or two opposite charges.

potential Usually synonymous with voltage. The electrical charge of one body compared with that of another.

potentiometer A resistor with a rotating arm that can make contact with any point on the resistance. When a total voltage is applied across the two fixed terminals of the resistance, any portion of that voltage may be obtained from the rotating arm and one of the end terminals.

power-line frequency The frequency of the voltage source that supplies power to the instrument.

power supply A circuit that supplies various a-c and d-c voltages and currents for a specific purpose.

preaccelerating electrode The electrode of the gun of the cathode-ray tube which is located between the control grid and the focusing electrode. Its function is to provide the initial acceleration to the electron beam.

probe A circuit connected to a piece of coaxial cable to connect the vertical channel of an oscilloscope to a high-impedance signal source without producing serious loading effects.

pulse A momentary sudden change in voltage or current.

push-pull circuit A circuit of two tubes operating simultaneously but 180 deg out of phase with each other to produce twice the output of a single tube.

push-pull deflection Applying a signal to two opposite deflection plates of a cathode-ray tube. The signal applied to one plate is 180 deg out of phase with the signal applied to the opposite plate, resulting in one plate pulling the electron beam and the other plate pushing it away.

Q

Q (of a coil or circuit) A figure of merit for a coil or resonant circuit. It is obtained by dividing the reactance by the a-c resistance at the operating frequency.

quadrant One quarter of the area of a circle.

R

raster The rectangle of light seen on a television screen. The picture signal varies the intensity of the raster to form definite images.

actance The opposition of inductance and capacitance to the flow of alternating current. The vector sum of reactance and resistance is equal to impendance.

ctifier A device that converts alternating current into direct current.

-F, r-f Abbreviations for radio frequency.

gulator A device used to vary or to prevent variation in a desired characteristic.

sistance The opposition to the flow of an electric current.

C circuit A circuit composed of resistance and capacitance.

sistor A component part that offers opposition to the flow of an electric current.

MA The abbreviation for Radio Manufacturers Association.

ns The abbreviation for root mean square.

tary switch A switch that operates when the control knob is rotated.

tor plates The plates of a variable capacitor that rotate when the knob is turned.

m The abbreviation for revolutions per minute.

S

w-toothed wave A waveform resembling the teeth of a carpenter's saw.

canning The process of discharging successively the photo-electric light energy into electrical impulses. Mechanical scanning is also possible but is now obsolete.

chematic A diagram showing the electrical connections of an electrical circuit and using symbols to represent the various components.

hunt Any device or component that is connected in parallel with another device or component.

deband A deviation in the frequency of a carrier wave caused by modulation.

gnal Any varying voltage.

ne wave The waveform of any oscillation that follows the sine law. Usually, a pure a-c signal is an example of a sine wave.

ngle-ended deflection The deflection of the beam of a cathode-ray tube by applying a signal to only one deflection plate of a pair. Usually, the other plate is grounded.

ound traps A device or circuit for preventing the sound signal from appearing in the picture signal of a television receiver.

pot The effect produced when a stationary electron beam impinges upon a fluorescent screen.

quare wave A waveform having flat, horizontal peaks and steep, vertical sides.

tage A circuit that performs a single function. Usually, a stage includes a single electron tube.

tator The stationary plates of a variable capacitor.

tepped attenuator An attenuator that has fixed values of attenuation connected to various positions on a switch.

weep circuit The circuit that generates the linear time base of an oscilloscope.

weep frequency The frequency at which the sweep generator is operating.

weep generator The stage of the oscilloscope that generates the sweep signal.

ync The abbreviation for synchronize or synchronizing.

ynchronize To cause two or more actions to occur at the same instant or in step with one another.

T

ank circuit A circuit usually consisting of an inductor and a capacitor which may be tuned to resonance.

erminal A device to which electrical connections are made.

hyratron A three-element gas-filled electron tube.

time-base generator An oscillatory circuit for generating a time base for application to the horizontal deflection plates of the cathode-ray tube.

time constant A time value that indicates the time required for a capacitor to discharge to about one-third of its original charge through a given value of resistance.

toggle switch A two-position switch operated by means of a lever.

tolerance The permissible variation from a given value.

trace The line formed on a cathode-ray tube by the application of an a-c signal to one pair of deflection plates.

tracking A term applied to tuned circuits that follow the frequency indicated on the receiver tuning dial as the receiver is tuned over its entire range.

transducer A device for converting one form of energy into another form.

transient A signal which occurs only once for a given set of conditions.

trapezoid A geometric figure of four sides in which two sides are parallel and the other two sides are not.

traveling detector A crystal detector that may be wired into a probe for separating the intelligence being transmitted from the r-f carrier. The advantage of the traveling detector is that it permits the examination of each i-f stage individually.

triggered A circuit that has been caused to start operation by the receipt of an external signal is said to have been triggered.

triode An electron tube that contains three elements, usually a cathode, a control grid, and a plate or anode.

V

variable Having the ability to change in value.

vector A quantity that has both magnitude and direction.

velocity Speed that is measured by the ratio of distance to time.

vertical amplifier The amplifier that is associated with the vertical channel of an oscilloscope.

vertical channel Those circuits of an oscilloscope that are connected to the vertical deflection plates, thus deflecting the beam of the cathode-ray tube in a vertical direction.

video The television picture signal. (It is the same as the Latin word meaning "I see.")

volt The unit of electrical potential. A potential of one volt will cause a current of one ampere to flow through a resistance of one ohm.

voltage Electric potential or potential difference expressed in volts.

voltmeter An electrical instrument for measuring volts.

W

wave envelope A pattern that appears on the screen when a modulated r-f carrier is viewed on a linear time base.

waveform The shape of a wave; the plotting of the instantaneous values of a signal.

winding One or more turns of a conductor which make up a continuous coil.

wobbulator A signal generator that frequency-modulates an r-f signal.

writing rate The total distance through which an electron beam writes on the screen of a cathode-ray tube in a given unit of time.

Index

INDEX

321

x